"In *Treating Trauma and Addiction with* Winhall introduces a new strategy to trea̲ ad̲d̲i̲c̲t̲i̲o̲n̲ ̲t̲h̲a̲t̲ ̲c̲o̲m̲b̲i̲n̲e̲s̲ Gendlin's classic concept of a felt sense with Polyvagal Theory. The author shares her intellectual journey in which unique insights transform two disparate perspectives into obvious complements leading to a powerful treatment model. As Polyvagal Theory gives the language of neuroscience to Gendlin's felt sense, the phenomenological world of Gendlin becomes transformed by Polyvagal Theory into observable shifts in autonomic state. The product of this creative journey is an integrated therapeutic strategy with the potential to decode the wisdom of the body with its full repertoire of survival reactions into positive outcomes that promote optimal mental and physical health. These successes are highlighted by new abilities to co-regulate with others that lead to successful trusting relationships."

Stephen W. Porges, PhD, *Distinguished University Scientist,*
founding director, Traumatic Stress Research Consortium,
Kinsey Institute, Indiana University Bloomington; professor of Psychiatry, University
of North Carolina at Chapel Hill

"In this insightful volume Jan Winhall brings together the essence of ground-breaking modern therapeutic practices with her own decades of hard-won clinical experience to fashion a new, deeply humane and promising model of addiction treatment, illustrated by poignant clinical vignettes."

Gabor Maté, MD, *is the author of*
In the Realm of Hungry Ghosts: Close Encounters with Addiction

"Reframing addiction and its treatment through the lens of Experiential Psychotherapy, Polyvagal Theory, Interpersonal Neurobiology and Imago Relationship Therapy, Jan Winhall has produced a brilliant synthesis and expansion of addiction theory and treatment that should be read by all therapists, not just addiction specialists."

Harville Hendrix, PhD, and Helen LaKelly Hunt, PhD, *authors of*
Doing Imago Relationship Therapy in the Space Between

"Based on Porges' biologically-based theory of trauma, this book shows how addiction is a brilliantly adaptive way to 'bear the unbearable' rather than a sickness. Integrating this framework with her intuitive grasp of body-centered therapy, Winhall helps us both reinterpret and treat this most formidable of habits."

Marc Lewis, PhD, *author of* The Biology of Desire:
Why Addiction is Not a Disease

"Brave and revolutionary in her thinking, Jan Winhall has written a compelling book on addiction—a must-read for both clinicians and the general public alike. Compassionate, wise and profound, this book will leave its mark for years to come."

Ann Dowsett Johnson *is an award-winning journalist,*
and newly trained trauma psychotherapist.
She is the bestselling author of Drink,
A Woman's Intimate Journey with Alcohol

Jan Winhall has developed a powerful healing model that integrates polyvagal theory and felt sense experience. The model comes to life in this beautifully written book. It engages you in a process of discovery that helps you make it your own from the inside out.

Serge Prengel, LMHC, *is a psychotherapist trained in Focusing, Core Energetics and Somatic Experiencing. He is a co-editor of* Defining Moments For Therapists *and the editor of the* Relational Implicit & Somatic Psychotherapy podcast

This is an inspiring book that invites therapists to see addiction freshly, not as a disease but as a way of regulating the nervous system to adapt to the person's social context. Jan combines Porges' polyvagal theory with Gendlin's Focusing-oriented therapy in a creative manner that embraces both theory and practice. Her models for understanding and working with addiction are brought to life with case examples, personal sharing, and invitations to the reader to explore their own experience and understanding of the subject.

Peter Afford, *author of* Therapy in the Age of Neuroscience

Jan Winhall's book is wise, emotionally compelling and hopeful. I highly recommend it to any clinician who wants to expand their therapeutic toolkit for addressing addictive behaviour.

Andrew Tatarsksy, PhD, *founder and director,* The Center for Optimal Living

Jan Winhall blends Gendlinian bottom-up process of *felt sensing* with Stephen Porges' *polyvagal theory*. Her book is both broad and deep and a remarkable contribution to the field of addictions. Jan's wise and heartfelt human presence is fully embodied throughout the book as she takes us on her own journey over 40 years as a psychotherapist. Clinicians will be able to easily take in these fresh clinical avenues, perspectives and practical clinical treatment methods. I will continue to savour this book as a theoretical resource and as a clinician's handbook for treating addictions.

Karen Whalen, PhD, www.relationalwholebodyfocusing.com

This book is a powerful illustration of Eugene Gendlin's 'Thinking at the Edge' methodology for working with the Felt Sense. The integration of Porges' Polyvagal theory with the author's bodily knowing creates a brilliant model for working with trauma and addiction. Her courage to challenge the disease model benefits all who are impacted by addiction. The writing is elegant, comprehensive, and touching in a transformative way.

Dr. Evelyn Fendler-Lee, www.fendler-lee.com

Treating Trauma and Addiction with the Felt Sense Polyvagal Model

In sharp contrast with the current top-down medicalized method to treating addiction, this book presents the felt sense polyvagal model (FSPM), a paradigm-shifting, bottom-up approach that considers addiction as an adaptive attempt to regulate emotional states and trauma.

The felt sense polyvagal model draws from Porges' polyvagal theory, Gendlin's felt sense, and Lewis' learning model of addiction to offer a graphically illustrated and deeply embodied way of conceptualizing and treating addiction through supporting autonomic regulation. This model de-pathologizes addiction as it teaches embodied practices through tapping into the felt sense, the body's inner wisdom. Chapters first present a theoretical framework and demonstrate the graphic model in both clinician and client versions and then teach the clinician how to use the model in practice by providing detailed treatment strategies.

This text's informed, compassionate approach to understanding and treating trauma and addiction is adaptable to any school of psychotherapy and will appeal to addiction experts, trauma specialists, and clinicians in all mental health fields.

Jan Winhall, MSW, FOT is an author, teacher, and psychotherapist. She is an adjunct lecturer in the Department of Social Work, University of Toronto. She is director of Focusing on Borden, a psychotherapy and training centre. Jan presents internationally on trauma and addiction.

Treating Trauma and Addiction with the Felt Sense Polyvagal Model

A Bottom-Up Approach

Jan Winhall

Routledge
Taylor & Francis Group

NEW YORK AND LONDON

First published 2021
by Routledge
605 Third Avenue, New York, NY 10158

and by Routledge
2 Park Square, Milton Park, Abingdon, Oxon, OX14 4RN

Routledge is an imprint of the Taylor & Francis Group, an informa business

Library of Congress Cataloging-in-Publication Data
Names: Winhall, Jan, author.
Title: Treating trauma and addiction with the felt sense polyvagal model : a bottom-up approach / Jan Winhall.
Description: New York, NY : Routledge, 2021. | Includes bibliographical references and index.
Identifiers: LCCN 2020053996 (print) | LCCN 2020053997 (ebook) | ISBN 9780367408114 (hardback) | ISBN 9780367408121 (paperback) | ISBN 9780367408183 (ebook)
Subjects: LCSH: Compulsive behavior--Treatment. | Addicts--Rehabilitation. Classification: LCC RC533 .W56 2021 (print) | LCC RC533 (ebook) | DDC 616.85/22706--dc23
LC record available at https://lccn.loc.gov/2020053996
LC ebook record available at https://lccn.loc.gov/2020053997

ISBN: 978-0-367-40811-4 (hbk)
ISBN: 978-0-367-40812-1 (pbk)
ISBN: 978-0-367-40818-3 (ebk)

Typeset in Times New Roman
by MPS Limited, Dehradun

For all shaky beings, may you find moments of liberation in the pages that follow.

Contents

Acknowledgements

The first acknowledgement must go to the women in my incest survivor groups. Without your willingness to risk vulnerability with me and each other, this book would not exist. By sharing your secrets, you helped me to understand the true nature of addiction. Together, we welcomed the wisdom of the body. Deep gratitude forever.

To all of you who travel down the wondrous path of psychotherapy with me, it is an honour to accompany you. To protect your privacy no one person is in any of the case vignettes, rather pieces of our shared experiences formed the fictional characters in the following pages.

Steve Porges generously agreed to meet with me, to be available via email and to support my work. Without this validation the book would not have been born.

To my international focusing community, I continue to be nourished by your presence. Focusing on Borden, my local community has sustained and supported me through this long process. A special thanks to our focusing trainers Jenna Chevalier, Jessica Zormann, Zainab Kazi, Ann Dowsett Johnson, Lorri Pacheco and Raelene Hopper for their input on the embodied assessment tool. Annette Dubreil deserves credit for creating the body cards that have become central to our practice.

Many thanks to Jenna Chevalier and Haley Malcho who worked with me on the creation of graphic depictions in this text.

My dear friend Serge Prengel encouraged me from the very beginning of this project, helping me to make important connections with people and ideas.

Thank you to everyone who took the time to read my work and give me helpful feedback. Tony Cohn, Serge Prengel, Annette Dubreil, Jenna Chevalier, Steve Moscovich, Jen Wesenko, Ann Dowsett Johnson, Nomi Drory, Mark Lewis, Steve Porges, Yacine Haffar, Bonnie Badenoch, Heidi Juniper, Rochelle Rubinstein, Mary Poppe, Katarina Halm and Jeffrey Halliday.

Thank you to Evelyn Fendler-Lee for helping me formulate my ideas and experiences into a *thinking at the edge* process. You have a wonderful brain that honours the sweet spot of integration.

Thanks to Gabor Maté for ongoing support and connections with like minded people working in harm reduction.

A hearty thank you to Harville Hendrix and Helen LaKelly Hunt who gave me such encouragement and spirited dialogue. I so appreciate your ongoing support.

To Ann Dowsett Johnson who gave me the courage to really believe in myself as a writer. You have been a midwife in this project.

For my husband, a deep gratitude for many things, not the least of which was holding the fort while I was consumed. Thank you for your well formulated thoughts, your technical expertise, your abiding companionship in all things work, and love related. You are one of the few in your field who embrace the body as a living organism. Your patients are lucky indeed.

Thank you to Leslie Ellis, my chief midwife, who kept me company the whole length of the journey. You edited each page with such care and intelligence, gently suggesting, asking, and validating my work. Your presence was a gift and a major contribution to the creation of the manuscript.

A huge thank you to my editor from Routledge, Amanda Devine, for believing in this project.

For my children Marika and Peter, thank you for being you. For bringing your own unique energies into the work of healing our planet. You are each a gift to me.

A Prologue: My Women's Group

Eight pairs of eyes sitting in a circle, staring at me, but not with me. We each try to settle in to this stark, green-walled hospital room. The sun has no place here. The room feels as suffocating and unyielding as the belly pain carried inside each of these remarkable young women. I notice a tall brunette with a strong clenching jaw slouch down in her plastic chair. She holds herself together with rage. There's a slender, pretty blonde with rings on every finger. Her little dirty hands look like they belong to a 50-year-old woman who has lived a hard life. Young women in their twenties, checking each other out as they awkwardly avoid gazing.

I look down: stiletto heels, shiny patent-leather pumps, steel-toed boots, black-and-red running shoes. Back to stiletto heels, I follow her sexy body up to find a face encased in a layer of thick pale makeup, big red lips, long caked eye lashes, and a soft and welcoming smile. She tries so hard to hide her relentless freckles; they belong to the little girl in her, and that part must be hidden. Our eyes meet and I feel myself soften and take a breath as I smile in return. From the very beginning this one found her way to a place deep inside me. I am twenty-five, a brand-new therapist, and I am leading this group for incest survivors. I know two essential things: I can listen with curiosity and freshness, and I have to start by addressing safety for us all.

I began my career as a social worker/psychotherapist 40 years ago. I found myself leading this group for young women who were survivors of possibly the worst imaginable experience. I listened with non-pathologizing ears and heard shocking stories of sexual torture and responses that confused me. Women were cutting themselves, burning their bodies, sucking on bars of soap, having compulsive sex with strangers, bingeing and purging huge quantities of food, and abusing drugs and alcohol. As I listened, I learned that somehow these self-harming behaviours were "helping" them to escape intolerable emotional states. They were shifting their mood from flooding anxiety to numbing deadness, or vice versa. Because these behaviours were so helpful they were compulsively repeated and often became addictions.

I began searching the literature to help me understand. *The Courage to Heal* became my go-to book: "The problem survivors experience with their bodies ... splitting, numbing, addictions, began as attempts to survive. You cut off from your body for good reasons, but now you need to heal ... to move from estrangement from your body to integration" (Bass & Davis, 1988, p. 208). The authors encouraged women to see themselves a *survivors*, not victims. They spoke of "honouring our defenses" instead of pathologizing clients and calling them patients. Bass and Davis were criticized for not having an academic background to support their claims, but I would argue that precisely because of that, they were able to really hear with fresh ears the *meaning* behind the behaviour.

I recall one of my earliest teachers. Feminist therapist Sandra Butler (1978) wrote one of the first books about incest. She taught us that when a woman behaves in these ways that are labelled "borderline personality disorder," she is simply showing us what she learned to do to survive. I took this knowing back to the group and gently asked the women to share more about what they experienced in their moment-to-moment quest for relief of intolerable feelings.

Bridgette's Mixed Memories

Bridgette describes feelings of deadness that terrify her. She remembers a foggy Saturday morning. She is sitting at the kitchen table, a little skinny seven-year-old part of herself. Daddy is making her pancakes. Thick doughy sweetness sticking to the roof of her mouth. She is gagging, sinking into a tunnelling, funnelling journey, down into a place of floating oblivion. No one can find me here, I am safe...deadened.

A piece of memory comes. "Daddy on top of me, suffocating...can't breathe...the pancake lodges in my throat." She sees the glistening sunlight on the kitchen table...terror in the stomach. Hide from Daddy.

Over many weeks Bridgette shares how she would feel the funnelling sensation and accompany it with sharp, razor cuts to her vagina. This would help her to stay away from the agony of awareness of Daddy's attacks to her little, private opening.

The experience of the women's group stays with me. I still carry it in my bodily knowing as a kind of referent and anchor for sifting through and comprehending life and clinical practice. Why is that? What about that group of women brought so much richness and heartache and wisdom to me? The answer to these questions is the basis of this book.

Reference

Bass, E. & Davis, L. (1988). *The courage to heal.* New York: Perennial Library, Harper & Row.

1 Early Days: The Initiation of a Trauma Therapist

Addiction: It helps you in the short term,
hurts you in the long term,
and you can't stop doing it. – JW

As far back as I can remember I have been curious. I wondered about all kinds of things, mostly to do with feelings and relationships. How could some people that I love hurt me so much? How could others be so kind? What made people so different, and how was I going to find my way in this kind of world? When I look back now, it feels like I was a born psychotherapist, questioning the nature of relationships from the beginning. I spent much of my life exploring ways to find answers to these questions. This exploration led me to run an incest survivor group for young women in their twenties. Here I found many more questions, and many experiences that were like mine, and not like mine. These relationships accelerated my search. I became particularly curious about how the body responded to such horror. The myriad of ways that these young women were poking and prodding themselves both fascinated and repelled me. They described how these ways helped them and how they became addicted to them. Out of this experience I came up with this definition: Addiction is something that helps you in the short term, hurts you in the long term, and you can't stop doing it.

Addiction as Behavioural Affect Regulation: A New Frontier

I felt an urgency to help, but how? The answers I was searching for evolved over time. In reading trauma treatment books by Van der Kolk (1996) and Herman (1992), I came to understand that these self-destructive behaviours were common to all survivors of trauma as ways to manage affect regulation. Herman noted that such heightened states of attack could not be managed by ordinary means. "Abused children discover at some point that the feeling can be most effectively terminated by a major jolt to the body. The most dramatic method of achieving this result is through the deliberate infliction of injury" (p. 109). She went on to say that while self-injury is the most "spectacular" soothing mechanism, children find many other ways to induce major alterations in affective states. "Purging and vomiting, compulsive sexual behaviour, compulsive risk taking or exposure to danger, and the use of psychoactive drugs become the vehicles by which abused children attempt to regulate their internal emotional states" (p. 109).

It is only within the past decade that we see researchers begin to discuss these actions as behavioural or process addictions. Prior to this, we viewed addiction as substance related, and therefore self-injury was not viewed as an addiction. *However, while not all self-injury is addictive, all addiction is self-injurious.* It helps you and harms you. What many of us hear in our offices is that because these behaviours are so needed and effective, they become compulsively repeated as powerful mechanisms of comfort. Thus, habit-forming behaviours can become addictive when they are needed to survive.

The understanding of behavioural or process addictions has emerged at the same time as, and perhaps because of, a current technological revolution. We now have access to neurobiological information about the body that is guiding us in our broader understanding of psychological struggles. Since the *decade of the brain* in the 1990s, the field of trauma has been greatly enhanced by the use of modern imaging technologies such as fMRI and PET. We can now see the impact of traumatic experience on brain functioning. Lewis (2015) states, "The neural consequences of behavioural addictions indicate the same cellular mechanisms and the same biological alterations that underlie drug addiction" (p. 23). New theories are emerging as we learn more about trauma and the brain.

Finding Interpersonal Neurobiology (IPNB)

IPNB, as it is called, was created by Dan Siegel (1999) in the 1990s. It draws from 40 different academic disciplines. The beauty of the theory is its emphasis on *consilience*. Wilson (1998) defines consilience as "the discovery of common findings from independent disciplines" (p. 7). Thus, we can learn to appreciate and integrate findings from branches of the natural and social sciences, and the humanities. We will see in Chapter 2 a new and fresh way to integrate these disciplines called *thinking at the edge* (TAE). This way comes from Gendlin's *philosophy of the implicit* (2018). The concept of the *felt sense* is central to this philosophy. A felt sense is a bodily knowing that can be subtle at first but opens up more and more as one gently attends to it. The central importance of attending to the felt sense has been widely adopted in trauma and therapy circles. It also forms an integral part of the *felt sense polyvagal model* (FSPM) of addiction that forms the central idea for this book.

IPNB provides a view of mind, brain, and relationships that seeks to bring a more strength-based approach to mental health. This theory suggests that well-being is a state of integration, and that states of suffering are difficulties with emotion regulation. Siegel views these states on a continuum from an emotionally flooded, chaotic response at one end, to a numb and rigid response at the other. Integration is the linkage of differentiated parts. Without integration, a person will cycle between chaos and rigidity. Linkage creates integration of left and right hemispheres and of top-down and bottom-up processing, and this helps a person stay away from the extreme ends of the continuum.

Experiential Response to Siegel's IPNB Model

When I first read about the chaos/rigidity continuum, I recognized how it was helpful in understanding the women in my group. Because of trauma, they were all swinging back and forth from chaos to rigidity. They were seldom able to experience a grounded state because they felt so unsafe in their bodies.

The whole demeanour and physicality of the women's presence changed depending on where they were on this emotional continuum. If they were flooding in chaos, they were anxious, fidgety, distracted or sometimes irritable and rageful. If they were numbing, they presented as rigid, lost, depressed, dissociated. How they viewed the world was also determined by their state. If they were in a chaotic/angry state, the world was a boxing ring. If they were in a shut down, depressed state, the world was boring, grey, deadened. This dramatic shifting of states was a key to my future understanding about the nature of the autonomic nervous system.

Discovering the Missing Links: The *Polyvagal Theory*

It was when I discovered Porges' (2011) work on the *polyvagal theory* that I really began to make headway into a deeper understanding of the mysterious behaviours of the women in group. Polyvagal theory is the study of the *autonomic nervous system* (ANS), the linked, massive network of nerve fibres that keenly monitors our needs for survival without our conscious awareness. The *vagus nerve* is the primary focus of the theory. It is the tenth cranial nerve, connecting brainstem areas to several visceral organs.

Polyvagal theory has had a huge impact on the field of trauma. This book takes it into the field of addiction, challenging the disease model by providing a radical paradigm shift. Through this lens addictive behaviours that I saw in my women's group are *adaptive* attempts to regulate the ANS. The central goal of the healing journey is to support autonomic regulation through embodied practices.

Origins of the Felt Sense Polyvagal Model of Addiction (FSPM)

Over 40 years of keeping my clients company, I have developed a model to understand what I saw and heard as I sat with their stories and ways of managing their intense experiences. As I began to learn about polyvagal theory, I realized that I was applying the theory as I explored the field of addiction. The theory enhanced my understanding of what I knew intuitively: *Clients were using addictive behaviours to propel themselves from a state of sympathetic arousal to a dorsal vagal response of numbing, and vice versa. Through understanding how the ANS operates, we see these behaviours as adaptive. They have developed over time to help the addicted person survive when enough safety isn't available.*

I now saw Siegel's continuum of emotional chaos and rigidity as reflective of the ANS. Chaos is the sympathetic state, and rigidity is the parasympathetic shutdown the body experiences when the dorsal vagus is activated. Thinking back to Brigette in the women's group, it became clear that her vaginal cutting was an adaptive response to intolerable experience. It propelled her from the overwhelming flooding of anxiety, terror, and ensuing chaos characteristic of sympathetic arousal, to the tunnelling, funnelling journey down into a place of floating oblivion and rigidity, which is a dorsal vagal response. This cutting behaviour became her addictive, adaptive response to trauma.

Addictive/Adaptive Responses Often Tell a Detailed Trauma Story

Another part of the mystery is the way in which the addictive response may tell a story about the client's trauma history. Sometimes the chosen addiction points to the source of the trauma. For example, some studies show that 80 per cent of sex addicts have a history of sexual abuse (Carnes, 2001). Another example is dysregulated eating, which can be a response for those with a trauma history around food.

Sometimes clients reenact specific behaviours that take place during the addictive experience that link back to early childhood abuse. The reenactment tells a piece of the story, hence puts the client in touch with the feelings, without directly making the link. The dissociated, fragmented story is held in the body.

Van der Kolk (2014) was curious about re-enactments. He asked the question, "Why are so many people attracted to dangerous or painful situations?" He found a paper written by Beecher (1946) entitled, *Pain in Men Wounded in Battle*. Beecher was a surgeon working with soldiers wounded on the Italian front. He observed that 75 per cent of the severely wounded did not request morphine. He then speculated in this paper that if emotions are strong enough, they can block pain.

Van der Kolk and some colleagues conducted a study with eight war veterans who agreed to watch violent scenes from the film *Platoon* (1986) and at the same time take a standard pain test. They measured how long the veterans could keep their hands in a bucket of ice water. They then repeated the process with a calm and peaceful movie scene. Seven of the eight veterans kept their hands in the freezing water 30 per cent longer during the violent movie. He states, "We then calculated that the amount of analgesia produced by watching fifteen minutes of a combat movie was equivalent to that produced by being injected with eight milligrams of morphine, about the same dose a person would receive in an emergency room for crushing chest pain" (Van der Kolk, 2014, p. 33).

In clinical settings it is apparent that clients' addictive behaviours of traumatic re-enactment – that is, re-exposing themselves to painful, humiliating, dangerously abusive experiences – activates a dissociative, dorsal vagal response. This response is often activated at the beginning of the addictive cycle, the phase of pre-occupation, and endures for hours after the event. Clients report that it brings them a powerful sense of relief and often the ability to sleep.

Now, it all begins to make sense through an ANS lens. The primary responsibility of the ANS is to ensure safety and hence survival, and the shift in states facilitates this mandate. Without safety, our body will automatically resort to survival mode, although our ancient survival mechanisms are not always the best response in the modern world.

Addictive behaviours are adaptive strategies for survival that kick in when there is no sense of safety. A sense of safety is a prerequisite for the ventral vagus to support a socially engaged state. Addiction occurs in isolation, during avoidance of social engagement. Instead of regulating our nervous system in safe connection with self and others, in addiction we regulate with objects, behaviours, drugs, alcohol, food, and with relational reenactments. Porges (2017) states, "When individuals have difficulty regulating state with others or co-regulating, they *adaptively* gravitate to regulating state with objects" (p. 119; emphasis added).

When I read this, I knew I had found an explanation that made intuitive sense. Now I set out to integrate the polyvagal theory with a method of psychotherapy that I teach called *focusing oriented therapy*. I wanted to create a methodology for working with self-harm and addiction that integrated these concepts.

Finding Focusing: Back to Women's Group

Seeing the distress and dramatically different presentations of trauma drew me to finding a way to attend to the body. I began working with these young women in a gentle embodied way called *focusing* (Gendlin, 1978/1981). This is a natural bodily process that can be taught as a contemplative practice. It helps people bring awareness of body wisdom into consciousness. Through learning how to listen and connect with embodied presence of feelings and thoughts and memories, called the *felt sense*, we discover a kind of *felt shift*, or physical release. This release or letting go of tension and uncomfortable feeling guides us in our direction of healing.

I began to integrate focusing oriented therapy (FOT) and the felt sense experience, into a model that is the subject of this book. I've called it the felt sense polyvagal model (FSPM) to treat trauma and addiction. We will see as the model unfolds, that polyvagal theory and focusing can be integrated within any psychotherapy framework.

How Porges Updated the Traditional ANS Model

We will now turn our attention to learning more about the autonomic nervous system so that you can orient yourself to the FSPM. Before Porges' ground-breaking work, the ANS was thought of as a paired antagonistic system with two opposing parts: the sympathetic nervous system that was activated during stress, (flight/fight) and the parasympathetic system, primarily the vagus nerve, which inhibited the sympathetic system. The result of these two opposing parts was a kind of balance. The traditional view of the system emphasizes the influence of the motor pathways (efferent nerves) and minimizes the importance of the sensory pathways (afferent nerves) that travel from the organs to the brain or brainstem. The view also minimizes the bidirectional nature of the pathways.

In his own detailed study of heart rate monitoring, Porges discovered that the nervous system is much more complex than originally thought. Unlike the traditional model, polyvagal theory acknowledges and emphasizes the bidirectional nature of the motor and sensory pathways. Because 80 per cent of the fibres in the vagus nerve are sensory, most of the information carried to the brain from the vagus is coming from the bottom up, from the viscera to the brain, and *not the other way around*. So, it makes sense that PVT would emphasize the embodied approach.

When asked how the nervous system interplays with our visceral feelings, Porges says that although an understanding of how the nervous system regulates our bodily state is highly relevant to the practice of psychotherapy, his theory is not taken into account in the current theory, practice and teaching of psychotherapy. "Psychology and psychiatry primarily use top-down models that conceptualize emotions and affective processes as central phenomena and minimize the role of the body in these experiences" (2017, p. 216).

The beginnings of the polyvagal theory occurred as Porges was monitoring infants' heart rates. He discovered that some babies' health risks could not be explained by the traditional model. This led to an understanding that there was indeed a second path of the vagus nerve that was employed when the system was under serious threat: the dorsal vagus.

The Dorsal Vagus

This second pathway of the vagus, the dorsal branch located below the diaphragm, is activated when the system is under threat and the sympathetic response is not adequate. It is a state of immobilization with fear. Under threat, the autonomic nervous system will first try to connect and solve the problem. If that doesn't work, the ANS will go into fight/flight, chaos. If *that* doesn't work, the system will seek survival by activating the dorsal branch of the vagus, the shutdown response.

Appeasement or "fawn", sometimes confused with the dorsal vagal shutdown response, is a term coined by Walker (2013) that refers to the state of acquiescing in order to stay safe. It is a behaviour chronically abused children often employ to reduce harm. It is not a total immobility response because it is also a form of social engagement, and a blocking of protective fight responses that could lead to more harm. It is one of the hybrid states that can be identified in more complex interpretations of Porges' theory.

Polyvagal theory posits an evolutionary timeline in the development of the ANS. The dorsal branch is the oldest, originating 500 million years ago. Next is the sympathetic nervous system that evolved 400 million years ago. The newest system, the uniquely mammalian ventral vagal circuit, is 200 million years old.

The Ventral Vagus

A major idea offered by polyvagal theory is that the ventral branch of the vagus nerve contributes to the *social engagement system*. This part of the vagus supports health, growth, and restoration. Brainstem areas (i.e. ventral vagal complex) regulating the ventral vagal pathway are also involved in the regulation of the muscles of the face and head. The social engagement system helps us co-regulate with others and create safety. This part of the vagus communicates with organs located above the diaphragm and enables bidirectional neural communication between the heart and face. This explains how we are wired to connect through facial expression.

When we are connected to the ventral vagus we can be creative, exploring the edges of experience. We feel a sense of grounding and openness to new possibilities. A term from interpersonal neurobiology applies; it is the state of *integration*. It is the sweet spot of experiencing: safe, held, curious, full of life.

Sympathetic Nervous System

The sympathetic pathway is the fight/flight state of mobilization with fear. This state brings accelerated heart rate, sweaty palms and dry throat as our bodies mobilize to escape or fight our way out of a stressful situation. We lose our appetite, pumped up on adrenaline to prepare for the worst. This is the triggered state that so many of our clients chronically inhabit. In IPNB terms, this is the emotional state of *chaos*. While it is essential when we need it, it can wreak havoc when we are in fact safe but don't recognize safety due to triggers that hamper our ability to accurately read our environmental cues. Such confusion about the actual level of present danger is common in those who have experienced trauma.

Polyvagal-informed therapist Dana (2018) describes the system this way:

> To follow the autonomic hierarchy, envision your stomach and its digestive processes as the ancient dorsal vagus, move up to the middle of your back as the next layer in the evolution of the system with the sympathetic nervous system and its spinal nerves, and then move to your heart and face and the newest part of the autonomic nervous system, the ventral vagus. (p. 22)

The Felt Sense Polyvagal Model (FSPM)

The FSPM comes from years of thinking through and applying various theories and treatment strategies. Because I am a visual person, I needed a map for organizing my thoughts. The model provides a graphic representation of the integration of felt sense experiencing, and the neurophysiology of the autonomic nervous system. As the clinician model evolved, I shared it with clients. They showed me how they were using it to help themselves orient to their ANS state. They encouraged me to make a simple client version and we created the *6 F's*.

The client version (see Figure 1.1) is designed to be a simple way to explain the model, starting with the six states in the autonomic nervous system. I called them the 6 F's, flight/fight, fun, flock, flow, fold, fixate. This makes it fun to work with and easy to remember. In its simplest form, we teach our clients how to identify and map their state on the model. As they learn about focusing, they map their felt sense onto the states. I've attempted to make the model pleasing to the eye, intriguing in its presentation, and playful in its use. I want the whole experience for clinician and client to be a grounding, validating, ventral vagal experience. (Figure 1.2)

The FSPM clinician version of the model is an integration of several theories, hence it is complex and multi-layered. Looking at the graphic depiction of the clinician's FSPM, we can see:

A. *Three circuits of the ANS.* These are depicted in the solid line triangle at the bottom right. Ventral, flock, is in yellow at the bottom of the

THE FELT SENSE/POLYVAGAL MODEL OF TRAUMA AND ADDICTION
Client Version 6F's

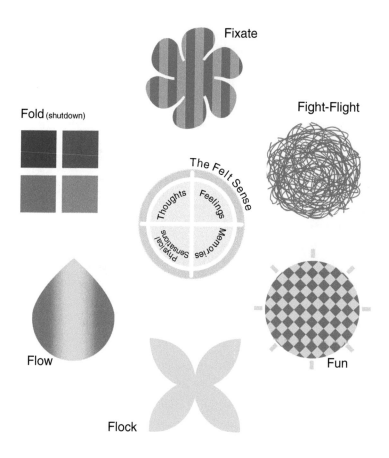

Figure 1.1 FSPM client version.

page, sympathetic (flight/fight) in red on the right, and dorsal (fold) in grey on the left.

B. *Intertwining States.* These are depicted in the dotted line triangle at the bottom right. Intertwining states utilize two pathways in the nervous system. The ANS has the capacity to blend states. This offers us a greater capacity for varied experiences. Intertwining states are

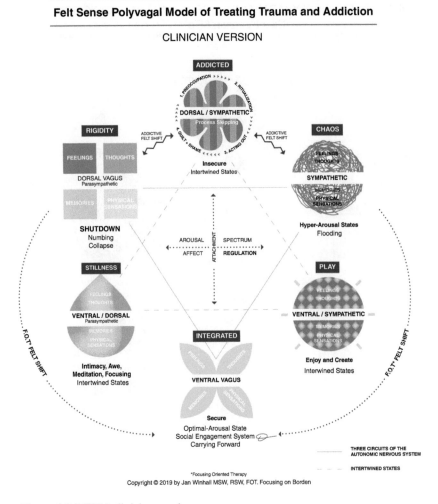

Felt Sense Polyvagal Model of Treating Trauma and Addiction

CLINICIAN VERSION

Copyright © 2019 by Jan Winhall MSW, RSW, FOT. Focusing on Borden

*Focusing Oriented Therapy

Figure 1.2 FSPM clinician version.

represented in the model in mixed colours. Play, or fun on the client version, is on the bottom right in yellow/red. Stillness, flow on the client version, is bottom left yellow/grey. Addiction, fixate on the client version, is at the top, red/grey.

Play: Mobilization with Safety (yellow/red)

This state is an intertwining of ventral, (safety and co-regulation), and sympathetic, (mobilization), to create energy and vitality. We can see how quickly children can switch into a full sympathetic response when the safety of play turns to a fight/flight response if someone gets hurt or frightened.

Stillness: Immobilization with Safety (yellow/grey)

This state is a blending of the safety of ventral and the still, calmness of dorsal. The system is designed to promote a state of deep relaxation, and intimacy with others. This promotes a regulated, connected, fully satiated experience of life. Focusing and deep experiential therapy take place in this state.

Addiction: A Propeller of Dysregulated State Change (red/grey)

The FSPM proposes a third intertwined state: addiction. This state is a blending of sympathetic and dorsal. When trauma and other states of emotional dysregulation occur, the capacity to regulate through social engagement (ventral vagus) is compromised. The ANS shifts into survival mode and will often employ addictive behaviours in an effort to seek relief from suffering.

The Current and Desperate State of Addiction

Confronting the profoundly relentless hold that the mechanism of comfort has over the addicted person is daunting. How can the grueling path of healing ever compete with the quick and dirty salve of soothing? (Winhall, 2014).

Addiction is eating us up. While it used to lick around the edges, it is now flourishing in the belly of our culture. And it's on the rise in most countries. What does that mean? What are we showing ourselves in such painful and damaging ways?

These questions and more need so desperately to be addressed. While the language that we use to speak about addiction can sound hyperbolic, the destruction speaks for itself. Every day, people are dying on the streets from fentanyl overdoses in greater numbers than ever before. As clinicians we find ourselves encountering clients struggling with compulsive, self-harming, addictive behaviours in increasing numbers, and yet, we don't always feel competent to help. Traditional ways of understanding and treating the problem are not effective. Many people find it hard to even truly comprehend someone continuing to damage themselves and those around them, when all the facts point to the need to stop. We search for ways to appeal to the addicted person ... mostly through cognitive means, yet the current results show that we are fighting a losing battle.

The Polyvagal Paradigm Shift ... A Powerful Dance of Connection

The capacity to ground ourselves, to feel safe and regulated inside our bodies, is the most fundamental skill we can achieve in a lifetime. Some of us are lucky and we learn these skills and the "felt sense" in our bodies from our loving caretakers. Some have this capacity early on in life but lose it with experiences of pain and suffering. Others spend the better part of their existence trying to create this safe nest in which to grow and heal.

In my view, polyvagal theory implies a radical paradigm shift. Our current pathologizing model of addiction fails to see the helpful, *adaptive* nature of these behaviours. Its hierarchical *top-down* approach inadvertently shames people. We can do better than this!

Addiction is an embodied response to emotional dysregulation. When we call addictive behaviours maladaptive, we need to really appreciate the power of such language. These behaviours do not come from sickness; they come from a natural bodily response to threat and a wired in method of survival. *We have forgotten that we live in our bodies.* Polyvagal theory reminds us that we are part of the natural world, the world of mammals. We do better when we travel in packs, in loving families of safety and connection.

Porges (2017) writes:

> If we want individuals to feel safe, we don't accuse them of doing something wrong or bad. We explain to them how their body responded, how their responses are adaptive, how we need to appreciate this adaptive feature, and how the client needs to understand that this adaptive feature is flexible and can change in different contexts. (p. 122)

If we accept that safety is, first and foremost, a prerequisite for healing, then we begin to shift our lens of understanding our clients. Rather than having an ever-growing list of diagnostic categories, we can assess people's *capacity* to self-regulate and co-regulate their physiological state with others. We need to move into this emotion regulation paradigm, and away from the disease model of addiction.

Every good trauma/addiction therapist knows this intuitively because we are curious with our clients and listen to the meaning and function of these behaviours. Now we have a neurobiological explanation that can be developed in conjunction with our clients lived experiencing, to enhance our capacity to articulate that knowing.

Summing Up the Journey to a More Sophisticated Model for Addiction

In this chapter, we have journeyed through the evolution of my understanding of the process of addiction facilitated by those who have changed the way we view this challenging state. Sadly, the more outdated models for addiction treatment are still quite prevalent, which is why we need the FSPM. Through this lens we understand addiction as the body's attempt to regulate when safer ways are not available. Viewing all this as adaptive paves the way for healing.

References

Beecher, H. (1946). Pain in men wounded in battle, *Annals of Surgery, 123*(1), 96–105.

Butler, S. (1978). *The conspiracy of silence: The trauma of incest*. Volcano, CA: Volcano Press.

Carnes, (2001). *Out of the shadows: Understanding sexual addiction* (3rd ed.). Center City, MN: Hazelden Publishing.

Dana, D. (2018). *The polyvagal theory in therapy*. New York: W.W. Norton & Co.

Gendlin, E. T. (1962/1997). *Experiencing and the creation of meaning*. Evanston, IL: Northwestern University Press.

Gendlin, E. T. (1978/1981). *Focusing*. New York: Bantamdell.

Gendlin, E. T. (2018). *A process model*. Evanston, IL: Northwestern University Press.

Herman, J. (1992). *Trauma and recovery*. New York: Basic Books.

Lewis, M. (2015). *The biology of desire: Why addiction is not a disease*. New York: PublicAffairs.

Porges, S. (2011). *The polyvagal theory*. New York: W.W. Norton & Co.

Porges, S. (2017). *The pocket guide to the Polyvagal Theory: The transformative power of feeling safe*. New York: W.W. Norton & Co.

Siegel, D. J. (1999). *The developing mind: Toward a neurobiology of interpersonal experience*. New York: The Guilford Press.

Siegel, D. J. (1999). *The developing mind: Toward a neurobiology of interpersonal experience*. New York: The Guilford Press.

Van der Kolk, B. (1996). *Traumatic stress: The effects of overwhelming experience on mind, body and society*. New York: The Guilford Press.

Van der Kolk (2014). *The body keeps the score*. New York: Penguin Books.

Walker, P. (2013). *Complex PTSD: From surviving to thriving*. USA: An Azure Coyote Book.

Wilson, E. O. (1998). *Consilience, the unity of knowledge*. New York: Alfred A. Knopf, Inc.

Winhall, J. (2014). Understanding and treating addiction with the felt sense experience model. In G. Madison, (Ed.), *Emerging practice in focusing-oriented psychotherapy*. London: Jessica Kingsley Publishers.

2   Finding Focusing and Thinking at the Edge

This book proposes a model for understanding and treating addiction that is the result of an advancement in thinking since my earlier introduction of the *felt sense experience model* (Winhall, 2014). A major addition is that I have integrated the polyvagal theory (Porges, 2011) to create a more sophisticated way of understanding emotional regulation. The *felt sense polyvagal model* (FSPM) invites clinicians to explore the implications of the theory as a paradigm shift, moving us from a pathological model to a strength-based model. However, what remains the same is that my model of addiction theory and treatment is grounded in the embodied practice of *focusing* (Gendlin, 1978/1981).

Back in the 1980s, I went searching for a more body-based practice because I could see that talk therapy alone was not accessing the deeper place of trauma. In watching my clients' bodies, I saw the aches and pains of trauma reveal themselves in facial expression, bodily-felt movements of constriction, the rhythm of breath flow, and in their capacity for connection with me. Where they held joy and sorrow revealed itself in wordless movement.

Focusing and the Felt Sense

Focusing is the work of Gendlin whose best-selling book *Focusing* (1978/1981) has sold more than a half million copies around the world. But despite that success, it is not well known as a practice. Perhaps that is partly because its applications are many. It is a natural bodily process that can be taught as a contemplative practice. It has been incorporated into teaching/learning models, coaching models, religious practice, physical therapies, a philosophy (the philosophy of the implicit), a methodology for developing theory *(thinking at the edge),* and a method of psychotherapy (focusing-oriented psychotherapy). It's a generic practice hence its applications are endless.

Focusing is based on research conducted at the University of Chicago by Rogers, who was teaching and researching in psychology, and Gendlin, who was doing his PhD in philosophy. Together, they explored the answer to this question: "Why does therapy work sometimes and not others?" Through analysing thousands of client-therapist recordings, utilizing a wide variety of therapies, Gendlin discovered that clients who showed tangible change were easy to spot. They were not so much influenced by the therapist's technique; rather, they were doing something specific in therapy. They were focusing. These successful therapy clients were capable of deep levels of experiencing. They intuitively knew how to skilfully concentrate on their problems and listen to their bodies' way of knowing. Gendlin decided to create six steps of focusing as a way to teach this process. For many people, the process does not come naturally, but is a skill that can easily be learned.

Focusing in Partnership: Learning to Listen

Focusing is unique as a contemplative practice in that we most often experience it in partnerships. Sitting across from each other, we explore, face to face, and open-bodied, our felt sense experience. We learn to emotionally regulate and to co-regulate with each other in our practice. While meditation and focusing both involve ventral vagal activation, focusing practice invites and enhances social engagement and co-regulation through partners' deep listening to each other.

In interpersonal neurobiology (IPNB) terms, focusing is a process that engages right and left hemispheres, linking differentiated parts and promoting integration of top-down and bottom-up processing. In Gendlin's philosophy, he framed it as moving from the implicit (bottom-up) to the explicit (top-down) process. Gendlin (1978/1981) wrote:

> We all know people with whom it is best not to share anything that matters to us. If we have experienced something exciting, and if we tell it to those people, it will seem almost dull. If we have a secret, we will keep it safe from those people, safe inside us, untold. That way it won't shrivel up and lose all the meaning it has for us. But, if you are lucky, you know one person with whom it is the other way around. If you tell that person something exciting, it becomes *more* exciting. A great story will expand, you will find yourself telling it in more detail, finding the richness of all the elements, more than when you only thought about it alone. Whatever matters to you, you save it until you can tell it to that person. Focusing and listening are like that: like talking to a person who makes your experience expand. In focusing you must be that kind of person within yourself. And you can also be that way with others and show them how to be that way for you. (p. 131)

In our focusing community we spend equal time learning how to focus and how to listen. This creates a powerful energy between us. I call this the *relational felt sense* (Winhall, 2014). In our international community people form lifelong focusing partnerships where they take time to be with each other as part of their weekly practice.

Of course, you can focus alone much like people meditate on their own. It is an important skill to be able to do by yourself, particularly when working on reducing harmful addictive behaviours. When you become very skilled in the process it becomes a way of living. You are able to find the felt sense as part of your daily embodied awareness. Then, time in and time out are seamless.

Focusing: The Fundamentals

So, what is focusing? I want to give you a taste of this remarkable practice, one that I use with my clients and in my life. I am inviting you to come with me now, into the experience. I will be your partner as we begin the process.

Step 1: Clearing a Space

We are going to soften our gaze and turn attention inwards. Say *hello* to whatever is there. We will slowly go through the steps. It is important to take time to prepare. Give yourself a quiet, uninterrupted place for roughly 20 minutes. Sit comfortably in your chair. Close your eyes and allow yourself to take a deep breath, and follow your awareness down, somewhere into the centre of your body. Ask yourself: "How am I today? What is coming between me and feeling great?" Usually five or six issues will be floating around in your head. Without going into them, take each one and imagine that you are stacking each up, out in the hall. Ask one at a time to get some distance, just for now. You can come back to any one of these later. But for now we want to make a nice, clear space inside, to be able to breathe. If one is particularly difficult, imagine floating it up into the air like a balloon or you can put it in a boat and float it offshore. There will be time to be with these issues. Just for now, we want to clear space inside. Eventually, the space down in the centre of your body is clear. Notice what that is like. Remember that it takes time to learn and to develop your own ways of clearing space. In our centre we practice in groups. This is very helpful because we can share and learn from each other's process. Clearing space can be very challenging, so feeling the power of the group coregulation supports us.

Step 2: Getting a Felt Sense of the Problem

Let your inside self decide which of the issues would like your attention now. Which feels the most in need, the most awful or urgent or sticky or prickly. Now, ask into your body – keeping your attention down inside:

What does this *whole* problem feel like? Don't answer in words: just let your inner sense of it form. Notice how you feel, what thoughts come, what physical sensations emerge – and if there are memories that come in the felt sense. Be patient, and quiet with your inside self, allowing a sense of all of it to form. This is a matter of learning what to pay attention to and what to ignore. Let the jabbering go. Bring your attention back to the centre of the body, staying with a gentle, curious attitude. The felt sense is often fuzzy and vague – not something we are used to paying attention to.

Step 3: Finding a Handle

What is the quality of the felt sense? Is it sticky, hungry, longing, jumpy-restless? Is there a word, phrase, colour or movement in your body that captures its essence? This is what we call the *handle*.

In this third movement, you may begin to find your problem changing. It may begin to feel different from what you expected, before you started focusing; different from anything you might have figured out by rational means. The difference may be small and subtle and perhaps puzzling at first. This is what we are looking for; something that comes along with a body shift. Discard everything else (Gendlin, 1978/1981, p. 63).

This step symbolizes the experience. *Languaging*, or saying aloud the qualities of the felt sense enhances and sometimes crystalizes the meaning making.

The Felt Shift

I find that when a handle comes, it often brings with it a sense of physical release, an "Aha!" or a "Yes, that's it" kind of feeling. This we call a *felt shift*. It may be small; we have to be quiet and attend to the inside place with patience and respect. It's like learning how to be with yourself the way you would be with someone you really love who is shy and needs to feel safe. It doesn't always come during a focusing round, but the process is alive in the body and carries on as we move forward.

Sometimes, the felt shift is enormously powerful. Ageless tears well up and flow, or tight painful feelings in the chest release and ease in a new way. This is the body's way of shifting states in the autonomic nervous system. The shift moves us from a tight flight/fight sympathetic state to a calm safe ventral vagal state, or from a dead-end, numb, dorsal vagus state back to ventral vagus. Listening to the bodily knowing, informed by the nervous system and our conscious awareness, reveals our own unique direction in healing. We become our own experts in carrying our path forward.

The heart of focusing is the felt shift. Without understanding and attending to this natural process of healing, we miss the most important information available to us. This shift, I am arguing, is the body's link to and expression of the ANS and the inherent will to survive and thrive. Many therapies today add a body scan as a way of paying lip service to the need for embodied approaches. But this is only halfway into the body. The other half is the listening for direction through the wonders of the felt shift. The shift brings the meaning of the experience with it. The process of focusing is summed up in the title of Gendlin's first book, *Experiencing and the Creation of Meaning* (1962/1997). He invites us to go down inside to the place of experiencing and we follow the body back up to symbolizing the experience through the handle. This creates the embodied next step, the meaning step in our life process.

The Addictive Shift

You will notice on the clinician version of the *felt sense polyvagal model* (FSPM) that there are two kinds of shifts noted. The dotted lines circling the outside of the states from dorsal and sympathetic down to ventral, and the squiggly lines going from dorsal and sympathetic to addicted. The focusing shift is an embodied, grounded shift that seeks integration. The addicted shift is also a release in the body, but it is not connected to the integrated state. This can be very confusing for the addicted client, as they struggle to identify their bodily process, and claim their safe and connected self. The addicted shift does not contain meaning. It does not carry life forward. It carries life process around and around in endless vicious (and we mean *vicious*) cycles. As we see on the model, the addicted cycle is in the upper half, the emotionally dysregulated part of the cycle. This is where the FSPM model is so useful. Clients can see visually and map out their current state, the place where they need to be, and what they need to do to get there.

Step 4: Resonating Felt Sense and Handle

Here we take the handle word or phrase or movement and check it against the felt sense. Make sure – as you say it back – it resonates perfectly. You may want to change your handle. Your partner may repeat your handle back to you and it may not sound right.

Wobbly?

No, not quite wobbly.

Jumpy?

Yes, that's it! Jumpy.

Step 5: Asking

Using the handle to make the felt sense vivid, you ask into it. What does it need? What about this whole problem makes me feel jumpy? Or, what would it feel like in my body without all of this? Or, what is the worst of all of this? Asking is a powerful step that requires skill in finding the right questions and the right time to ask. If you hear a lot of thoughts or answers, just go right past them and back down into the bodily sense of it all. This step is particularly powerful when a skilled listener can help you go deeper into your felt sense. This is the power of focusing partnerships. This is polyvagal theory in action. The power of coregulation to enhance the healing journey.

Step 6: Receiving

Take the time to welcome whatever comes and savour it. Often, the most uncomfortable places yield the most information. This is just one step along the way. Enjoy the new knowing. Let yourself resonate with the felt shift. Notice how it sits in your body. This step can bring you to a deep level of experiencing, an *aha* moment which needs to be appreciated. Take your time to claim your truth.

George's First Focusing Session

Now that you are acquainted with the six steps of focusing, I want to share with you how we bring the practice into the therapy room.

George, a tightly wound, 35-year-old architect comes in for his third appointment. His tone with me is curt, and I feel an angry burst of energy about to erupt. "I'm frustrated with this process. I feel confused about it. What am I supposed to be doing? I feel so pissed off with everyone at work, and at home I am yelling at my son all the time. I thought we were going to get to the bottom of this here. But I just feel mad!"

I look over at George and take a deep breath. I feel into his bodily felt sense. Clenched jaw, furled mouth. He is ready to pounce. I hardly know George. In the last two sessions he was more anxious than angry. He talked about a lot of stress at work. As an architect he worked long hours, and pressure to produce was wearing him out. It was hard to sleep, and hard to take care of his six-year-old son on the weekends. Separated a year ago, he lived alone during the week. He used to look forward to seeing his boy on the weekends, but in the last while he can hardly drag himself out of bed. In fact, he even cancelled the last visit with his son. Just as we were ending the last session, he shared that he has lost ten pounds. He feels this hard pit in his stomach, and he can't eat.

This comes back to me now, as I sit with tight, seething George. I sense an opening here to go into the body, but I'm not sure what will happen. We need to slow things down some, so I ask him if he will try something with me. "You are so angry and uncomfortable. Will you try something with me?"

He sighs, a big sigh, and looks straight at me. I hold the gaze. We stay like that for what feels like a while. I breathe down into my belly and soften my face, especially the little muscles around my eyes and mouth. I relax my jaw. "Humour me George." I slowly let a warm little smile emerge. I'm testing his nervous system to see if he can find a bit of ventral energy. I feel a slight settling in his body, and we connect ever so slightly.

"I want you to bring your attention to your feet." He shuffles his feet in a self-conscious way like a reluctant kid. "And close your eyes if it feels ok." He looks down at his brown birkenstocks, and slowly closes his eyes. "I'm wondering how that pit in your stomach is feeling right now?"

Immediately, George opens his eyes, wide, and starts to tighten up. I wait, and let the body show us the next step. He looks afraid so I say, "Something here wants your attention. We have to be gentle and go slowly. We can take our time and learn to be with it." I wait and see what his body says. To my delight he closes his eyes again, and we are off to the embodied exploration of the felt sense. In time George learns that he is protecting this deeply anxious pit in his stomach with drugs and rage. He learns to welcome the bodily knowing and the felt shifts that help him to understand his fears.

This is one example of how we bring the body into our work. We learn how to find openings, embodied signals like tears, or tight rage, or references to physical sensations. We lean in and help our clients feel safe enough to enter an implicit world of inner wisdom.

Thinking at the Edge (TAE)

Gendlin took the six steps of focusing into the conceptual world. TAE is the methodology that comes from his philosophy of the implicit. He developed it when teaching theory construction at the University of Chicago. In this multidisciplinary course he taught philosophy and logic and engaged in what he called,

> ...the difficult task of getting students to attend to what they implicitly knew but could not say and never considered trying to say. Whereas everywhere else in the university only what was clear counted at all, here we cared only about what was as yet unclear. (2004, p. 1)

He was speaking of the murky edge of the felt sense, the place where you have a sense of knowing, but also not knowing, a place where there is more to come. That is the place where we connect into the bottom-up process of focusing and invite the body to tell us what this *more* is. Together with his wife and intellectual partner, Mary Hendricks, Gendlin developed 14 steps in the TAE process. The steps, just like the six steps of focusing, are simply to help connect with the process. Once you get it, you can drop the steps. But in the beginning, it is valuable to lay them out.

The 14 Steps of TAE

1. Let a felt sense form about your subject, project, theme.
2. Find what is more than logical in your felt sense, a paradox.
3. Notice that you don't mean the standard definitions of the words.
4. Write a sentence or fresh phrase to say what you wanted each of the three words to mean.
5. Expand what you wanted each word to mean by writing fresh, linguistically unusual sentences.
6. Collect facets.
7. Allow the facets to contribute detailed structure.
8. Cross the facets.
9. Write freely.
10. Choose terms and link them.
11. Ask into the inherent relations between the terms.
12. Choose permanent terms and interlock them.
13. Apply your theory outside your field.
14. Expand and apply your theory in your field.

As I began the research for this book, I became interested in finding out more about TAE, and sought out training Evelyn Fendler-Lee an organizational psychologist and TAE specialist. In writing and learning about the process, and as the journey unfolds, I realize that, unbeknownst to me, all along I have been using the TAE process to guide me in developing the FSPM.

TAE as a Three-Step Process

Steps 1–5: Speaking From the Felt Sense

My felt sense of the problem in how we understand addiction evolved over many years. I know in my bones that I developed the model from a bodily response to the women in my first therapy group. In exploring the strands of the felt sense I discovered a crux of the problem in a paradox, "What helps you, harms you." I knew that the help was not being heard, and therefore the way in which addiction was being treated was missing this point. We had to acknowledge the help in order to deal with the harm. The implicit intricacy of how addictions worked for people needed to be thoroughly explored. I remember an explicit example with Bridgette in the group. She helped me to understand how important it is to listen freshly to what is being experienced. Brigette could not have endured the pain without her addictive behaviours. I welcomed all the contradictions in logic. When I went into my body, the contradictions merged into an image of a singular path, still murky, but slowly becoming defined. A sentence came: "One without the other is an incomplete truth." The help without the harm was an incomplete picture of the truth about how addiction works in the body. I trusted that the way forward in understanding addiction would come from a bodily knowing.

Steps 6–8: Finding Patterns From Facets (Instances)

I collected instances from my clinical work and began to develop patterns that emerged. Understanding how Bridgette would flood with emotion, and then numb led me to search for patterns in emotional states. I noticed the felt shifts in my clients' bodies, and in my own experiencing. I linked the shifts to the help that they reported feeling. The physical relief in the body could be initiated with addictive behaviours. This pattern repeated over and over with client instances.

Step 9: Write Freely

Exploring the felt sense led to the crossing of help and harm and the interaction that came from them formed the sentence, "The help embraces the harm."

Steps 10–14: Building Logical Theory

A TAE theory is logical and experiential. The logic comes through working with the paradox. We define our terms with three words or phrases that become A, B, and C.

In my case, I chose A: addictive behaviours; B: addictive behaviours are helpful and C: addictive behaviours are hurtful. Then we build a logic by playing with the three terms as follows: A = B, A = C, B = C.

A = B Addictive behaviours are helpful
A = C Addictive behaviours are harmful
B = C Addictive behaviours are helpful and harmful.

One without the other is an incomplete truth. The whole model is the experiential and logical continuation of the earlier steps. As an example, retrospectively, we see how the paradox, when put into the logical structure that Gendlin names "new pattern" (step 12), develops the whole model. As Fendler-Lee says, "This is the 'goal' of the first TAE steps – to find a way to say what the crux of the experience is, what the new thing is that you know, first in a bodily way and then you find the words for it" (personal communication, October 29, 2020).

Step 13, applying your theory outside your field, helped me to understand the interaction and inherent logic of my three terms. Hearing clients' descriptions of the felt shifts from flooding to numbing helped me to link the concepts of chaos/flooding and rigidity/numbing in interpersonal neurobiology. This patterning led me to study the autonomic nervous system and polyvagal theory. This added understanding helped to resolve the paradox. Our nervous system is designed to help in ways that are also hurtful when the environment requires this to survive. So, A: addictive behaviours are helpful; B: they are hurtful; and C: they are helpful *and* hurtful. A then equals C.

The TAE process is complex and requires much more study than this book can cover. As we move through the chapters, we will use TAE to experience the concepts from each theory. While the steps may be new, the felt sense of the process will unfold as we go on.

My step 14, expand and apply your theory in your field, is the creation of this book.

References

Gendlin, E. T. (1962/1997). *Experiencing and the creation of meaning: A philosophical and psychological approach to the subjective.* Evanston, IL: Northwestern University Press.

Gendlin, E. T. (1978/1981). *Focusing.* New York: Bantam Books.

Gendlin, E. T. (2004). Introduction to thinking at the edge, *The Folio, 19*(1), p. 1–8.

Porges, S. (2011). *The polyvagal theory.* New York: W.W. Norton & Co.

Winhall, J. (2014). Understanding and treating addiction with the felt sense experience model. In G. Madison, (Ed.), *Emerging practice in focusing-oriented psychotherapy.* London: Jessica Kingsley Publishers.

3   Thinking About Thinking About Addiction: Integrating Top-Down and Bottom-Up

It's essential to think about *how* we think about something as a place to start an inquiry since the approach will shape our definition of addiction and the suggested treatment path. Our way of seeing and knowing informs our path of discovery. Let's take some time here to ponder, to wonder about how we are thinking about addiction. How might we study it if we begin to integrate the *felt sense polyvagal model* (FSPM)?

As we start our conceptual exploration, it is vital that we take time to connect with our whole being, to greet addiction where it lives, in the body. If we don't give ourselves this sense of connection with body, if we don't settle inside ourselves, we create theory that is disembodied. Much of our Western thinking comes from this kind of disconnection. When we take first-person experiencing out of the process of developing new ideas, we create an intellectual world that is devoid of lived experiencing and connection with the natural world. And when we create disconnection, we cannot feel safe because we *are* unsafe. Living in our post-Descartes culture has resulted in a travesty. Descartes, a 17th-century French philosopher, is the architect of the mind-body split that privileges thought over embodied ways of knowing. This bias is creating a world that is destroying itself. This then leads to a cycle of trauma, whereby people grow up in a dissociated state, hurting and being hurt by each other.

Gendlin (1997/2018) states in his philosophical work *A Process Model*:

> The whole body *is* an interaction with the environment. In traditional Western philosophy the whole body was ignored. Experience had to be built out of perceptions by the five sense-organs. In order to think of those as the source of experience, one had to jump from colours and smells to the experience of objects, things, and situations. One was not supposed to notice that even the simplest situation cannot be thought of as bits of colour and smell. (p. 112)

In focusing practice, we have an embodied way of exploring and developing theory via *thinking at the edge* (TAE; 2004)). This process was created by Gendlin and Mary Hendricks and involves 14 steps, with three stages of inquiry. In seeking a bottom-up approach to the study of addiction, I found myself exploring more of Gendlin's writings. My experience of reading his early work, *Experiencing and the Creation of Meaning* has been profound. Here Gendlin (1962/1997) lays out the struggle to integrate top-down (logical and objective) and bottom-up (felt dimension of experiencing) processing. He states:

> The task at hand is to examine the relationships between this felt dimension of experience and the logical and objective orders. How can logical symbolizations and operational definitions be related to felt experiencing? Or, to reverse the question: what are the functions of felt experiencing in our conceptual operations and in our observable behaviour? (p. 1)

Important to notice is Gendlin's very clear caution about how to answer this question. He is emphatic about the importance of both methods. "The study of human behaviour can be guided and aided if we can learn what kind of concept *can* relate to felt experience and how concepts of this kind can, in turn, relate to objective concepts and measurements" (p. 3). The FSPM is an attempt to relate the felt experiencing of addiction with objective concepts and neurophysiological measurements.

Top-Down Processing

Our Western culture favours cognition over emotion, leaning heavily on the mind/body split as a way of organizing reality. As discussed, this split originates with Descartes, who believed that mind and body are distinct and separable. As a result of the powerful influence of this way of thinking, many of us live in our heads and tend to dismiss or dissociate from our bodily awareness. From birth we receive messages that confirm this bias. In our education system, if constraints apply, the first two classes to be cancelled are often physical education and art. Cognition reigns supreme. This orientation represents *top-down processing*, an approach that dominates our way of being. It is infused in everything we experience. It is hard to get enough distance from it to appreciate its presence. Sometimes it feels like it is simply "reality".

Top-down processes look for already known patterns and models to organize and understand new information. They are mediated by the brain's left hemisphere. The left hemisphere has a historical rather than a present-moment perspective, so it tends to sort perceptions into categories based on our prior experiences (Siegel, 1999, p. 256).

McGilchrist (2009) speaks of the left brain as prizing consistency and offering familiar, simplified models to explain complex human problems, at the expense of a more sophisticated and nuanced understanding of experience. McGilchrist is deeply concerned with the dominance of the left-hemisphere biased, top-down monopolization of our current culture.

A cognitive approach relies on memory. When we see a tree, we say to ourselves: "There is a tree," and we move on to the next thing because we know what a tree is and we put it into a category. The strength in this approach is that it helps us to create order from novelty. It seeks precision and commonality. It anticipates what will happen next based on past experience. It cuts to the chase, containing the chaos. Top-down thinking uses logic and our knowledge of the tangible, observable world. This orientation towards concrete, focused thought enables us to create airplanes, the computer I am using to write this book, buildings, refrigerators, electrical and plumbing systems, and advanced medical treatments to help those who become physically ill due to addiction. It leads to the advancement in medications that improve and save people's lives. Imagine if everything we perceived was new to us. Life would be overwhelming and scary. At its best, top-down processing is practical and comforting, and it can help us to feel safe in an ever-changing environment. This is essential for well-being. So it is not that we reject top-down thinking, but that we need more of a balance between this and the kind of information that comes from the bottom up, from the embodied experience of living.

Brain-Disease Model

Lewis (2018) aptly describes the prevalent brain-disease model of addiction: "According to the brain disease model, addiction is a chronic disease brought on by changes in the brain systems that mediate the experience and anticipation of reward and in higher-order systems that underlie judgment and cognitive control" (p. 1).

Our current way of understanding addiction as a brain disease reflects a top-down approach that suggests addiction changes the brain and that these changes represent disease. The brain-disease model has been prevalent for the past 30 years, and the medical profession is a key player in diagnosis and treatment. The advancement of neuroimaging technologies promotes the change to a neurobiological model. It has shifted our understanding of addiction from a morality model (the addict is morally impaired) to a medical model (the addict is sick). Some people draw comfort from this shift. Certainly if one had to choose between being seen as bad, or sick, sick would trump.

Addiction According to the Diagnostic and Statistical Manual (DSM)

If we understand addiction as a disease, diagnosing becomes the next step in treatment. The *Diagnostic and Statistical Manual of Mental Disorders*

(1952) was first published by the American Psychiatric Association as a way of offering a common language and standard criteria for diagnosing mental disorders. As a top-down process, it offers specific units, or diagnostic categories, with which to understand psychological distress. It has become the bible for treating people suffering from mental "illness". It's interesting to note that the preamble to DSM-III in 1980 "warned explicitly that its categories were insufficiently precise to be used in forensic settings or for insurance purposes" (in van der Kolk, 1999, p. 137). Nonetheless, a DSM diagnosis has gradually become a requirement in the psychiatric system, and in billing for most insurance companies.

The DSM forms the basis for all medical, psychiatric, and psychological training programmes. Many faculties of social work do not include the teaching of the DSM but rather focus on a sociological critique of "mental illness". (In Chapter 4, we will delve into alternative models for understanding addiction.) It's important to appreciate how much human suffering has become medicalized. There is much controversy, for example, about the increasing number of diagnostic categories with each addition of the DSM. The first edition in 1952 mentions 102 disorders. By 1980 that number became 265. The DSM-IV (1994) increased the number to 297. The system changed for DSM-V, and the number of diagnostic categories is hard to get a consensus on. It ranges from 157 to 541, depending on how you classify the categories. What is clear is that over the years, there has been a marked increase in the ways to call us crazy, unwell, diseased, or maladapted.

The DSM claims that "Alcohol use disorder runs in families, with 40–60% of the variance of risk explained by genetic influences" (p. 494). This statement is highly controversial, yet it is presented in the DSM as fact. The only behavioural addiction that is included is gambling because it was decided that there were not enough peer-reviewed studies of other behavioural addictions to warrant inclusion.

Critiquing the DSM

Much has been written about the major problems with the DSM, mostly in relation to the lack of reliability in diagnosis, and the nature of, and increasing number of diagnostic categories, hence an ever increasing medicalization of what may actually be simply "problems of living" (Szasz, 1960, p. 113).

The Rosenhan experiment is famous for illustrating the problematic nature of the DSM. It was designed to determine the validity of psychiatric diagnoses. In order to be admitted to psychiatric hospitals, the experimenters pretended to be hearing voices in their heads that said "thud". Once they were admitted to the psychiatric ward they acted normally. In spite of their return to normal functioning, all were diagnosed with schizophrenia and put on antipsychotic medication. They spent an average of 19 days in hospital. Rosenhan (1973) called the resulting article, published in the prestigious journal *Science,* "On being sane in insane places". It is still referred to today when people are critiquing the system.

The DSM-III did establish more diagnostic reliability and has been used to facilitate research and clinical practice as well as providing credibility in court proceedings. However, DSM-V had abysmal results. Frances (2010), professor emeritus at Duke University and chairman of the DSM-IV task force, was highly critical of this edition. He described the grave consequences of false-positive epidemics of disorders that would be constituted through inappropriate usage of new diagnostic entities. In so doing, DSM-V would "expand the territory of mental disorder and thin the ranks of the normal". In other words, it would help to further "medicalize" society.

To be fair, it is not my intention to paint all psychiatrists or those who adhere to the DSM as enemies, or uncaring fools. Quite the contrary, I believe that most people working in the system want to do a good job in taking care of their patients. None of what I am saying is personal. In fact, my partner is a psychiatrist. "Wow," you might say. "How does that work?" Well, interestingly, in our clinic, we are developing a progressive new way to be with people who seek us out for help. We have a non-hierarchical circle of care for each client. Whoever has the most expertise to help with the issue leads that aspect of care. We do not have a "medical" model. We have an embodied wholistic model.

First-Person Experiencing of DSM

In my early days as a psychiatric social worker I was employed at a small community hospital in a very challenged neighbourhood. This was where I ran the group that I wrote about at the beginning of this book. In the mornings I attended rounds where we discussed patients, then I went from ward to ward responding to requests for psychiatric consultations. My job was to meet with the patient and take a life history, specifically regarding any mental health issues. Then I would go with the psychiatrist to interview the patient and complete the assessment. We covered all medical wards and the emergency department of the hospital. We saw it all. It was a shocking, traumatic, incredibly informative experience. And it is from this first experience that I immersed myself into a disturbing world ... disturbing in many ways.

Firstly, as demonstrated in Rosenhan's study, I was shocked by what I read in patient charts. It wasn't unusual for one person to have five or six (or more) diagnoses from at least that many admissions to hospital. In addition, they would often be taking at least the same number of medications. Right from the start, this simply did not make sense to me, although it was a predictable outcome of an ineffectual system of diagnostic categories. Secondly, the medical hierarchy, although familiar, was still infuriating to my young, eager-to-be-impactful, professional self. My role was clearly to assist in history taking so that the psychiatrist could make a diagnosis of mental disorder even though these women were far better understood as victims of horrific crimes.

A Group Vignette

Let's return to the women's group from Chapter 1, and I will share my experience and how it shaped my search for a new understanding of what I was witnessing. One bitterly cold day about six months into weekly group meetings, the women are gazing at me as they often do when we are looking for a way back into the sludge.

Mary, as I will call her, is being challenged by Bridgette, the brunette who carries her anger like a shield. "Why do you always wear those stupid stiletto heels in the winter? Aren't you freezing?" This is so interesting, I think to myself. Bridgette is attacking and caring at the same time. She has to present her caring about Mary in an angry way.

"I have to wear them, I can't walk without them," Mary replies, looking ashamed and afraid.

"What?" says Brigette.

"My dad started buying me high heels when I was eight years old. I can't walk without them now. My feet don't go flat." Silence.

Mary takes off her shoes and tries to walk around the room. She wobbles and winces and reaches for her heels in a hurry. This leads into Mary's story of sexual abuse by her father and his friends. They would dress her up to look "sexy" and then take turns sexually assaulting her. This then leads into many stories of being abused, and many more stories of how each woman has developed ways to cope with the atrocities committed against them. I learn to listen, to hold and contain the unspeakable.

Over many weeks we meet and merge in this precious group. We soak the murky wall of this hospital room with the energy of excavated trauma. As I listen to all that is emerging, I become increasingly curious about what I am hearing. All of the women are engaging in "self-harming" behaviours, many of which have become addictive. They are cutting themselves on their arms and legs and sometimes their vaginas. They are picking at their faces and pulling at their hair. They are drinking huge amounts of hard liquor, smoking marijuana daily, chain smoking cigarettes, bingeing on inordinate amounts of food, starving themselves, purging. The more they share, the more they reveal a bizarre array of behaviours. And they describe these behaviours as mechanisms for dealing with the pain. Somehow, and I am not sure how at this point, these behaviours are "helping" them. Helping and hurting simultaneously.

If I listen to the psychiatric community in the hospital, they will tell me that these women have *borderline personality disorder*. They will say the women's behaviours are because they are masochistic and manipulative. They are trying to get attention. The staff urge me to distance and not engage with patients, since I will be viewed as condoning their "obnoxious" behaviour.

Herman (1992) noted this stigmatization of trauma victims:

> Patients, usually women, who receive these diagnoses evoke unusually intense reactions in caregivers. Their credibility is often suspect. They are frequently accused of manipulation or malingering. They are often the subject of furious and partisan controversy. Sometimes they are frankly hated. (p. 123)

Hated. Yes. I feel that deep inside me, and it motivates me to continue this work. To bring change to outrageous and deeply misogynistic ways. What is it about these young women that activates such an appalling response from the very people who are mandated to help them? This is a crucial question that we will revisit throughout the book. Surely it comes from a place of fear, a profound lack of a sense of safety and grounding on the part of the healers. Thus, I will argue, we need a model that starts with the premise of safety first. Safety is the fundamental beginning. In safety we find curiosity and courage to explore new frontiers. In safety, we find the capacity to afford dignity to all living creatures.

In my reality at the hospital, I am becoming increasingly emotionally engaged with my group of survivors. I see the twisted ways in which they ask for what they need. I might be young, but I am no fool. I see Bridgette's attack and care for Mary as a pairing of anger and vulnerability. A guarded way to communicate care by couching it in a container of contempt. I keep my eye on her caring energy. I hold it with her so she won't let it go, so she will learn to feel safe being with her loving self.

Sometimes I am scared, angry, appalled by their ways, but I know in my felt sense that these ways come from a very wounded place. It is my job to create enough safety and respect in the group, so that we can dig down underneath these ways and come to a more direct experiencing of life, a fresh way of being with each other that isn't defined by past experience. I never assume that this is easy, or that it will happen. But I believe that it is possible. This belief is the key to safety and healing. This belief, in allowing each person to come freshly and to be received freshly, without preconceived biases, or categories of understanding, is absolutely crucial to the healing process. And to the process of being truly alive. We cannot get there with *only* top down thinking. We have to also welcome our personal embodied response. We have to connect through the felt sense of the interaction to create change.

I know too that these young women have *almost* given up on love, on needing another person. Of course they have. They have turned to their trusted and twisted sources of survival for nourishment. They are drinking from the only well that they can rely on. But we all know, although we don't yet speak of it in the group, that this is not sustainable. They will have to find another source of nourishment if they want a good life.

Critiquing the Twelve Steps: The Origins and History of AA

It is fair to say that the twelve-step approach to treating addiction is by far the dominant method recommended by professionals and those struggling with addiction. Initial treatment often involves both in-and outpatient hospital settings and residential treatment programmes. Within these settings, twelve-step programmes are usually recommended, often with meetings occurring right in the facility. Over the past ten years, privately-run and very expensive residential programmes have become popular with those who can afford to attend. Obviously, this creates an unacceptable situation. Most people cannot afford fees up to $30,000 US per month. Some of these programmes offer trauma treatment in addition to cognitive behavioural therapy. I haven't heard of any that offer an embodied psychotherapy approach. By far, the majority of all facilities adhere to the brain disease model, in keeping with the twelve-step approach. While there are now many kinds of twelve-step programmes, including alcohol, narcotics, sex, shopping, gambling, marijuana, to name a few, alcoholics anonymous (AA) was the first of its kind.

AA began in 1935. Think about that. It was a very different time than we are living in now, particularly with the advent of the *decade of the brain* in the 1990s and the neuroplasticity revolution. Many of us are working hard to integrate the knowledge that has come from this new understanding of the brain. In 1935, we believed that the brain was fully developed at birth and that brain cells did not regenerate. Now we know that most of the brain develops after birth and that brain cells continue to reproduce as we age. Back then neuroscientists also advocated a *localization theory*. Like a machine, the brain was seen as made up of parts that occupied a location and performed a single function. If part of the brain was damaged, nothing could be done to repair it. Now we know that this is not the case. In fact, the brain can change and grow in many fascinating ways that exceed anything we had imagined. In addition, and perhaps most important, rather than seeing the brain as disconnected from the body, as Descartes would have us believe, we now know that the brain is *part of the body. Who would have thought?*

How did AA get its start? In 1934, just after Prohibition's repeal, a struggling stockbroker named Bill Wilson was admitted to a hospital in Manhattan for severe alcoholism. He had several admissions before achieving sobriety and going on to start what would become the most influential organization in North America for treating addiction. Wilson (2002) describes his heart-wrenching personal story, a tale as profoundly desperate as it is transforming. After years of daily, excessive, soul destroying drinking, Wilson was visited by an old friend who claimed to have overcome his addiction and wanted to help him.

> The door opened and he stood there, fresh-skinned and glowing. There was something about his eyes. He was inexplicably different. What had happened? I pushed a drink across the table. He refused it. Disappointed but curious, I wondered what had got into the fellow. He wasn't himself.
>
> "Come, what's all this about?" I queried.
>
> He looked straight at me. Simply, but smilingly, he said, "I've got religion." (p. 9)

Wilson (2002) describes his religious journey from a kind of passive belief in a power greater than himself to a profound conversion experience. "I must turn in all things to the Father of Light that presides over us all" (p. 14). He describes a sense of victory, peace, and serenity that was new to him. Wilson made a connection with the Oxford Group, a Christian organization founded by American missionary Frank Buchman. Buchman believed that all problems were a result of living in a state of fear and selfishness. One needed to surrender one's life over to "God's Plan". Wilson wrote, "God comes to men gradually, but His impact on me was sudden and profound" (p. 14).

Wilson based the AA approach on the beliefs of the evangelical Oxford Group founded by Buchman. Interesting to note is that the role of religion versus spirituality was part of the discussion in the formation of AA. While Wilson started out as a passive believer in a power greater than himself, perhaps closer to the spiritual experience, he had a profound conversion experience that lead him to adopt a more formal Christian doctrine. Today, the organization seems to be struggling to come to terms with this issue. While it is stated that you can believe in a power greater than yourself, however, you experience it to be, many of my clients do not feel that this is actually accepted in their group. They report that it is standard practice to close your eyes and pray to God, and they do not feel comfortable. It's like saying we accept vegetarians and then serving meat.

Wilson had a powerful conversion experience that finally led him to achieve sobriety. For him, the movement from the spiritual path to the evangelical path literally saved his life, and perhaps this trajectory is more deeply embedded in the organization than is realized. Thus, the implicit sense is that one will "get there" to a religious conversion with time.

The AA Controversy

So, here is my thinking about the AA approach. Wilson created a method for treating addiction that came out his own experience and worked for him. Chances are that it will be most successful for those who are like him. For clients who meet the following preconditions for membership, AA is a helpful method of treatment for addiction:

1. You believe in a higher power and are comfortable praying to God.
2. You believe that addiction is a brain disease and you will always be an addict.
3. You believe that family members are co-dependent. That is, the whole family system is sick, not just the addict.
4. You believe that total sobriety is essential to healing.
5. You believe that you must attend meetings for the rest of our life.
6. You believe that addiction is genetically predetermined.
7. Once you have achieved sobriety, you feel a sense of safety and trust in your embodied self.

Of course, many clients are willing to pick and choose what they like and don't like about the programme. They somewhat secretly continue to believe otherwise about things that may not be so important to them because they value much that works well: the connection with the fellowship, the financial and geographical accessibility, the sponsorship relationship, the structure of the twelve steps. The crucial issue from a FSPM perspective is that while you may pick and choose, you are able to achieve Number 7, a sense of safety and trust in your body.

Noel, a focusing trainer, has developed a method that integrates the six steps of focusing into the twelve-step programme. Her book, *Loving at the Edge: Recovery Emerging* (2010) provides a detailed outline of the path.

The Twelve Steps: Dancing with the Devil

Why do I emphasize this sense of embodied safety in relation to the twelve steps? It is very common in the twelve-step philosophy, and in general, to see the addict as devil-like, or as a trickster. This metaphor for addiction appears frequently in our culture. In tarot cards, the devil is associated with temptation and addiction. Homer Simpson sums it up in his image entitled "Butterfinger". Here we see Homer, caught in a struggle between the angel whispering in one ear and the devil with pitchfork in the other. With great gusto, he is pulling a big piece of Butterfinger chocolate bar out of the package and gazing into the devil's eyes. We all know this moment. But what happens if you have to deal with a multitude of these moments when trying to stop addictive behaviours, and you see the part of you that *wants and desires* as the devil?

There is a saying in the twelve-step tradition. Just when you think you are on top of your cravings, beware, "The addict's in the corner doing pushups." In other words, *you can't ever totally relax*, once an addict, always an addict. Hence, a lifelong journey of attending meetings and identifying as an addict forever.

Focusing Practice

I invite you to pause here and let yourself feel into your felt sense of the devil, or the trickster. What comes for you as you let yourself feel into this place? How would it be in your body to carry a part of you that feels evil, bad, greedy, and terrifying?

We will each have our own response to this, our own way of coming to terms with the dark side of ourselves. The key is to honour the response and ensure that the embodied self feels enough safety and is respected. For some, adhering to a twelve-step model puts them in a bind: wanting and needing the programme yet feeling diminished by the devil metaphor. There is a sense for some that this way of being with their addictive behaviours doesn't fit their experience, doesn't fit their embodied sense of themselves. Some clients also speak of feeling diminished by the sense of having to admit to powerlessness. Rather, they feel a growing sense of seeing the addict part as small and scared, more like a needy child. And they crave a sense of empowerment to help that little child to become stronger and free of shame.

For many of us, the idea of the addict devil, trickster creates a very unsafe, shaming feeling in the body. When working with clients in a focusing or mindful way, I can feel their embodied hyperarousal. The body can become permanently stuck in the hypervigilant state of flight/fight even though they have achieved years of sobriety. There is a part of the self, this addicted self in the corner, that will not let the body settle. Although they have achieved years of sobriety, they are unable to trust themselves because they have been indoctrinated with the belief that they must remain hypervigilant and deeply untrusting and even disgusted with this part of self.

I recall one client who had five years of sobriety and no conscious awareness of any concern about relapsing. However, his body was plagued with fear. As we worked more and more deeply with this felt sense of fear, he began to be able to separate out his own angst from the story that he was told in his AA group. Over many months, he slowly came into his own experiencing. Through clearing space in focusing practice, he was able to move into a more ventral state, slowly, slowly ... allowing himself to come home to trusting. From a felt sense polyvagal perspective, the crucial issue here is that clients feel safe enough in their bodies. Without enough safety, addictive behaviours will flourish.

If you return to the FSPM, you can see the addiction state at the top of the model. This intertwining state propels the person back and forth from a dysregulated sympathetic to a dorsal parasympathetic response. The addicted person lives most of the time in the upper half of the model, unable to settle into a calm, grounded ventral vagal state. It's telling that the grounded state is directly opposite the addicted state in the FSPM diagram.

Our job is to listen to how the body is responding to any kind of treatment. If there is a lack of sensing safety, the treatment is wrong for this person. On the other hand, if the twelve-step programme, or any other method of healing, is sitting well in the body, we honour that. Our job as psychotherapists is to support safety and growth and to respect each individual's way of healing.

Cognitive Behavioural Therapy: A Top-Down Approach

Within the field of psychology, paradigms have shifted from behavioural models in the 1960s to 1970s, to cognitive models in the 1970s and 1980s. Just as advancements in brain imaging impacted psychiatry, so followed psychology. The decade of the brain spanned between 1995 and 2005. The cognitive behavioural therapy (CBT) model flourished, and it continues to flourish now. Its emphasis is on changing the client's "maladaptive" cognitions in order to change behaviour. The trouble, it seems, is all in our heads.

Many of the addiction programmes utilize a CBT model, often in conjunction with the twelve-step programme. *Motivational interviewing* is also used. Each of these approaches appeals to a person's thinking and subsequent behavioural change making them a top-down method. In spite of an overwhelming body of research that speaks to the need for embodied psychotherapies, CBT remains a treatment of choice. It offers a brief course of therapy that appeals to insurance companies. Many CBT programmes are now attempting to incorporate a mindfulness component. When this is done well it can be effective.

Top-down thinking has its short comings. It can prevent us from experiencing life in a fresh, spontaneous, unbiased way because it anticipates what will happen next based on past experience. With too much top-down emphasis, life can become stale and repetitious, stuck in old ways and thinking. It can lead to dead ends and rigidity. In addition, a top-down approach has negated the importance of engaging the client in attending to bodily awareness. However, over the past decade or so, there has been a growing acknowledgement of the importance of physical well-being. Mindfulness meditation and yoga practices are making their way into treatment programmes.

So how do we allow for this fresh experiencing within the context of a need for some kind of shaping, categorizing, and common understanding of our clients' experience? Yes, we do need to seek out commonalities. But, how to describe these commonalities while honouring the nuance, the uniqueness of each person that we sit with who is suffering? In our quest for familiarity, it becomes very difficult to step back from the top-down approach and see where all those pieces that *don't* fit into the prevailing theory will go. Those pieces that are left over after the rest has been positioned into the theory are discarded. But what about those pieces? This brings us to bottom-up processing.

Embodied Processing: A Bottom-Up Approach

> The experts tell you not to be fixed in your thinking, but they don't tell you how to become free and open. If you pay direct attention to your sense of anything, that opens you up.
>
> (Gendlin, 1979)

The bottom-up approach privileges information that comes from bodily attention to the senses. It's important to note that 80% of the information travelling between the brain and the vagus nerve is afferent (moving up from body to brain), so we see the important connection with polyvagal theory and bottom-up processing. Someone with a bottom-up approach is curious about those pieces that don't fit into the theory. The inquiry takes place in the present moment. We see a tree and sense the breeze that comes from its branches as a new, fresh experience, with no pre-conceived notions of what tree means.

> Direct experience is a kind of texture – it doesn't have boxes. It's more like a Persian rug – even *that* is too structured. Experience is non-numerical and multi-schematic. No one scheme will ever explain it. You can always create another aspect of experience by putting any two elements together.
>
> (Gendlin, 1979)

Bottom-up experiencing is related to right brain processing. Siegel (1999) says,

The right brain is able to create the gist or context of experiences and the overall meaning of events. The nonverbal codes of the right hemisphere are predominately based on sensations and images. These rapidly associated images give us a more direct and immediate representation of the world and of ourselves. This gives us a perceptual advantage: We can perceive the world for "how it is" from a bottom-up perspective. (p. 256)

Bottom-up welcomes feeling and experiencing of all inside and outside awareness. Embodied awareness, information that flows up from the body to the brain (which is part of the body) and sensory awareness are experienced as one interaction in the present moment (Gendlin, 2018).

Key to bottom-up processing is that we start with first person experiencing. This makes it an inherently more vulnerable kind of inquiry. In revealing more about our personal embodied journey, we open our whole being: thoughts, feelings, physical sensations, and memories, our felt-sense experience, to our subject of study. An example of bottom-up processing is focusing and meditation practice.

The Marvellous Metaphor

Recall our journey inside to the six steps of focusing practice. We begin by bringing attention down into the body and asking into the felt sense. We find a shape, colour, image, or word that captures the quality of the felt sense. This becomes a metaphor, a way of being with the essence of the felt sense. We go back and forth from being down inside bodily knowing, back up to thinking and bringing words, sometimes beginning with gestures or movements, to conceptualize our process. In symbolizing our felt sense, we help to bring clarity and meaning to our experiencing, describing the felt sense as a metaphor for our lived experience. We saw the metaphor idea in the twelve-step description of the addict as devil, or the addict can be seen as the traumatized child. Another example of metaphor in focusing practice might be a rat in a box, struggling to find its way out, or a fierce windstorm that is sweeping through your home, or you as a little child being held by a big warm cloud. We often find metaphors in focusing with dream work.

McGilchrist (1999) states:

Only the right hemisphere has the capacity to understand metaphor. That might not sound too important – like it could be a nice thing if one were going to do a bit of lit crit. But that is just a sign of the degree to which our world of discourse is dominated by left-hemispheric habits of mind. Metaphoric thinking is fundamental to our understanding of the world, because it is the *only* way in which understanding can reach outside the system of signs to life itself. It is what links language to life. (p. 115)

"Linking language to life" is the process of focusing. Language is both left and right hemispheric in nature. "Language is the province of both hemispheres and, like everything else, has different meanings in either hemisphere. Each uses it differently, and different aspects of it stand out in the use that either hemisphere makes of it" (McGilchrist, 2009, p. 99). Words that come from deep experiencing often don't make sense in the world of the left hemisphere. But, never mind, they make sense from the right. They become the handle for the felt sense, symbolizing the essence of the practice. Moving from inside, implicit experiencing to outside, explicit *languaging* is the weaving, or zig-zagging, from bottom up to top down and back again of our focusing practice.

While top-down approaches involve a more cognitive style for the therapist, which allows for a certain distance from experience, vulnerable opening to our felt sense engages the therapist and client in a new way. Bringing bodily awareness into the relationship touches into the heart of what is happening in the room. We open to an experiential therapy that monitors moment-by-moment interaction. This demands a deep and courageous presence for the therapist. It involves great sensitivity in titrating the intensity of that presence so as not to frighten the client. We take gentle steps, staying with our bodily, bottom-up awareness, to hold a grounded, calm, healing space.

The Safe Edge: Where Bottom-Up Meets Top-Down

We can develop a capacity to be curious, bold in our stepping into fresh territory (bottom-up), and safe in our familiar knowing (top-down) at the same time. I call this the *safe edge*. In this space, we can explore our experiences through a felt sense journey. This gentle act of bravery involves thinking, feeling, physical sensation, and memory. All are welcome and enlivened. We can step into the edge of experience and step back when we need to rest in a safe nest. Stepping back also allows us to reflect and look for already known patterns or ways of understanding our experiences. This powerful knowing – I can step in, I can step back – provides us with a wide *window of tolerance* (Siegel, 1999) for experiencing and for thinking about experiencing.

Siegel (1999) coined the term "window of tolerance" to describe the zone of arousal in which a person is able to function most effectively. In this zone, we are able to respond to life's ups and downs without getting thrown off course. In this grounded place, a person's state of arousal is neither over-stimulated (flight/fight, chaotic) or under-stimulated (fold, rigid). The wider the window, the more varied experiences a person can integrate, while staying grounded in a ventral vagal state. It enables us to be more deeply connected to ourselves and to each other.

In a broader sense: the wider the window of tolerance, the more we can integrate top-down and bottom-up experiencing, both in our personal lives and in our intellectual work. This safe edge is a place of integration. In the words of Badenoch (2008), "Some would say it is precisely when top-down crashes into bottom-up that creativity flourishes" (p. 180). The safe edge embraces both processes, honouring the need for safety/ familiarity, and freshly new. It's a sweet spot of contained exploration. The following is a wonderful example that describes the "primacy of human presence" in the process of psychotherapy. Gendlin (1990) wrote:

> I want to start with the most important thing I have to say: The essence of working with another person is to be present as a living being. And this is lucky, because if we had to be smart, or good, or mature, or wise, then we would probably be in trouble. But what matters is not that. What matters is to be a human being with another human being, to recognize the other person as another being in there. Even if it is a cat or a bird, if you are trying to help a wounded bird, the first thing you have to know is that there is somebody in there, and that you have to wait for that "person", that being in there, to be in contact with you. That seems to me to be the most important thing.
> So when I sit down with someone, I take my troubles and feelings and I put them over here, on one side, close, because I might need them. I might want to go in there and see something. And I take all the things that I have learnt – client-centred therapy, reflection, focusing, Gestalt, psycho-analytic concepts, and everything else (I wish I had even more) – and I put them over here, on the other side, close. Then I am just here, with my eyes, and there is this other being. If they happen to look into my eyes, they will see that I am just a shaky being. I have to tolerate that. They may not look. But if they do, they will see that. They will see the slightly shy, slightly withdrawing, insecure existence that I am. I have learnt that that is o.k. I do not need to be emotionally secure and firmly present. I just need to be present. (p. 205)

Here we see Gendlin's capacity to create a safe and connected space. He welcomes and indeed, celebrates, both ways of processing. He names already known top-down theory, and bottom-up first-person experiences, and places them on either side. He creates a cleared space inside and then he is ready to be in a fresh, bottom-up process with the client. He encourages us to move back and forth from bottom-up to top-down to see if we have already-known theory that may help the client. But the crucial difference is that he does not interpret the client's experience to fit into the box. He *suggests* it, and the client checks in to bottom-up knowing, the bodily felt sense, to see if it fits. The body then guides the process. If it fits, he works with it through the six steps of focusing, or other methods. If it doesn't fit, he simply discards it.

This way of being, open, fresh, knowledgeable, and fully present creates a very safe and respectful way of holding our clients. We are not the expert in their process. We are keeping them company and offering our ways of understanding as they zig-zag back and forth from experiencing to symbolization to meaning making. They begin to gain a sense of grounding and confidence about their process through following this gentle path. The emphasis on safety and respect is a fundamental part of focusing and polyvagal theory.

Thinking at the Safe Edge: A Non-Pathologizing Approach to Addiction

My felt sense polyvagal model (FSPM) embraces the safe edge and crosses it with TAE. This allows is to be as creative as we can be in our exploration. Instead of starting from the top down with what we already know (which is a lot), let's start from the body up and see where we meet top-down. Then we can truly embrace both ways of knowing freshly, bodily, and with clear thinking. If we pause and allow ourselves to take a fresh look at addiction with no preconceived theories or recommended treatments, we create a bottom-up approach to being with our client.

When I listened to the young women in the group, I heard how their self-harming, compulsive behaviours were in fact helping them cope with unbearable pain. Some of the behaviours were not addictive. However, many developed into addictions over time, as they were so desperately needed in the moment and brought relief into the body. I understood that in the context of inescapable abuse, the body was unconsciously protecting itself, although I had *no idea* how that worked. I understood that I needed to direct attention gently into the embodied experience because it was the body that was speaking clearly from a place of no words. The events were unspeakable.

Now, with the knowledge of polyvagal theory, we can explain the self-harming behaviours through the lens of the ANS. When we do that, we see that the disease model is not compatible with the experience. According to the polyvagal theory, the body is designed to shift into a dissociative state for survival. These behaviours act as very efficient propellers that facilitate this shift. If the shift helps the person to endure otherwise unbearable experiences, then how is this a disease? What other so-called diseases are a result of the body's natural process and provide help to survive?

The capacity to be present, with nothing in the way, is very challenging for therapists. In the top-down climate of treatment, with ever-pressing concerns about health-care costs, and proving our effectiveness, it is difficult to hold a quiet, still, embodied place with people who have been, quite literally, running from stillness for dear life. Stillness is dangerous if you are being attacked. Filling the space with drugs, alcohol, food, sex, and computers is about survival. And for therapists, words, ideas, and prescriptive methods are hard to resist. They help us to deal with our own overwhelming feelings of sadness and grief when hearing such horrific stories. They are invaluable when we are trying to help. And yet, it is this very capacity to be with our client, in safe, quiet stillness, that must be embraced for the next step to come.

References

American Psychiatric Association. (1980). *Diagnostic and statistical manual* (3rd ed.). Washington, DC: American Psychiatric Association.
Badenoch, B. (2008). *Being a brain-wise therapist: A practical guide to interpersonal neurobiology.* New York: W.W. Norton & Company.
Frances, A. (2010). The first draft of DSM-V if accepted will fan the flames of false positive diagnoses. *BMJ, 340,* 492.
Gendlin, E. T. (1962/1997). *Experiencing and the creation of meaning.* Evanston, IL: Northwestern University Press.
Gendlin, E. T. (1979). Gendlin: Experience is richer than psychology models. *Brain-Mind Bulletin, 4*(10), 2.
Gendlin, E. T. (1990). The small steps of psychotherapy process: How they come and how to help them come. In G. Lietaer, J. Rombauts, & R. Van Balen (Eds.), *Client-centred and experiential psychotherapy in the nineties.* Leuven: Leuven University Press (pp. 205–224).
Gendlin, E. T. (1997/2018). *A process model.* Evanston, IL: Northwestern University Press.
Gendlin, E. T. (2004). Introduction to thinking at the edge, *The Folio, 19*(1), p. 1–8.
Herman, J. (1992). *Trauma and recovery.* New York: Basic Books.
Lewis, M. (2018). Brain change in addiction as learning, not disease. New England Journal of Medicine, *379,* 1551 1560 10.1056/NEJMra1602872.
McGilchrist, I. (2009). *The master and his emissary: The divided brain and the making of the Western world.* New Haven: Yale University Press.
Noel, S. (2010). *Loving at the edge: Recovery emerging.* Author.
Rosenhan, D. (1973). On being sane in insane places. *Science, 179,* 250–258.
Siegel, D. J. (1999). *The developing mind: Toward a neurobiology of interpersonal experience.* New York: The Guilford Press.
Siegel, D. J. (2016). *Journey to the heart of being human.* New York: W.W. Norton & Company.
Szasz, T. S. (1960). The myth of mental illness. *American Psychologist,* 15, 113–118.
Wilson, B. (2002). *The big book of alcoholics anonymous* (4th ed.). New York AA Services.

4   Addiction: A Very Bad Habit

So, if addiction isn't a disease, what is it? The felt sense polyvagal model (FSPM) of addiction uses a *learning model* from the work of Lewis (2015). I am a seeker. I look for new ways, fresh approaches that include first-person experiencing. As I was creating the FSPM, I searched for a way of understanding addiction that is compatible with the non-pathologizing, embodied approach reflected in the polyvagal theory and focusing oriented psychotherapy. I looked for a way of understanding the complexity of addiction from the body up, viewing the body as a living organism that is imbued with a knowing of the right next steps for surviving and thriving. Lewis (2018) states, "Learning models propose that addiction, though obviously disadvantageous, is a natural, context-sensitive response to challenging environmental contingencies, not a disease."

A natural, context-sensitive response. Yes. If we view the body as alive, and wise, we see addictive behaviours as ways to survive when all else fails. And if we view the neurobiology of addiction as a natural process that occurs in emotionally dysregulated experiences, then addiction is a learning process, not a disease process. I knew I had found a kindred spirit when I read this: "If we are to understand anything so complex and troubling as addiction, we need to gaze directly at the point where experience and biology meet" (Lewis, 2015, p. xv). Now that is *thinking at the safe edge.*

The following quote exemplifies how Lewis views addiction:

> Addiction can therefore be seen as a developmental cascade, often foreshadowed by difficulties in childhood, always boosted by the narrowing of perspective with recurrent cycles of acquisition and loss. Like other developmental outcomes, addiction isn't easy to reverse because it rides on the restructuring of the brain. Like other developmental outcomes, it arises from neural plasticity, but its net effect is a reduction of further plasticity, at least for a while. *Addiction* is a habit, which, like many other habits, gets entrenched through a decrease in self-control. Addiction is definitely bad news for the addict and all those within range. But the severe consequences of addiction don't make it a

disease, any more than the consequences of violence make violence a disease, or the consequences of racism make racism a disease. What they make it is a very bad habit. (2015, p. xiii)

Lewis has a unique relationship with addiction. In his remarkable book *Memoirs of an Addicted Brain* (2011), he shares his story of battling severe addictions until he reached the age of 30. At this point in his life, he realized that he was at a crossroads and he eventually stopped all addictive behaviours. Returning to graduate school, he completed a PhD and became a neuroscientist. His book is a unique blend of his personal story and the neuroscience behind addiction. We see how Lewis' work resonates with a thinking at the edge (TAE) approach by exploring concepts and felt experiencing, weaving back and forth as one informs the other. The journey is an integration of top-down and bottom-up processing. As a neuroscientist he is rigorous in his pursuit of a sophisticated model that deals with the complexity of addiction. As a formerly addicted person, he is passionate about integrating lived experiences. Who more suited to help us unravel this multi-layered behavior than a former heroin-addicted person turned neuroscientist?

Lewis (2011) weaves a tale of desperation. At the same time, we can step back and understand what is happening to neuropathways and the nervous system. The addictive cycle repeats and repeats in an endless loop, a stuck place that narrows one's choices. This narrowing occurs both in neuropathways in the brain and in life choices for the addict. This is tragic as we literally see a shrinking capacity for aliveness, a dorsal vagal shutdown response ... surviving, but not thriving. The social engagement system is not as available in the state of addiction. The person becomes trapped in their own deadened sense of isolation. Interestingly, this narrowing, deadening spiral is also present in states of depression and post-traumatic stress. All represent the dorsal shutdown response.

Lewis understands, from the inside out, that we need to be more connected to lived, embodied experience in our approach. He muses about the difficulty in conveying his thoughts to his students.

> Look up from your notes and feel what your brain is doing. You can get this directly. Not from your notes ... [Your brain is] not just an organ of rationality, as you've no doubt been taught; it's also the biological engine of our striking irrationality – it has a dark side. How does that work? (2015, p. xiv)

Here we see Lewis' passion about bringing felt experiencing into the process. In true TAE style, he began to reveal to his students his own lived experience as a drug addicted person. Indeed, that got their attention.

Neuroplasticity, The Brain's Way of Learning

Lewis postulates a learning model of addiction. The main reasoning behind the argument for calling addiction a disease is that it changes brain chemistry. Lewis agrees that this is so. But, he argues, the brain is always changing. This change process, called neuroplasticity, is present in changing cell density, the size, and shape of the cortex, gene expression, and with learning and development. Neuroplasticity underlies all new skill development like driving a car, reading and understanding this book, and healing from brain injury or emotional trauma. So brain change that occurs with addiction would have to be pathological in order for it to be called a disease. However, Lewis argues, "The kind of brain changes seen in addiction also show up when people become absorbed in a sport, join a political movement, or become obsessed with their sweetheart or their kids" (2015, p. 26).

A good example of neuroplasticity is the brain in love. That our brains change when we fall in love makes sense from an experiential point of view. Most of us know what it feels like when we are infatuated with a new love. We can't stop thinking about the object of our affection. All of our attention is pulled to them, we daydream about them, can't wait to see them again, fantasize to the point where we can be frustrated when pulled away. Our attention becomes narrowed. We even neglect responsibilities, and sometimes do things that we don't morally agree with. We are besotted and out of our minds.

Cozolino (2006) writes about this state in his book *The Neuroscience of Human Relationships*. He speaks of the experience of being in love as being similar to an addiction and even to madness. In fact, we even say that we are "madly in love" when we are smitten and have lost a sense of grounding. The madness of addiction overtakes us and we behave in ways that we would not normally do. Cozolino draws a parallel between the withdrawal from drugs and the withdrawal from a lover:

> The anguish caused by separation from the mother or abandonment by a lover has also been likened to the experience of drug withdrawal (Panksepp et al. 1978). Cocaine craving results in robust activation of the anterior cingulate and decreased activation in the frontal lobes (Leon & Shadlen, 1999; Wexler et al., 2001). Remember that the anterior cingulate evolved to allow for maternal behavior, nurturance, and bonding, whereas the frontal lobes control foresight and inhibition. This combination drives the addict towards a drug as it drives others to a lover, with little inhibitory control or consideration for future consequences. (p. 114)

First Person Experiencing – The Fear of Shameful Sharing

It feels like a good time to pause and check down inside to that bodily sense of experiencing our concept, "addiction as a bad habit." I close my eyes, breathing deeply, and say the phrase to myself: Addiction as a bad habit.

I feel myself resisting this search for a felt sense. The fear of shameful sharing.

Open eyes ... In this top-down world, it is shameful to share personal embodied experiences while developing ideas, or in our professional work. I fear being judged and misunderstood. I feel the sharing as risky.

Closing eyes ... sitting with that. Being understood, understanding me and why I did those crazy things. I did those things because ... Going back to the body ... sitting quietly. So hard to stay here in this place of feeling shame. I feel into the women in my group ... how they were objects of contempt.

Fear sharing my story ... feel tightening in my chest. They will judge me. Misunderstand me. I won't be taken seriously. My book will be seen as some woman's personal meanderings. Men reign. Men speak objective facts. Women babble.

Tightening in my gut ... building into hot anger. The beginnings of a powerful felt sense come into my belly, extending up into my arms and jaw. I feel the sympathetic flight/fight response in my core. How can I write about a process model, Gendlin's philosophy, without being true to the process? Personal meanderings are precious in creating embodied conceptual models. Felt sensing into personal meanderings ...

A bit of a shift as I hear my grounded self knowing and believing in the process. Seeing how it helps to be with the truth down inside. And to fight for the truth. The embodied truth. The power of speaking my own truth and helping other people to speak their truth.

An instance comes. Back to 1968. I am sixteen. I feel how young I am in my body. Blowing warm summery breeze, summery brown skin, blonde hair ... swish swishing down my back, panting hard as I run for my sense of my life.

Remembering panicky, hard-to-be-with terror ... some tightening in my chest ... aching lonely flows through me as I run down the main street of Bracebridge, our cottage town, chasing my means of survival. I'm truly, madly, deeply in first love. And terror. I've smothered him with fear and now he is bolting for dear life down the street to who knows where? I watch him pack his suitcase many times, I watch myself chasing him many times. I am lost, no place inside for comfort and strength. I am desperate for him ... I will do anything to make him come back ... just come back ... so I can breathe.

He comes back. Blissful reuniting ... swirling sinking into his warm holding feeling safe place. The ahhhhh place of rapture. Wrapped in rapture. But I know I can't live without him. My body does not know how to live, to breathe without him. I am in deep trouble. I am addicted to this boy/man.

Rapture ... and rupture. The insidious horror of rapture/rupture ... This is my addictive place. A bodily shift comes with this phrase ... it symbolizes my felt sense of addiction. The insidious horror of rapture/rupture. Knowing that something is deeply wrong with me, and I must hide it. Shameful sharing will not happen for a long time. Addiction as a bad habit. Desperately bad.

Focusing Practice

I invite you to take a moment to check to see how your body carries "addiction as a bad habit." Or you may simply start with saying "addiction" and dropping your attention down into the centre of your body. Chances are that something about the topic has drawn you to my book. Notice what comes. Notice any feelings, thoughts, physical sensations, memories. Explore your felt sense. See if you can find a handle, a word or phrase, or an image or gesture that captures the quality of the felt sense of addiction. Take time to be with this, letting it form inside, welcoming a knowing, meaning, that carries you forward in your thinking ... You will take this experience with you as we return to conceptualizing.

Back to the Origins of Neuroplasticity

The shared neuropathways of love and addiction extend to our experiences with our children too. We have periods of time where we think about them constantly, count hours away from them, delight in how precious they are, obsess over their health and well-being, and choices in life. The saying, "You are only as happy as your most unhappy child" illustrates our powerful connection and sometimes obsession with our children.

It happens at sports games. Thousands of fans, screaming, crying, obsessively recounting plays, scores, spending enormous amounts of money to be there where it is all happening, to be caught up in the frenzy. These experiences show up in the same way in the brain. They give us a taste of the experience of addiction. The key here is that the *process* by which the brain changes is the same in all of these activities. Therefore, Lewis (2015) argues, it is not pathological. It is simply the brain doing what it is designed to do. Granted, too much of a good thing leads to trouble. We shall see how this happens in addiction.

Let's back up a bit to take a brief look at the history of neuroplasticity before we venture more deeply into the learning, developmental model of addiction. Because I am no neuroscientist, and you probably aren't either, we will dip into a very complex field knowing that our goal is to get a general sense of what happened during the *decade of the brain* in the 1990s, and how that is changing the fields of addiction and trauma.

As we saw in Chapter 1, the decade of the brain occurred in the 1990s as a result of the advent of increasingly sophisticated neuroimaging machines. Once we had the capacity to see into the brain it became apparent that cells were indeed reproducing. This knowledge led to the *neuroplastic revolution* (Doidge, 2017). Revolutions are intriguing. They signify a paradigm shift, a fresh response. They represent moments in history when, despite the need for homeostasis, the status quo is overturned. Although we humans seek the safety of familiarity, we are also compelled to continue searching for novelty, something outside of what is familiar, something inhabiting the safe edge of experience, something that will carry us forward into new growth.

While this new way of understanding the brain was very exciting and intriguing for some, it was not met with such enthusiasm by all. A major contributor to the field of neuroplasticity, Merzenich, states,

> Almost everybody I knew in the mainstream of neuroscience thought that this was sort of *semi*-serious stuff – that the experiments were sloppy, that the effects described were uncertain. But actually the experiments had been done enough times that I realized that the position of the majority was arrogant and indefensible. (In Doidge, 2017, p. 61)

Resistance, often expressed through arrogance and contempt, erupts when we are trying to introduce new ways of understanding. Although we are often quick to label and pathologize this defensive response in our clients, we desperately need to pay attention to our own response. I believe this place of fearful resistance was evident in the hospital setting where I ran the women's group. The fear of change, of radical transformation, can overtake us. As human beings we live out a paradox. We need safety to feel grounded, to have the prefrontal cortex – the adult, mature part of our brain – functioning well, so we can think clearly. Yet, we need to be courageous in our capacity to welcome the freshness of bottom-up processing. When we achieve this state of integration we experience the sweet spot of thinking at the safe edge.

Focusing Practice

Let's take a moment to check down inside. To be with the paradox
… searching for something new and holding onto safety. Resisting
what we don't want to be true. Resisting the possibility that we are
wrong. Can you welcome the uncomfortable? Can you imagine a
whole new way of understanding addiction?

When we think at the edge, we welcome paradox as a natural
starting point, a place to be curious. It is really only in our Western
dualistic top-down culture that we distrust contradictions. Bottom-
up processing welcomes contradictory information. The body holds
many different kinds of experiences all at once. Cold feet, warm
heart; tight chest, relaxed thighs. Bodies speak without logically
imposed limitations.

The Changing Brain: Dispelling Myths

Doidge (2007) tells the fascinating history of the neuroplastic revolution.
His stunning examples of brain neuroplasticity reveal the very best of a
revolutionary shift and demonstrate the brain's capacity to heal itself.
Examples include accounts of stroke patients' remarkable recovery, aging
brains rejuvenated, and most relevant to this book, healing from addictive behaviours.

Up until the 1990s, scientists viewed the brain as a digital computer.
This mechanistic view was a reflection of Descartes mind/body split that
is part of top-down thinking. Two firmly held beliefs about the brain were
about to be challenged:

Myth #1: Brains Don't Change

Formerly, brain anatomy was believed to be fixed or hardwired. The only
time the brain changed was when we began to age, or due to illness or
injury. In this view, once brain cells were lost, they could not be replaced.
Therefore, people's limitations were forever. Doidge (2007) talks of a
"neurological nihilism" that occurred whereby treatment for brain problems was viewed as impossible. This created an attitude of futility and an
overall rigidity in thinking about the brain. This exemplifies top-down
thinking at its worst.

Myth #2: Brain Parts Perform Specific Functions

The theory of *localization* states that each part of the brain has a distinct
location, performing a single function. If damage occurs to one of those

parts, nothing can replace them. Brain circuitry is hardwired, a term borrowed from the computer world. This idea was firmly applied to our senses as well. It was believed that once one lost capacity in one sense, it was gone forever.

Bach-y-Rita (in Doidge, 2007), a pioneer in neuroplasticity research, proved this wrong. He invented a bizarre-looking hat that his patient Cheryl wore for periods of time every day to help with her problems with balance. She had been told by doctors that she had no vestibular function due to damage from medication she was taking for a post-operative infection. The doctor told her that there was no cure; she would be dizzy for the rest of her life. Luckily for Cheryl, Bach-y-Rita's hat invention replaced her vestibular apparatus by sending balance signals to her brain through a connection between her tongue and a computer. Cheryl experienced a neuroplastic miracle through the rerouting of tingling sensations on her tongue. Normally, they would go to the sensory cortex, the part of the brain that processes touch. Now with this neuroplastic intervention these sensations connected with a new pathway in the brain that processes balance. With time Cheryl was able to remain balanced without the necessity of any device. So amazing.

Bach-y-Rita explains it this way:

> If you are driving from here to Milwaukee, and the main bridge goes out, first you are paralyzed. Then you take old secondary roads through the farmland. Then, as you use these roads more, you find shorter paths to use to get where you want to go, and you start to get there faster. (In Doidge, 2007, p. 9)

This is an example of the wonders of neuroplasticity, but it isn't all wonderful, as we shall see.

Brain Regions Most Relevant to Addiction

Let's take a look at the areas most involved in addiction in terms of Lewis' (2018) learning model. A caveat: the brain is very complex, and many more areas are involved. For simplicity's sake, we will discuss these five areas:

Dorsolateral PreFrontal Cortex: "The Bridge of the Ship" (Lewis, 2015, p. 45)

This is the region involved in self comprehension and self-regulation. I think of it as the responsible-adult part of the brain. It matures gradually with cognitive development. This is the part of the brain involved in problem solving, judgement, reasoning. Important to note, it loses its connection with the striatum as addiction develops, and as a result, we see the addicted person becoming capable of actions that are not reasoned or empathic. The addicted person is then seen as *immoral* due to this loss of contact with the responsible adult self. This is the area connected to the ventral branch of the vagus nerve that brings grounding, safety, and insight.

Ventral Striatum: Motivational Engine

This area is deeply involved in addiction as it focuses on feelings of desire, craving, and reward. It focuses on a goal and then sends an action signal to other parts of the brain to execute the goal through the movement of muscles. This action brain, or striatum, learns from experience. It assesses how well the goal was achieved in the past and adjusts itself to better achieve the goal in the future. Hence, goals that are associated with the addiction take precedence over goals like finishing your homework or being faithful to your partner. This area of the brain is fuelled by dopamine, a powerful neurotransmitter pumped up from the midbrain. Dopamine is the fuel that increases the firing rates of the neurons causing craving to intensify to the point where nothing else matters. More than liking, dopamine is about *wanting*. Dopamine determines what is most relevant and salient and motivates the system to acquire it at all costs.

Midbrain: Dopamine Pump

The midbrain controls and regulates dopamine production. It is the centre of visual and auditory reflexes and coordinates movement. Cells in this area pump dopamine to the striatum, amygdala, and prefrontal cortex.

Amygdala: "Emotional Spraypaint" (Lewis, 2015, p. 79)

The amygdala is subcortical, meaning it is a lower, more primitive part of the brain. It is responsible for reading emotional tone and responds immediately to fear, excitement, and pleasure. It the part of the autonomic nervous system that says, "Pay attention!"

Orbitofrontal Cortex: Connector

This area forms a connection between the amygdala and the prefrontal cortex. It connects emotion (amygdala) with expectancies (prefrontal cortex). It creates an action plan based on past experiences and assesses the best path to achieve the goal. It assesses the best way to act out, without getting caught. The OFC recruits the more reflective skills of the prefrontal cortex (where, when, how) to better achieve its goals. However, these reflective skills can develop into rumination and preoccupation with addiction.

As Lewis (2015) explains it, this is part of how the brain is designed.

If that reflection turns into rumination, we can't suddenly look for some foreign entity, point our finger, and shout, "Disease!" Rumination is the result of a normal brain, doing what it's designed to do when the brain's owner has entered a cycle of seeking and finding the same thing over and over again. (p. 82)

This is exactly the process that occurs in love or infatuation as well.

How Addiction Works in the Brain, A Case Example

My client, we'll call him Joe, is one of my favourite people to work with. I know, we aren't supposed to have favourites, but of course, our relational felt sense varies from client to client. Some like Joe are easy to connect with right from the start. Joe is a young, creative guy with a quirky sense of humour. He is curious and open to new ways of seeing and experiencing life. If I go too far or too fast, he is quick to pull in, arms crossed, tightness around the eyes. He warns me, but he softens just as fast. I like this about him. We can be mischievous and playful together, and I use this to help him stretch and gently ask more of himself.

Joe comes to see me because he struggles with alcohol addiction. He is like so many young men these days. He started drinking when he was 14, at first occasionally when he and his friends could get their hands on their parents' alcohol. Over time he drank more and more, especially when he moved to residence in university. He never really saw his drinking as a problem. All of his friends were doing the same thing, getting drunk every weekend. But inside Joe's brain huge quantities of dopamine were pumping from the *midbrain* into his *striatum* on a regular basis. A pattern was beginning to develop every five days. Cravings would build up and he would become more and more preoccupied with Friday night bingeing. *Now appeal*, the notion that immediate rewards are always more appealing than long term rewards, was beginning to set in for Joe. Now appeal is driven by dopamine uptake into the striatum. Joe couldn't resist the pull to Friday night, even though it was getting harder and harder to concentrate at work, and his girlfriend was complaining about his drinking. Joe's striatum, fuelled by dopamine, was activated and busy planning the next binge.

Luckily for Joe, he was more than able to hold down a job and continue to develop professionally. But everything else in his life was slowly deteriorating. He started drinking after work most nights, and feeling increasingly disconnected from his friends, and from his ability to enjoy anything in his life. His family was worried but didn't know what to do after they approached him and were met with his anger and denial. Joe was lost in a fog of swirling isolation.

At times Joe was able to realize that he was in trouble. He would feel the craving start up again by Wednesday night in anticipation of the weekend, and he would tell himself to resist. Sometimes he would really put in effort to redirect his attention, worrying that the drinking was hampering his performance at work and with sex. But *ego fatigue*, exhaustion from trying to resist alcohol, was taking over. The more he tried to stop, the more fatigued he became, the less he was eventually able to resist. A vicious cycle.

Lewis says, "Ego fatigue is like a microcosm of addiction, augmented rather than diminished by attempts to suppress impulses" (2015, p. 199).

In a state of ego fatigue, Joe's *dorsolateral prefrontal cortex (DPFC)*, the bridge of the ship, would disconnect from the striatum. This would become evident in his inability to think ahead to the horrible consequences of the bingeing. He simply didn't give these consequences any thought. As addiction develops the connection between the *DPFC* and the striatum slow down, dampen and fade. Joe himself began to fade into an empty, shadowy being. His adult self was nowhere to be found, at least on the weekends. Once he sobered up by Tuesday he could feel his head clear a bit as the DPFC awakened from the foggy Friday binge.

Bad things began to happen. Joe was driving home from the pub one night having consumed a lot of his favourite beer. He felt himself getting very sleepy and actually drifted off at the wheel. Later he remembers thinking that he needed to stay awake, but this was just before he slipped into a deep reverie. Waking with a huge cracking sound, he found himself buried in a thick bush. The car had slipped off the road as Joe lost consciousness. When he showed up in my office the next day, he stroked the huge bump on his head as he cried and cried. The little boy inside him was terrified, and deep shame rippled through him. He felt lost. He didn't understand how this could happen to him. More shame was coursing through his limbs up into the centre of his body. He was done with drinking. Never again. He had learned his lesson. Joe's close call activated his *DPFC*, helping him to connect with a mindful, wiser part of himself that understood the consequences of his dangerous behavior. This part of him knew he had to change. All good.

Until it wasn't all good. Joe was able to stay sober for about six months. One night after a particularly vicious argument with his girlfriend, he stormed out of the house and past his old drinking spot, an irresistible trigger for Joe. Seeing the pub activated the cues associated with his previous alcoholic escapades. His midbrain lit up and sent large quantities of dopamine into his striatum, the motivational engine. Recall that dopamine, the fuel of desire, works in the striatum to focus attention to the most salient aspects of achieving the goal. The more dopamine, the more craving, leading Joe back to the pub, back to the cycle of addiction. Over time Joe became more and more consumed with craving. The neural networks that support the pursuit of the craving for more alcohol become salient, and the networks that don't support the pursuit die off. This narrowing of attention is part of the process of what is called *pruning*. Like pruning a hedge, what is not needed is discarded, and what the striatum considers important for goal acquisition is repeated over and over again until the addictive neuropathways become rigid and single-minded.

Pruning is a natural process in the development of the brain. Adolescence is a time when much pruning occurs as the brain becomes more efficient and evolved in its capacity to operationalize functions. In addiction, pruning leads to efficiency of goal acquisition. But, like too much of a good thing, it also leads to a deadening of other pursuits, as Joe experienced again and again. This is how neuropathways are shaped and impacted by addiction.

"Neurons That Fire Together Wire Together"

Plastic change is a process, occurring over time in the brain. How to demonstrate this process? Merzenich (1984), a neuroscientist at the University of California, decided to conduct a series of experiments with monkeys to illustrate these changes. He and his research team used a method called brain mapping. This involves collecting many different images of the brain and using the data that is collected to analyse what is occurring as the brain develops. Merzenich mapped a normal monkey's hand, then sewed together two of the monkey's fingers so they became like one, and remapped. After the monkeys had been using the sewn-together fingers for several months, Merzenich remapped again. The two maps of the originally separated fingers now merged into a single map. When the researchers touched either finger the new merged map would light up. Because all the movements in the fused fingers occurred simultaneously, they formed a single map. Canadian neuropsychologist Hebb (1949) coined the term, *neurons that fire together wire together,* to illustrate this point. The research showed that neurons that fire together *in time* wire together to form one map. If maps could change, then Merzenich posited that it would be possible to help people who were born with problems in brain map-processing areas, learning problems, strokes, or psychological problems, by helping people form new neuronal connections. New firing, new wiring.

Now we move to another finding that enhances our understanding of neuroplasticity based on the above experiment with humans. When researchers separated the webbed fingers and the patients' brains were remapped, two separate brain maps occurred for each finger. When the fingers were able to move independently the neurons no longer fired together. This demonstrated that *neurons that fire apart, wire apart*, creating two separate brain maps. These findings help us to create neural exercises for rewiring the brain.

We know that what fires together, wires together. The more exciting and engaging a behavior is, the more we tend to repeat it. And the more we repeat it, the more neurons fire and wire together, the more learning takes place. All good. But, frequent repetition of behaviours that are engaging is a slippery slope and can result in a narrowing of choices as we travel the same pathway over and over again. As we saw with Joe, the chosen pathway becomes more and more rigid, and soon we are lost in the obsessive world of addiction. So while neuroplasticity creates mental flexibility at the beginning, it can lead to mental rigidity. Doidge calls this the plastic paradox.

Let's go back to the felt sense polyvagal model (FSPM) of addiction. Looking at the model, recall the intertwining state of addiction in polyvagal theory. This is where Joe got stuck, swinging from sympathetic flight/fight to dorsal vagal shutdown. Alcohol becomes the substance that propels Joe from one state to the other. A rigid pathway is created under extreme stress as the ANS shifts into survival mode, employing addictive behaviours to creates shifts in the body. Joe's world is shrinking into disconnection.

Embodied Cognition Leads to an Integrated Approach to Addiction

I'm having lunch with Lewis in a great Italian restaurant one wintry day. He has generously agreed to meet with me to share ideas and talk about my book. Our ideas converge and I decide to share a pet peeve of mine: while I find the learning model of addiction very helpful and fitting, I am frustrated by the disembodied approach of current cognitive science. He asks if I have heard of embodied cognition, a concept he had recently published an article about in the *New England Journal of Medicine* (2018). I become quite excited by this idea and look up the article as soon as I get home.

Let me to put this information in context. Psychology, particularly cognitive psychology, was shaped by Descartes' notion of the mind/body split. However, ideas that emerged during the decade of the brain continue to influence these traditional approaches, and embodied cognition is an outgrowth of this influence. Embodied cognition challenges this split notion and provides an integrated model. The beginning of the field dates back to early 20th century phenomenologists: Heidegger, Merleau-Ponty, and Dewey. McNerney (2011) offers a salient comment:

> The mind arises from the nature of our brains, bodies, and bodily experiences. This is not just the innocuous and obvious claim that we need a body to reason; rather, it is the striking claim that the very structure of reason itself comes from the details of our embodiment ... Thus, to understand reason we must understand the details of our visual system, our motor system, and the general mechanism of neural binding. (para. 2)

I'm excited to see that these same phenomenologists were deeply influential in Gendlin's thinking and development of his philosophy. Gendlin (2018) takes these ideas further by utilizing the focusing method to understand and experience body/environment as one process. He states:

> The current gap between physiology and psychology is not a gap between the body and behavior. It is rather the gap between the current vocabularies and concepts of the two fields. If one doesn't develop concepts for the bodily development of sentience, both sides become mysterious. Then the body seems to be a machine, and the behavioural terms have to come from a new and false beginning that floats without the body. Then our concept of body and behavior never acquire the inherent internal connections. If we have succeeded in thinking of body process and behavior within one paradigm, we can show how the bodily structure of each species is just what is needed for its behavior. This is not quite so mysterious if behavior is a certain kind of carrying forward and change of the "body". (p. 110)

Lewis' definition is strikingly similar to Gendlin's. The concept of embodied cognition suggests that all cognitive activity (including learning) results from iterative, self-perpetuating interactions between the animal and the environment (Lewis, 2018, p. 1552).

Lewis (2018) suggests that an integrated approach to understanding addiction embraces the embodied-cognition paradigm. In this view, it is important to understand how all factors *interact* with each other to create the complex state of addiction. "A comprehensive, balanced model of addiction needs to recognize that the organism and its environment are connected at every level, from perception to cognition to behavior, and interact continuously as an open system" (p. 1557). He suggests that we start with early psychosocial adversity as a predictor of addiction.

Lewis (2018) describes how most alternative models of addiction highlight social and environmental causes, such as poverty and trauma. He goes on to say that these models often don't address the neurobiological changes in the brain. He proposes a more integrated model that addresses all of these levels of analysis, including the neurobiology of addiction, in order to provide a more comprehensive and robust alternative to the brain disease model.

What implications does this have for our notion of recovery from addiction? In the traditional medical model, and according to AA programs, once an addict, always an addict. It is a chronic disease that one has to be wary of forever. "The addict is in the corner doing pushups!" is a common saying in AA. In my experience with clients, this is a fear-based approach and one that leads to a life-long state of chronic, sympathetic angst regarding relapse.

In shifting paradigms from disease to a learning model, our concept of recovery changes. We begin to see how healing can be a profound developmental process of learning how to live in a more secure, socially engaged community. The FSPM supports the development of neural exercises that facilitate state shifts. These exercises are based on contemplative practices such as focusing, meditation (particularly in groups to facilitate social engagement), psychotherapy, journaling to track, and map ANS states using the visual maps and increasing social engagement activities. Moving to the FSPM in no way diminishes the horrors of addiction. Any way you look at it, a rigorous approach to healing is required. It's hard, hard work to rewire, and reshape your brain. And, it is possible.

References

Cozolino, L. (2006). *The neuroscience of human relationships: Attachment and the developing social brain.* New York: W.W. Norton and Company.

Doidge, N. (2007). *The brain that changes itself: Stories of personal triumph from the frontiers of brain science.* New York: Viking.

Doidge, N. (2017). *The brain's way of healing.* New York: Penguin Books.

Gendlin, E. T. (2018). *A process model.* Evanston, IL: Northwestern University Press.

Hebb, D. (1949) The first stage of perception: Growth of the assembly. In *The organization of behaviour.* New York: Wiley.

Leon, M. I., & Shadlen, M. N. (1999). Effect of expected reward magnitude on the response of neurons in the dorsolateral prefrontal cortex of the macaque. *Neuron, 24,* 415–425. doi: 10.1016/S0896-6273(00)80854-5

Lewis, M. (2011). *Memoirs of an addicted brain: A neuroscientist examines his former life on drugs.* Melbourne, Australia: Scribe Publications.

Lewis, M. (2015). *The biology of desire: Why addiction is not a disease.* New York: PublicAffairs.

Lewis, M. (2018). Brain change in addiction as learning, not disease. *New England Journal of Medicine, 379,* 1551–1560.

McNerney, M. (2011, November 4). A brief guide to embodied cognition: Why you are not your brain. *Scientific American.* Retrieved from https://blogs.scientificamerican.com/guest-blog/a-brief-guide-to-embodied-cognition-why-you-are-not-your-brain/

Merzenich, M. M., Nelson, R. J., Stryker, M. P., Cynader, M. S., Schoppmann, A. & Zook, J. M. (1984). Somatosensory cortical map changes following digit amputation in adult monkeys. *The Journal of Comparative Neurology, 22*(4), 591–605.

Panksepp, J., Herman, B., Conner, R., Bishop, P., & Scott, J. P. (1978). The biology of social attachments: Opiates alleviate separation distress. *Biological Psychiatry, 13,* 607–618.

Siegel, D. (2016). *Mind: A journey to the heart of being human.* New York: W.W. Norton and Company.

Wexler, B. E., Gotteschalk, C. H., Fulbright, R. K., Prohovnik, I., Lacadie, C. M., Rounsaville, B. J., et al. (2001). Functional magnetic resonance imaging of cocaine craving. *American Journal of Psychiatry, 158,* 86–95.

5   Facing the Truth About Addiction

We humans in the Western world tend to like to cling to simple, consistent ways of understanding. The complexity of paradox and murky experiencing is met with suspicion. Our top-down approach fosters yearning for concrete, easy-to-target solutions. Addiction isn't like that. As much as we are bound and determined to see it as the result of drugs, it simply isn't. And it is high time that we accept this truth. I believe that it is our job as trauma and addiction therapists to stand up and shout this out from the rooftops, lovingly and fiercely.

The irony, of course, is that while our top-down societal approach speaks of objectivity and following the evidence, we are actually responding to the evidence with dysregulated emotion. Either we are angry and disgusted with the addicted person, wanting to punish, or we are dissociated and shut down, choosing to deny the truth about the cause and consequence of this horrific and ever-increasing wound. Either way, we are not doing justice to the problem.

Facing the Truth, Settling Our Nervous Systems

We all have to settle our nervous systems. Addicted or not, we are often emotionally dysregulated, which affects our thinking and responding to the problem. So the irony continues. The very mechanism of denying and dissociating painful experiences is at play with those suffering from addictions, and those denying the problem. We are all so very much the same. We are all wired to survive any way we can. Polyvagal theory teaches us to pay attention to our bodies' awareness of safety/danger and to notice and honour our autonomic nervous system's bodily response. What is happening in our society that makes us increasingly unable to feel safe and settled in our bodies?

Alexander (2014), a pioneer in the addiction field, stated that *addiction is our teacher*. It couldn't be said any better than that. As we work through this chapter, we will come back to this wise statement and learn from Alexander, other teachers, and addiction.

As we shall see in this chapter, the evidence is clear. Addiction isn't about *things*. It's about bad habits and feelings: sad feelings, scary feelings, desperate feelings, exciting feelings, powerful feelings, empty feelings, hard-to-be-with feelings, and above all, lonely feelings. The evidence points to addiction as the result of painful experiences, and in spite of this, our culture insists upon dealing with this very real and growing problem of suffering as a "war on drugs". Our society tends to lock people up, or label them as sick, rather than acknowledging the deep-seated problems in our communities and in the world. How do we feel safe in our bodies and how do we create safety for our children in an increasingly unsafe world?

Maté, in his classic book, *In the Realm of Hungry Ghosts*, (2008) states:

> The drug addict is today's scapegoat. Viewed honestly, much of our culture is geared towards enticing us away from ourselves, into externally directed activity, into diverting the mind from ennui and distress. The hardcore addict surrenders her pretense about that. Her life is all about escape. The rest of us can, with varying success, maintain our charade, but to do so, we banish her to the margins of society. (p. 266)

In this chapter, I advocate for viewing addiction through an anti-oppressive lens. Doing so is not meant to exclude other approaches. That would be too simplistic, falling into the enticing top-down approach. No, I see it as more complex. The face of addiction is transforming in younger generations. Maybe growing up with smartphones as a constant companion creates more fertile ground for addiction. The impact of technology on the development of addiction is important to think about. That being said, let's take a closer look at oppression, the precursor to trauma, and how it creates fertile ground for addiction.

Five Faces of Oppression

The traditional definition of oppression is concerned with the ways in which dominant groups try to control or terrorize weaker groups. The Latin root of the word means to press against or hold down. We tend to associate oppression with large scale, political struggles, the kind of deep systemic oppression that runs right through the veins of our society. These we call macro aggressions.

More recently, we have come to understand that this deep systemic oppression manifests in many ways, often subtly bleeding into everyday discourse in the form of micro aggressions. These are the subtle ways in which we hurt each other, for example by not listening to, and/or dismissing someone of another gender, race, or class. By holding someone back, or down, we limit them and we limit ourselves. Everyday, first-person experiencing of micro aggression is key to understanding how traumatic childhoods lead to addiction.

Young was a professor of political science at the University of Chicago. She wrote about the systemic nature of oppression, how it seeps into political, economic, legal, and cultural institutions. Young (1998) was concerned with developing a more sophisticated study of oppression by understanding the intersection and complexity of macro and micro aggressions. She emphasized the hidden nature of oppression, the way in which well-meaning people can contribute to the holding down of others unconsciously. Acknowledging oppressed groups also requires that we acknowledge privileged groups. It becomes very murky territory when we encounter our own experiences as being members of both oppressed and privileged groups. Life becomes increasingly complex when we dig deep.

Young (1998) identified oppressed groups to include, women, blacks, Spanish speaking Americans, Jews, queer folks, the poor, physically and mentally disabled, Arabs, Asians, Native Americans. Young noted that while not all groups will be oppressed to the same extent, all experience limits in their capacity to develop themselves as a result of structural norms, habits and symbols. She divided oppression into the following five categories:

Exploitation occurs when one group benefits from the labour of others without adequate compensation. Those groups that possess wealth exploit those that don't in a system that reinforces class division. The rich get richer on the backs of the poor.

Marginalization refers to the process whereby people are excluded from the mainstream of society. They are often unemployable because they belong to a racialized group, or are women, or because they have a criminal record, are single mothers, are struggling with mental health and addiction issues, or are physically disabled. Young sees marginalization as the most dangerous form of oppression because it creates poverty and thus, shame and fear. Receiving social welfare is experienced as demeaning and creates a cycle of food and home insecurity.

Powerlessness manifests in the sense of futility, hopelessness in one's capacity to affect change in one's destiny. Young makes the point that a person's class impacts their sense of power. The more educated you are the more respected you are, especially if you are a white male.

Cultural imperialism involves the way in which the dominant culture shapes the norms, habits of society to the exclusion of other groups in that culture. An example of this would be the way in which our Judeo-Christian culture has silenced groups who don't follow the traditional heterosexual, nuclear family-based norms. The stereotypes are so taken for granted that people no longer question them. As a result, victims of cultural imperialism can feel both silenced and targeted.

In addition, there is often a sense of what Du Bois (1897) called "double-consciousness, this sense of always looking at one's self through the eyes of others, of measuring one's soul by the tape of a world that looks on in amused contempt and pity" (p. 95). This way of seeing oneself brings with it a sense of embodied shame that is hard to shake. There is another paradox here. The victims of cultural imperialism experience themselves as invisible and at the same time targeted.

Violence is more common amongst those already oppressed. Many groups, as a result of the above forms of oppression, live in constant fear of being attacked for their beliefs, gender, sexual orientation, race, and class. This violence is systemic in that it is directed at any person who is part of the targeted group simply because they are part of the group. Young gives the example of women fearing rape simply because we are women.

Focusing Practice

Let's pause and take some time to be with these five faces of oppression. How do they relate to each of us? Personally, I share both privileged and oppressed group experiences. I belong to a very privileged White, upper middle-class professional group. I belong to an oppressed, female group subjected to systemic misogyny. And I belong to a group oppressed by cultural imperialism. My family history includes addiction, (sex, drugs, alcohol) depression, and parental suicidal attempts with hospitalization, parental abandonment, and atheism (60 years ago when it was rare).

I grew up in Canada in a White, middle class, heteronormative, Christian, nuclear family based culture. While my family was middle class, we were in many ways oppressed by the prevailing cultural norms and values. My parents divorced when I was 5 and I knew no one else living in a single parent family. My father left the family. When asked why I didn't have a father I used to lie and tell people that my father was a travelling salesman. All of this led me to feel very marginalized as a child. Also, as a female I have been targeted by sexual violence.

What groups do you identify with? Do you have a sense of how this impacts you? Do you carry experiences of trauma and addiction? Please take some time now to be with this.

As we go through the chapter, we will keep in mind the intersection of oppression, trauma and addiction. Now let's turn our attention to the false story of addiction and what needs to take place to face the truth.

The Myth of the "Hook"

According to Hari (2015), as a society, we place too much emphasis on the chemical hook as the driver of addiction, likely because we don't want to face that the real culprits are trauma and isolation.

> We still think of addiction as mainly caused by chemical hooks. There's something in the drug that, after a while, your body starts to crave and need. That's what we think addiction is. But chemical hooks are only

a minor part of addiction. The other factors, like isolation and trauma, have been proven to be much bigger indicators. Yet, the drug war *increases* the biggest drivers of addiction – isolation and trauma – in order to protect potential users from the more *minor* driver of addiction, the chemical hook. (p. 271)

Before we go any further, let's clear up any doubts about the common belief in the *hook* as the main cause of addiction. This belief is so indoctrinated into our way of thinking that we must really take the time to think it through. *Let's pause*, and remember our bottom-up approach of being curious, and open to fresh ways of experiencing. We are thinking at the edge when we welcome something new and uncomfortable. The concept of behavioural addictions is still considered somewhat controversial. Are they really addictions? If so, how do they fit into the story about the hook?

We know that chemicals are involved in addiction, but to what extent? A study done by DeGrandpre (2006) shows that the addiction is not mainly driven by craving for a particular substance. The chemical hook in tobacco is nicotine, so the addiction should stop with the use of the patch by providing the body with the necessary supply. The level of nicotine in your bloodstream doesn't drop if you use the patch, so the chemical craving is gone. *But DeGrandpre's study showed that even with the patch, most people still wanted to smoke.* Only 17.7 percent of the subjects in this study were able to stop. This chapter is about the 82.3 percent of people who continued to imbibe and why.

The why can be found in the overwhelming research that links trauma and oppression to underlying causes of addiction. Interestingly, the relationship between the hook and the trauma is evidenced in the compelling story of the war on drugs. Hari (2015) tells us, in his page-turner of a book, where it all began.

Anslinger's Racist War on Drugs

It began back in the 1930s when Anslinger, the key player in the war on drugs, was a twelve-year-old boy. He was visiting his neighbors' farmhouse when he heard a desperate scream come from a woman upstairs. Her husband ran to Anslinger instructing him to go to the pharmacy, pick up a package and come back as fast as he could. Minutes after Harry's return, the package had been taken to the woman, the screams stopped and she calmed down. This experience, and undoubtedly others, seemed to have traumatized Harry. He wrote about it later in life saying that he never forgot those screams. He felt they were the result of evil drugs and he vowed to rid the world of such wild and degenerate behaviour. Anslinger devoted his life to this mission, going on to become the head of the first Commission of the Federal Bureau of Narcotics from 1930 to 1962.

When Anslinger arrived in office, prohibition had just been abolished, and while heroin and cocaine were outlawed in 1914 in the US with the Harrison Act, many drugs were still legal. His small beleaguered staff felt that they had lost the war on alcohol. Anslinger had to rally them and convince people that his way of criminalizing drugs was the way to go. He needed a focus and he found one in marijuana and in people of color.

The headline, "Mexican Family Goes Insane" appeared in the July 6, 1927 edition of the *New York Times*. The article describes a widow and her four children who had been driven insane by eating the marijuana plant. Doctors said that the children would die and the mother would be insane for the rest of her life. Because they were starving, the mother decided to feed her family marijuana plants from the garden. Apparently, neighbours heard outbursts of crazed laughter, and according to the article, rushed to the house to find the whole family inside and insane! Here we see the beginnings of the deep roots of racism intertwined with poverty in the drug war.

Anslinger read this article and began to formulate his plan against marijuana, and against racialized peoples. He believed that two groups of Americans, Mexican immigrants and African Americans, were using the drug more than others. He presented the House Committee on Appropriations with his nightmarish vision of where this would lead. He told them that coloured students at the University of Minnesota were partying with female students (White) and getting their sympathy with stories of racial persecution. This, he said, would result in pregnancy.

Anslinger told the public that the increase in drug addiction was "100 percent among Negro people" (Hari, 2015, p. 26) as a way of fuelling his racist war on drugs. In addition, he started to build a case against Chinese immigrants. He told stories of Chinese men luring young Caucasian girls into opium dens, getting them hooked, and forcing them into brothels for the rest of their lives.

In Canada, the Opium Act of 1908 was passed in response to the establishment of opium dens in British Columbia. This made it an offense to import, manufacture, possess, or sell opium. In the same year, the Proprietary and Patent Medicine Act prohibited the use of cocaine in medicines and required pharmaceutical companies to list heroin, morphine, or opium as ingredients. This created a black market for opium, which resulted in the Opium and Drugs Act of 1911 and created harsher penalties for drug offenders. We see the beginnings of the cycle. Criminalization leads to black market, leads to more arrests, and harsher sentencing.

Hari (2015) states:

> The arguments we hear today for the war on drugs are that we must protect teenagers from drugs, and prevent addiction in general. We assume, looking back, that these were the reasons this war was launched in the first place. But they are not. They crop up only occasionally, as asides. The main reason given for banning drugs – the

reason obsessing the men who launched this war – was that the Blacks, Mexicans, and Chinese, were using these chemicals, forgetting their place, and menacing White people. (p. 27)

And indeed, through scaremongering and appealing to notions of white supremacy, he succeeded. State level prohibition occurred in 1937 out-lawing possession or selling of pot in the United States.

In order to understand the impact of trauma on the development of addiction, we need to understand the links between racism, poverty, criminality, and loss of employment. Put simply, if you criminalize ad-diction, people will break the law and become criminals in order to feed the addiction. Stealing and prostitution become the way to survive along with the development of hard-core gangs to manage the drug trade. These gangs prey on youth living in traumatic environments, and a vicious cycle creates a violent and corrupt society. In addition, once people have a criminal record, it becomes harder and harder to achieve gainful employment. The cycle of poverty results and is often repeated over multiple generations.

Let's think back to the five faces of addiction. It now becomes clear that the folks being targeted and caught up in the vicious cycle are suffering from all aspects of oppression: racism, marginalization through unemployment and criminalization, cultural imperialism through colonialism, stereotyping, and horrific examples of misogyny, as we shall see shortly. Hart (2013) is a neuroscientist who wrote a detailed history of the roots of racism in the war on drugs, and the way in which this is still played out today:

Specialty police units saturate "troubled neighbourhoods" in search of drugs for weeks at a time, making excessive arrests and subjecting targeted communities to dehumanizing treatment. In the process, complex economic and social forces are reduced to criminal justice problems, while resources are directed towards law enforcement rather than the real needs of these neighbourhoods, such as job creation, education, and/or other opportunities. (p. 6)

The debate about decriminalizing drugs is a huge and volatile one. There are two countries who have had success with decriminalizing: Switzerland and Portugal. The reality is that this results in a remarkable reduction in criminal activity. The real problem is a different one. Digging deep down and facing our wrongdoing is the real problem.

First-Person Experiencing

I find myself soaring into a flight/fight response while reading Hari's book. I'm horrified by many of the stories. I feel embarrassed that I knew so little about the interconnectedness of race and the war on drugs. I'm not surprised, but I had no idea that Anslinger targeted racialized groups to such an extent. I find myself needing to pause and really take this into the body. I become very conscious of my white body. The more I read the more I feel this whiteness, the safety it affords me.

Focusing Practice

Let's pause again and take into the body our whole felt sense of this. Notice what information comes from your body as it travels up into your brainstem. Tapping into the autonomic nervous system, we slow down to process. Breathing into the centre of the body helps us to regulate as we go deeper.

I'm sharing with my daughter what I am learning about the extent of racism in the war on drugs. She suggests that I read Menakem's (2017) book, *My Grandmother's Hands, Racialized Trauma and the Pathways to Mending Our Hearts and Bodies.* I joke with her that when she was younger, she followed me around. Now she is all grown up and radicalized, and I follow her around. I learn from my two adult children about White supremacy. When they were growing up they attended an inner city school with kids from 43 nationalities. Perhaps because of this experience, I see in both of them a passionate, embodied sense of racial injustice. Their capacity to hold this space without the need to defend moves me deeply.

Understanding Harry: White Body Supremacy

Menakem (2017) has written a profound book about racism and trauma. The power and uniqueness of his voice comes from his direct connection with the body. He cautions the reader to challenge their bodily response as they read his words. He suggests that White supremacy should really be called "White body supremacy" because we are wired to respond through our nervous systems. He knows the power of the felt sense to unconsciously mobilize us to cues of safety and danger. What exactly is meant by *White body supremacy*? Menakem speaks of it as a powerful, all-encompassing assumption of white superiority, not so much individually focused, but infused in systems of economic and political oppression.

So what makes a man like Anslinger? Is he in all of us? Hari explores this question. He speaks of the anger that we can all feel when confronting the relentless hold that addiction has, particularly on people we love. When this anger merges with a need for domination, feelings of superiority, and a dangerous need to belong, it has monstrous outcomes. The Klu Klux Klan is an example of this, and so is white body supremacy. And, in case you are feeling defensive, thinking I am exaggerating, the following speaks for itself.

The Female Chain Gang

It is hard to believe the following exists in 2012 in Arizona, USA. And yet, the "hard to believe" is becoming all too commonplace. Hari (2015) writes:

> The female chain gang meets at five o'clock every weekday morning just as the sun is starting to rise over the Arizona desert. The women emerge unfed from the tents, surrounded by barbed wire, as they are ordered to put on T-shirts that display to the world why they are there. I WAS A DRUG ADDICT, is inscribed in bold black letters you can read from a distance. I watch as they clamber into their striped uniforms, their limbs flailing with hunger and exhaustion. Then they put on leg irons. Then the guards order them to begin their chant.
>
> *Everywhere we go*
> *People want to know*
> *Who we are*
> *So we tell them*
> *We are the chain gang*
> *The only female chain gang.*
>
> They have to stamp their boots and jangle their chains in rhythm to the song, as though they are the chorus line in some dystopian Broadway musical. And so their march out into the desert heat begins. (p. 104)

This is just not possible! And yet it is. Anslinger said that addicts were "lepers". Arizona has built something much like a concentration camp for them.

First-Person Experiencing ... Pause

> I realize that I am singing this chant as I read it. "Everywhere we go ... I realize that I know this chant! This is a children's campfire song. I first heard this when I worked as a camp counsellor at Dellcrest Children's Centre, a clinic for "emotionally disturbed" kids, as they were called. Here's how it went:
>
> *Everywhere we go,*
> *People always ask us*
> *Who we are*
> *So we tell them*
> *We're from Dellcrest*
> *Mighty mighty Dellcrest!*

Bizarre, absolutely bizarre. This is the place of trauma, where brutality floods into innocence

Big, thick block in my chest. I feel the adrenaline pumping through my body, and at the same time I want to shut it down. (Is it possible to feel flight/fight/freeze all at once? Or do they quickly switch?) This is the place of trauma. Forget thinking about it. This is the feeling place, and it stinks. This is the place we go to with our clients, and we become speechless, because in this place there are no words. We can only be real and be here with each other. And that has to be enough, because we cannot change what was.

I slowly find the energy to bring awareness into this horrendous story, the chain gang story, the image of these tortured women made to dance and prance like chained horses. It's a searing-on-the-brain kind of image.

Many images like this come with this work. I often wonder what we all do with them? Do any of us utter them aloud? Even if I could, I don't want to inflict them on another person. Do we as therapists carry them in our bodies?

I'm mobilizing, trying to act. To write, to speak, to fight with feet on the ground. Not with rage, but rage comes with this image, as it should.

But, wait a minute. Something doesn't feel right about Menakam's description of white body supremacy. I take time to feel into this ...

White male body supremacy is really different from white female body supremacy. I feel the male gaze. The lifelong assessment of female bodies. The male guards' abusive gazing at the female chain gang.

I think of White male queer bodies that I have worked with. They are very different from white male hetero bodies. I'm reminded of the embodied relational pain and shame that my gay or queer clients carry inside. Their fathers' contempt spills over them as they struggle to love who they are in the face of the fierce oppression of hyper masculinity. This is double consciousness. It is very important to notice and name these differences.

Childhood Trauma: The Underbelly of Addiction

"Addicts grow up in homes that are not homes, with parents that are not parents, so they seek escape. Girl or boy, this is a familiar pattern" (Anslinger in Hari, 2015, p. 161). Even Anslinger himself could see the connection between traumatic childhood and addiction, although this didn't stop him one bit from his vicious attacks. This kind of rage, born of fear, continues to fuel the racist war on drugs. It prevents us from acknowledging the facts: the evidence that links trauma and addiction is overwhelming.

Felitti's Adverse Childhood Experiences Scale (ACES)

The adverse childhood experiences study (ACES) is perhaps the most well-known and thorough study on the relationship between trauma and addiction. It was conducted by Felitti and Anda between 1995 and 1997. Felitti (2016) tells an intriguing tale about his journey into the field. As I hear him speak it feels good to realize that we share a path with some intersecting concepts and convictions.

It began in the 1980s when Felitti was running a weight loss programme in the Kaiser Permanente's Department of Preventive Medicine in San Diego. He discovered that patients who were losing weight were the most likely to drop out of the programme. This seemed counter-intuitive, and Felitti set out to discover what this was all about. He interviewed 286 people who had left the programme and discovered that the majority of them had been sexually abused as children (Felitti, 2002).

Patty's Tale of Sleep Eating. One patient in particular stood out for Felitti (2016). Patty was 28 at the time that they met. She was working as a nursing aide doing a nightshift job at a seniors' home. At the time that she entered the programme she weighed 408 pounds. At the end of 51 weeks of attending the fasting programme she weighed 132 pounds. Felitti was very pleased but this proved to be short lived.

Patty maintained the weight for several weeks, but then began to regain and within three weeks had put 37 pounds back on. Felitti was confused. How was it possible to gain this much weight in three weeks? Patty shared that as a child she used to sleepwalk. Now, she was waking in the morning in her apartment to find the kitchen full of pots and pans, leftover food and boxes, and she assumed that it must be her sleep walking and sleep eating, since she lived alone and had gained weight.

In true Felitti fashion, he asked, and asked again, why Patty thought she was gaining weight now. Finally, she answered that a married fellow at work had told her that she was looking good and suggested that they get together. While Felitti agreed that this was not a good idea, he was confused as to why it would lead Patty to such an extreme response. And then the connection came. Patty shared with him that her grandfather had sexually abused her for years as a child. It wasn't safe to be attractive.

Patty disappeared for 12 years. When she returned to the clinic, she weighed over four hundred pounds again. Meanwhile, Felitti had continued his search for answers and started a group for patients that weighed four- to six-hundred pounds and hadn't been able to lose weight in the programme. The group was formed to explicitly seek the answer to the following question: "What is the engine underneath eating yourself to death?"

Patty joined this group and continued her journey. She shared that several years ago she had bariatric surgery and had lost 94 pounds. She became suicidal, was hospitalized five times, and given three rounds of electroshock therapy. Eighteen months after this Felitti interviewed Patty and she shared that as the weight was coming off, she felt that her "wall was coming down" faster than she could handle it. It wasn't safe to lose the protective barrier.

Felitti's Aha Moment

An "aha" moment occurred for Felitti as he heard Patty say this. *He realized that what he had perceived to be the problem, Patty perceived to be the solution.* A moment of deep connection and validation came for me as I read this last line. This is exactly what I understood in my women's group. Their problems were actually disguised solutions. Our job as clinicians is to listen with non-pathologizing ears. Felitti (2019) says this very clearly: "We listened. Period." When we truly listen, we hear the truth and it all begins to make sense.

Felitti is one of my heroes. He heard horrific accounts of sexual abuse, and unlike Freud, he held on to his belief in his patients. He tells the story of presenting these findings to a large crowd at an obesity conference in Atlanta in 1990. During the presentation, a member of the audience suggests that he needs to understand that these patients are not telling the truth. We hear Felitti's impassioned response as he recalls "this miserable wretch". He takes the high road and keeps his outrage to himself.

However, he doesn't stop there. While having dinner at the same conference, he is approached by David Williamson, a researcher, who suggests that he needs to do a large study to get the attention of disbelievers. And so, ACES was born. This study has had a huge impact in the fields of addiction, trauma, and preventative medicine.

Felitti's Alternative Model of Addiction – A Psychodynamic Model

After all of his research into the effects of early adverse experience, Felitti (2004) draws the following sobering conclusion:

> Our findings are disturbing to some because they imply that the basic causes of addiction lie within us and the way we treat each other, not in drug dealers or dangerous chemicals. They suggest that billions of dollars have been spent everywhere except where the answer is to be found. (p. 3)

This large well-known study demonstrated the strong link between childhood adversity and chronic health problems. The first study was done within a single health care system in San Diego and a sample size of over 17,000 middle class American adults. The group was 80% White, 10% Black, and 10% Asian. A full 74% had gone to college, 49% were men, and the average age was 57.

The study included eight categories of adverse childhood experiences including:

- Recurrent and severe physical abuse (11%)
- Recurrent and severe emotional abuse (11%)
- Contact sexual abuse (women 28%, men 16%)

- Growing up in a household with:
- An alchoholic or drug user (25%)
- A member being imprisoned (3%)
- A mentally ill, chronically depressed, or institutionalized member (19%)
- A mother being treated violently (12%)
- Both biological parents absent (22%)

Participants scored one point for each category that was relevant. Therefore, an ACE score could range from zero to eight. According to Felitti (2004), a person with an ACE score of 6 is 2.5 times more like to be a smoker and six times more likely to be addicted to alcohol than a child whose ACE score is zero. The likelihood of injection of street drugs also increases dramatically and in direct correlation with ACE score increases. *A male child with an ACE score of 6, compared to a male child with an ACE score of 0 has a 4,600 percent increase in the likehood of becoming an injection drug user.*

Felitti disputes the current brain disease model of addiction, instead seeing it as experience-dependent and not chemically dependent. He suggests a psychodynamic explanation. He states that addiction involves:

> unconscious although understandable decisions being made to seek chemical relief from the ongoing effects of old trauma, often at the cost of accepting future health risks. Expressions like "self-destructive behaviour" are misleading and should be dropped because ... they overlook the importance of the obvious short-term benefits that drive the use of these substances. (2004, p. 8)

Note that Felitti says "unconscious although understandable" decisions being made to act out addictive behaviours. This is similar to the autonomic response of the nervous system to seek survival. Felitti also notes that the use of "self-destructive" is misleading, suggesting that a non-patholizing model is more fitting.

The Plot Thickens with Later ACES Study

The story of oppression deepens with Merrick's (2018) results of the largest ACES study to date. Significant in my reading of the first study is the over-representation of white middle class people. What do we find when we study a more diverse group? Merrick's sample came from 214,157 people living in 23 states in the United States from 2011 to 2014. This study asked similar questions to the first one except they added parental separation or divorce.

What Merrick (2018) and her colleagues found was interesting from a trauma perspective. Those who identified as Black or Latino, with less than a high school education, or annual income lower than $15,000 were more likely to have higher ACE scores. And a new finding was that multiracial, gay, lesbian, and bisexual people were the highest-scoring groups. Multiracial participants scored average of 2.5 ACES, and bisexual adults scored 3.1. Women, younger adults, unemployed people, and those unable to work also scored higher. What does this tell us? It tells us that if you are a member of an oppressed group in our culture you have a much higher chance of being traumatized, which leads to a much higher chance of becoming addicted.

Alexander: "Addiction is our teacher"

Alexander (2008) is a retired psychologist from British Columbia, Canada. He wrote one of the most important books on the study of addiction, *The Globalization of Addiction, A Study in Poverty of the Spirit.* He began his career working with heroin addicts in the very troubled downtown east side of Vancouver.

Similar to what shaped Maté's story, this early experience in Vancouver proved to shape much of Alexander's career. He was curious and able to listen to his clients without seeing their behaviour as pathological. What he heard compelled him to take a broader perspective, to *think at the edge* of the current understanding of addiction. The traditional brain disease model didn't fit well with his experience and he wanted to learn more about what addiction had to teach us. He felt that current medical and psychological theories were too small a box in which to really understand addiction. Like Maté and Felitti, he was struck by the pervasiveness of childhood trauma in the people he was trying to help. Alexander sensed a need to broaden the lens and to take a more historical perspective. This led him to read Polanyi's work on psychosocial integration.

"The discovery of the individual soul is the discovery of community … Each is implied by the other" (Polanyi, K., in, Alexander, 2008, p. 58). Polanyi was an economic historian and philosopher who was influenced by the psychoanalyst Eric Erickson. Erickson developed a theory that emphasized the importance of *psychosocial integration*. This is a process that "reconciles people's vital needs for social belonging with their equally vital needs for individual autonomy and achievement" (Alexander, 2008, p. 58).

Each individual is born into a family and a greater societal grouping. Integration occurs when people feel a sense of safety and belonging within both communities. A balance of meeting one's own and others' needs is achieved and this results in a sense of cohesion and harmony with self and the natural world. Social connection and individual autonomy work together to create a sense of belonging. In terms of polyvagal theory, this is a state of ventral vagal regulation. I called this state *flock* in the client version of the felt sense polyvagal model (FSPM). Flocking together with safety creates belonging and balanced emotional regulation. If you look at the model, this state of psychosocial integration includes flock, flow and fun, the full bottom half of the model.

According to Polanyi, the lack of psychosocial integration results in what he called *dislocation*. The term refers to a psychological state of alienation, isolation, and hence marginalization. Alexander recognized the state of dislocation in his heroin-addicted clients. He decided to use the term in his *dislocation theory* of addiction. In this state, the social structures that define and foster a sense of belonging have broken down. Dislocation includes, but is not limited to, geographical relocation, such as when indigenous peoples where colonized and sent to reserves. Looking again at the FSPM, the state of dislocation would include flight/flight/fixate/fold, the top half of the model. In its most severe form, it would represent the dorsal vagal branch of the autonomic nervous system.

Globalizing Free Market Society Creates Dislocation

Alexander (2008) argues that our whole culture is suffering from dislocation as a result of our free market economy. He is careful to point out that he is not advocating for communism when he makes the claim that free market capitalism is breaking down our sense of community. Rather he is emphasizing the fact that when free market capitalism is left to its own devices, the pursuit of materialism dominates society. This results in an obsession with acquiring "things" at the expense of building loving connections with family and community. In addition, too much emphasis is put on the needs of self. Psychosocial integration requires a balance between needs of self and community: "To be free and still belong" (p. 59). Through an anti-oppressive lens, we can argue that cultural imperialism has impacted our global economy to the extent that our whole North American society is suffering from dislocation.

Alexander (2008) states,

> The genius of a successful culture is that it provides adequately for individual autonomy and social belonging at the same time – a balancing act of the greatest virtuosity, since the needs often conflict with each other. The crucial flaw of globalizing free-market society is that the balance has shifted so far in favour of individuals that it is now extremely difficult to recover equilibrium because of the catastrophic damage-environmental, social, psychological, and spiritual-that this imbalance has already caused. The remedy for this imbalance is not a shift to the other extreme of all-encompassing collectivism, but re-establishment of the balance, if this is still possible. (p. 96)

Sustained Dislocation Creates Addiction

Human beings are very resilient and can withstand some degree of loneliness and marginalization that result from dislocation. However, a sustained environment of loss of connection results in adaptations such as addiction. We see how the addicted person attaches to the source of addiction (for example drugs, sex, food, shopping, or gambling) because the pain of connection becomes too great. Or, as we connect less and less with ourselves, quiet reflection becomes frightening and we seek distraction.

Increased online activity, long work hours, loss of spiritual connection, and pursuit of narcissistic goals all result in an overwhelming sense of dislocation. It is not surprising that in our society addiction is on the rise. Fellitti's ACES study demonstrates the evidence for dislocation theory: The greater the incidence of trauma and oppression, the higher the scores for addiction.

Alexander argues that if psychosocial integration is restored individuals should be able to overcome addictions. While this is not compatible with the current brain disease model, it is highly compatible with the learning theory of addiction, and polyvagal theory. We will see later, in our clinical vignettes, how we can restore psychosocial integration and thus help our addicted clients to not only achieve sobriety but also to sustain a ventral vagal state of emotional regulation.

Skinner Box Versus Rat Park

In the early 1960s, researchers did a series of rat studies to attempt to prove the demon-drug myth. They put each rat in what was called a Skinner box, an empty box that contained only a device that allowed them to self-administer drugs. Indeed, the studies found that monkeys, rats, and mice self-injected large doses of heroin, amphetamines, cocaine, and other drugs. These studies were cited as proof that drugs cause addiction.

Alexander was not convinced. He and others had the foresight to see the serious shortcomings in these experiments. Like so many psychological experiments in the laboratory, the element of real-life experiencing was not well thought out. Rats, like people, do not live in sterile environments. They are actually quite social creatures. So it shouldn't be surprising that when you stick them in an empty Skinner box with nothing to occupy their time, or to keep them company, they would seek out the drugs. In the 1970s, Alexander and colleagues decided to conduct a now-famous study that took this into account.

In order to see what would happen if rats had a more natural setting, Alexander and colleagues used two boxes. One was a Skinner box, and the other was what they called "rat park". This airy and spacious environment was 200 times the size of the Skinner box. They painted a peaceful British Columbia forest scene on the plywood walls, provided lots of empty tins and wood scraps, and about 16 to 20 male and female rats to play with. They compared the morphine consumption of rats in both boxes and found that rats living in rat park had little appetite for the morphine. In some of the experiments, rats in the Skinner box consumed nearly 20 times as much as those in rat park. The results have been replicated many times with the same outcomes.

Alexander (2008) concluded, "The intense appetite of isolated experimental animals for opioid drugs in self-injection experiments does not prove that opioid drugs have an irresistible addictive quality, even for rats" (p. 195). Psychosocially integrated rats, and people, do not become addicted to drugs or other substances or behaviours. They have no need.

It boggles the mind to see how, in spite of so much evidence to the contrary, intelligent people continue to distort the truth about addiction. We can't unpack this from a top-down approach because it doesn't make logical sense. We have to go deeper down, into bottom-up experiencing to explore this. As I allow myself to connect into a felt sense of what addiction teaches us, I come to this knowing: In our dislocated state, we as a culture can't know how to feel into the problem or the solution. We cling to our top-down explanation of demon drugs to avoid feeling into the embodied cultural trauma of our times. Like the addicted soul, we delude ourselves. We have lost our way. But only in our heads. The body knows the answer.

References

Alexander, B. (2008). *The globalization of addiction: A study in poverty of the spirit.* New York: Oxford University Press.

Alexander, B. (2014). *Existential analysis: Addiction panel discussion.* Vancouver, Canada: Simon Fraser University.

DeGrandpre, R. (2006). *The cult of pharmacology: How America became the world's most troubled drug culture.* Durham, NC: Duke University Press.

DiAngelo, R. (2017). What does it mean to be white? In R. Menakem (Ed.), *My grandmother's hands: Racialized trauma and the pathways to mending our hearts and bodies.* Las Vegas, NV: Central Recovery Press.

Du Bois, W. E. B. (1897, August). The strivings of the Negro people, *The Atlantic Monthly,* pp. 194–197.

Felitti V. J. (2002). The relation between adverse childhood experiences and adult health: Turning gold into lead. *The Permanente Journal, 6*(1), 44–47.

Felitti, V. J. (2004). The origins of addiction: Evidence from the adverse childhood experiences study. English version of the article published in Germany as: Felitti VJ. Ursprünge des Suchtverhaltens – Evidenzen aus einer Studie zu belastenden Kindheitserfahrungen. *Praxis der Kinderpsychologie und Kinderpsychiatrie, 52,* 547–559.

Felitti, V. (2016). *Addiction, trauma and adverse childhood experiences (ACEs): The neuroscience behind developmental/attachment trauma and adverse childhood experiences.* Eau Claire, WI: PESI.

Felitti, V. (2019, February 7). How childhood can haunt us. *Podcast.* Retrieved from https://www.acesconnection.com/blog/how-childhood-can-haunt-us-mowe-blog-podcast.

Hari, J. (2015). *Chasing the scream: The opposite of addiction is connection.* New York: Bloomsbury.

Hart, C. (2013). *High price: Drugs, neuroscience and discovering myself.* London, UK: Penguin.

Maté, G. (2008). *In the realm of hungry ghosts: Close encounters with addiction.* Toronto, ON: Alfred A. Knopf Canada.

Menakem, R. (2017). *My grandmother's hands: Racialized trauma and the pathways to mending our hearts and bodies.* Las Vegas, NV: Central Recovery Press.

Merrick M. T., Ford D. C., Ports K. A., & Guinn A. S. (2018). Prevalence of adverse childhood experiences from the 2011–2014 behavioral risk factor surveillance system in 23 states. *JAMA Pediatrics, 172*(11), 1038–1044. doi:10.1001/jamapediatrics.2018.2537

Young, I. M. (1998). The five faces of oppression. *Philosophical Forum, xix,* 4.

6   Bringing the Body to Mind: The Emerging Field of Interpersonal Neurobiology

This chapter will explore the area of interpersonal neurobiology (IPNB) with broad strokes. We will not delve deeply into the neurobiological aspects of IPNB. Others, including Siegel (2012b), Badenoch (2008), Afford (2020), and Schore (2012), have already covered this terrain with great skill and intelligence. Rather, I will review the basic ideas and then invite you to explore the field from an embodied trauma/addiction therapist perspective, drawing on our *thinking at the edge* (TAE) methodology.

From an embodied, experiential stance, we will inquire into the following questions: What does this *consilience* model (Wilson, 1998) bring to our field? How does it fit? Where do we place it in our more embodied, and, for some of us, radical approach to bodywork? How does it contribute to our understanding and treatment of addiction?

First-Person Experiencing

I am struggling to begin this chapter. Something is "niggling" away at me. I decide to go for a walk and check down inside. Breathing deeply as I walk through the brilliant red leaves, I'm reminded of the great resource within me, my focusing practice. It prompts me to breathe into the "niggling". Working from the bottom up, I ask myself the clearing space question, (step 1 in focusing).

"What is coming between me and beginning this chapter?" Now I am entering into what Gendlin (1962/1997, p. 100) calls "direct reference", which entails shifting my attention to my own internal felt experience. He describes this action as a change in itself: the stream of our experience becomes something new and different as we move into the bodily, implicit knowing.

I wait and walk. Something (I'm not at all sure what that "something" is), comes to me about the nature of crossing neurobiology with embodied trauma-informed psychotherapy, a crossing of a top-down with a bottom-up approach. This "something" feels bubbly and nervous in my chest and stomach. The felt sense is forming as I stay with it. The handle is a bubbly kind of nervous. The image of wobbly bubbles comes, and I laugh out loud.

I think back to how I heard about interpersonal neurobiology (IPNB). In 2011 I learned about the work of Siegel and Porges. The ideas grabbed my attention. When I attended a conference on polyvagal theory, I discovered that Badenoch (2008) was offering a course on IPNB, so I signed up. I found the weekend to be full of new exciting ideas, and a group experience that embodied the full spectrum of chaos, rigidity, and lovely moments of integration.

As I walk, I remind myself of how helpful it is to understand the body's biology. Something shifts inside and I feel myself settle. I am following my own felt sense of what feels right to pursue in the development of the felt sense polyvagal model (FSPM). I let myself stay with all of this in a quiet rhythmical walking way, sensing into something more.

Two issues come. First, the word caution. My chest tightens very slightly. I feel surprised by this heightened sense. After all, I am immersed in this world of IPNB and enjoying it. But, I did feel a caution at the beginning of this exploration, and my body holds it. Something comes again about trying to integrate neurobiology with our embodied practice of trauma therapy. After all, neurobiology is part of the top-down scientific community; a place that has not welcomed or respected our focusing-oriented work. Some therapists are concerned about this integration, perhaps because they see no need for it, and/or fear that it will reduce our understanding to biological explanations. Some feel that as clinicians we already know all that, so why do we need biological studies to "prove" it? And, they worry that it puts our work into a more medical context, reinforcing a top-down model.

Other therapists, perhaps as a result of feeling insecure and wounded by the disrespect, may be drawn to the field of neurobiology in a quest for status and recognition of our work. Ah, but there is a great irony in this. Siegel points out several times in his Mindsight lectures that IPNB is not embraced by the traditional scientific community. It appears that some academic disciplines, particularly medicine and psychology, are not ready for it. That's because Siegel's model is working at the edge of inquiry. He is offering a paradigm shift, a shift from a pathological illness model to a strength-based model of health and integration. This shift feels good in my body. It's as though my body feels deep appreciation for being understood and honoured. The word whole comes. This is a very familiar felt sense, coming from my focusing practice, and Gendlin's philosophy. My body is a knowing and ongoing process of growth and change.

Focusing Practice

I invite you now to pause, take time to go inside, and connect with your sense of this. How do you feel about welcoming neuroscience into the field of psychotherapy? What are your associations with science, objectivity, and brain research? Notice what happens as you breathe down into your body. The word "science" often brings up different gendered responses. Research shows that girls and women often experience misogynistic attitudes towards our abilities in the fields of science and mathematics. Girls perform much better when they learn these subjects in same-sex classrooms where we feel safe and free of judgment. Take time to notice how you carry this. Notice how the felt sense of this informs the direction of our inquiry. Where does all of this sit in your body?

Now imagine I am sitting across from you in focusing practice and I say back to you what you have just experienced and shared, resonating (focusing step 4) with your felt sense. Together, we build a relational felt sense of each other's inner world. A deeper sense of each other comes in a bodily way.

And now, I check back down inside, and I can take turns with you. I gently go inward. I take the word "science" in. I'm back in my first-year psychology class at university. The professor is showing us an image of a ruler. He says in a loud emphatic voice, "This is the study of psychology. Predict, measure, and control. If you don't like it go study religion!" I am devastated. Feeling into the place in my body where the impact of his words is most keenly felt, I sense my heavy chest, and sunken shoulders. Anger comes in my quickened breathing. I stuck it out to get my degree, but I sought solace in my Canadian writers' courses. I found the attempt to reduce the rich world of human felt experiencing to little "units" of study ridiculous and sad. At the time, the literary world gave me a much-needed lift. As I stay with all of this, I feel a felt shift. I knew then what I know now. It makes no sense to apply the scientific method to many aspects of subjective experience.

Bringing the Interpersonal into Neurobiology

So, here is the exciting thing: IPNB embraces the science of neurobiology *and* the subjective world of interpersonal experiencing. This consilience model integrates many different ways of knowing, with acknowledgement that the scientific method is not best suited to the study of subjective experiencing. IPNB embraces quantitative and qualitative research, depending on what is being studied.

Siegel is bringing the "interpersonal" into neurobiology in a respectful collaborative process of conceptualizing *and* experiencing. Much like Gendlin, Siegel is drawn to thinking beyond already known patterns. This is also the name of a brilliant paper by Gendlin (1992) in which he explores the edges of phenomena.

Thinking at the Edge: Crossing Concepts and Finding the More

I go back to our TAE methodology. We start with a place that precedes words, a place that we sense into and know more about than we can say. It is a niggling place that pulls at me to pay attention to the complexity of this crossing of neurobiology and subjective experiencing. Gendlin (2017) describes crossing concepts as looking into each facet through the other. "It isn't exactly what they have in common. It's more what will come out from them". Gendlin describes how, in a top-down model we reduce everything to the lowest common denominator, but in crossing we invite each facet to enhance the other. *We want to find more than what they have in common.* We want a fresh relating of two concepts that creates a new direction.

I began to map these IPNB concepts onto my model. As I look at the FSPM model, I can see how chaos maps onto the experience of flooding, rigidity onto the experience of numbing, and integration onto the grounded/safe place. I cross my clinically descriptive model with a neurobiologically informed way of understanding my client's emotional dysregulation. I begin to understand that flooding and numbing are part of the autonomic nervous system's natural response to threat.

Crossing Flooding/Numbing with Chaos/Rigidity

I ask the question: can emotional flooding be seen in some way like flight/fight chaos in the autonomic nervous system (ANS)? I feel into the relationship, sensing a similarity in some bodily way, sensing the body's physical knowing. It is getting ready to mobilize for survival. This way of understanding flooding as a chaotic state in the nervous system brings help in two ways: it shows how flooding helps to mobilize the body in a way that parallels the fight/flight response. And it offers help in understanding the adaptive way the body is designed.

Following the same logic, I wonder: can numbing be seen in some way to be like rigidity? Feeling into numbing and feeling into rigidity, I notice a deadening quality, a way of flattening, tightening. And yet, the words are not the same. Flooding and numbing feel *alive*. Clients use this language with ease. Chaos and rigidity feel distant, more technical. Clients rarely use this language to describe how they are feeling. Yet, one adds to the other. Flooding and numbing bring first-person experiencing to chaos/rigidity's intellectual, conceptual quality.

The Sweet Spot

Here we refer back to the discussion in Chapter 3. This is the place where top-down neurophysiology (chaos, rigidity), meets and informs bottom-up experiencing (flooding, numbing). Both are important ways of knowing and experiencing. Both bring richness to each other in the crossing. The crossing begins to reveal something new and fresh about the paradox: *what helps you harms you.* The help is in the autonomic nervous system responding to threat. The self-harm comes to activate the flight/fight fold response when flock is not available. More crossing will come.

This sweet spot feels so satisfying. What about this is so rich an experience for me? Do you sense this richness? On some deep level, I believe that we all seek the integration of *experiencing* and *thinking about.* The splitting of these ways of knowing feels foreign to me. *Our culture has distain for the rich intricacy of living.* Embodied experiential therapists seek to bridge this divide and heal this distain. The bringing together of top-down knowing with bottom-up freshness feels so alive, so whole and integrated.

The Brilliance of Consilience

Recall in Chapter 1, Siegel's (2012b) story about how the development of IPNB came as a result of a meeting of the minds, about the mind, with forty different academic disciplines. The consilience approach looks for similar processes at play in disparate areas of study. This does not mean that we try to fit all things into one box, or concept, but rather that we explore the commonalities while recognizing the differences.

Siegel (2012b) describes the ancient Indian parable of the blind men and the elephant as a way of understanding the concept of consilience. The story describes a group of blind men who have never come across an elephant before. Each of them touches a different part of the elephants' body and then assumes that the whole elephant can be described by the one part. For example, the man who touches the trunk describes the whole elephant as long and bumpy, whereas the man who touches the foot describes it as large and round. They assume that their limited description is the accurate one. This causes a lot of conflict with the group. The moral of the parable is that we humans tend to see our own version of reality and think that this is the one and only truth, without listening to others truth and looking at the big picture. A consilience approach brings together many different versions of the truth and seeks a kind of integration that honours all perspectives, enhancing an understanding of the whole.

How might we apply the concept of consilience to our work as therapists? For example, are there commonalities in different schools of psychotherapy? While techniques may differ, many of the approaches share a similar goal. They want clients to be able to regulate their emotional states, to feel stable and grounded. We can welcome divergent theories and treatment strategies, and also feel a sense of reassurance that many paths aim for related outcomes. While we may use many different methods, we need to develop a container that provides a basic framework for synthesizing the concepts. Otherwise we have nothing more than a hodgepodge of differing techniques, and that is not consilience. The framework I am suggesting is the FSPM.

A Definition of Mind

Eventually, Siegel entered psychiatric training and was deeply intrigued with the study of the mind. He was shocked to discover that we really have no definition of mind, so he began his inquiry by forming a working group whose first task was to create a working definition of "mind". Using the consilience approach, Siegel was driven to create a safe space for all forty academic fields to come together to begin to integrate ways of knowing. On a walk by the beach he came up with a definition of mind that all agreed to: "A core aspect of the mind is an embodied and relational process that regulates the flow of energy and information" (2012b, p. 2).

"Embodied" fits nicely with our bottom-up approach to psychotherapy. The brain lives in the whole body, and information and energy flow from the bottom up and the top down, but not equally. We know from polyvagal theory that 80% of the information flow along the vagus nerve moves *up* from body to brain.

Describing the mind as a "relational process" resonates with focusing language. This speaks to the deep ways in which energy and information flow between us in the relational felt sense (Winhall, 2014). This definition of mind gave Siegel a starting point to begin to build a model of health and well-being to replace the current pathologizing approach to mental health. With no clear notion of what wellness is, our current system is reduced to focusing on pathology. Much like Alexander (2008), Siegel stepped out of his own discipline, seeking help from other fields of study. He spent many years working with physicists and mathematicians, sharing ideas about the science of systems. This consilience approach led him to view the mind in terms of complex systems, or "complexity theory" (Siegel, 2012b).

First-Person Experiencing

I approached the chapter with a kind of excited trepidation. It is indeed daunting for a psychotherapist who has little training in science to begin to understand the complexities of IPNB. And yet, if one takes one's time, it is both accessible and fascinating. As those of us who practice embodied-experiential methods of psychotherapy are drawn to working with the body, it seems only fitting that we learn more about physiology. We needn't feel that we have to become experts in neurobiology. We can always go back to our plentiful sources to guide us. I return to Badenoch (2008) frequently when I begin to feel that my brain is going to explode (chaos) and subsequently shut down (rigidity).

When we think at the edge of experience we have to be brave, to step out and be able to acknowledge the place of "not knowing". Once we can welcome the unknown, and our lack of knowledge, we are free to be flexible, curious, excited to explore and learn in an embodied way. It is from this place that I write and share with you, and it is from this place that I invite you to learn along with me. We know from studying relationships that learning in the context of nurturing connection maximizes our potential for retaining new ideas. I invite you to sense how I am on this journey with you as we go deeper into the complexity.

Complexity Theory: A Push Toward Integration

We know that brains are complex systems, according to the strict mathematical definition of that term. Although the concept of complexity has many facets, one aspect has particular meaning for our endeavour: The theory says that there is an *intrinsic push toward integration, or the subjective experience of wholeness, in our neural circuitry* ... One way of talking about this push towards integration is that complex systems have an innate *self-organizing* capacity (Cicchetti & Rogosch, in Badenoch, 2008, p. 45).

Complexity theory comes from a branch of mathematics, and in the true spirit of consilience, it has been applied to many different fields of study including physics, chemistry, biology, technology, sociology, social work, engineering, ecology, and more.

I remember learning about systems theory, which is related to complexity theory, in my graduate training in family therapy. We were taught to see the family as a system in which each member is a part of the whole. In this model, we see the importance of relationships between the parts and their need to seek integration in order to function in a regulated way. When systems are dysregulated they move into chaos and/or rigidity. Our job is to help our clients find their way to a state of integration, the place of health, and restoration. Siegel (2012b) thinks of integration as being more like making a fruit salad than a smoothie. Individual parts do not become lost in the blender. They maintain their separateness within a whole.

We learned that the family system has an innate self-organizing capacity. The family naturally seeks integration through linking "differentiated parts" a phrase which, in this case, describes the individual family members. In order to understand the system, we assess which elements are linked and which are differentiated. Siegel has identified nine domains of integration that are used for assessing clients' aspects of integration. Blocked processes, arising from trauma and addiction, will impede the process of integration.

Self-organizing systems move from simplicity to complexity. In this case, complexity means developing more components that come together to create integration. Think of complexity as a richness, rather than a complication. As the system develops more parts that come together there is an *intrinsic push* toward integration. This means that the system is designed to work well together. This is a comforting thought. It resonates with a focusing approach. The felt sense carries an implicit knowing of the next step forward. An integrated state is flexible, adaptive, coherent, energized, and stable (FACES; Siegel, 2012a, pp. A1–73). Referring back to the FSPM diagram, integration is located at the bottom area and refers to the state in which the nervous system is governed by the ventral branch of the vagus nerve.

In terms of human development, in infancy our brains focus on differentiation in the first months of life and then gradually move into linking those parts into a more complex and harmonious system as the brain develops and matures. If, however, we experience a block in those linkages, our capacity for integration is impaired and the system moves to chaos and/or rigidity. As we shall see, this point of impaired integration is where trauma and addiction develop. Trauma creates blockages in the capacity to integrate our experiences and this then leads to addictions. The nervous system becomes dysregulated and moves back and forth between chaos and rigidity. Our grounded ventral state is nowhere to be found.

In working with clients, we can see where impaired integration, the state of trauma, occurs in the felt sense. Suzanne, a young woman that I saw for many years, would often have no bodily information accessible to her conscious mind when she would invite a felt sense. Her severe trauma history resulted in her need to *not* bring a fully integrated felt sense experience to her awareness. This state of blocked integration, a dorsal state of shutdown in the ANS, protected her from flooding into flight/fight. As her body began to integrate traumatic experience, we worked hard to establish a grounded ventral presence so she wouldn't swing to flight/fight and addictions. The process of integration developed slowly over years of focusing oriented psychotherapy.

Can you think of clients who you have accompanied on this journey? Instead of pathologizing the lack of integration, we deeply appreciate the body's way of compartmentalizing in order to survive.

First-Person Experiencing

As I read these words "intrinsic push toward integration" and "subjective experience of wholeness" (Badenoch, 2008, p. 4), I pause and allow bodily knowing to move into my awareness. According to Siegel (2012a, pp. 16–4), complex systems have a natural inclination toward well-being and health. I'm sensing a connection here between the concept of intrinsic push toward integration, and the felt shift in focusing. The felt shift brings a physical release that carries us forward into a place of wholeness.

I take the words down inside: intrinsic, natural, wholeness, integration, felt shift ... asking the body to be with all of this. I take my time. Something feels right about exploring these concepts further as I build my FSPM to treat addiction.

Focusing Practice

Take time to be with all of this learning. Some of the concepts need time to settle inside. The material can feel foreign and sometimes overwhelming. It can be very helpful to read and discuss with others as you go. Take the words intrinsic, integrated, and felt shift inside. Notice what comes in your body. Follow your felt sense as it unfolds.

Consilience and Crossing

I recall a conversation with Gendlin when I asked him about noticing similarities and differences. He asked me why I was interested in similarities because they don't lead to something new. I remember feeling nervous in my response and not feeling understood. I said that I was interested in both similarities and differences. Ah, he replied. That was all he said. I wish I had pushed for more.

I'm curious about the relationship between consilience and crossing. While consilience does begin with looking for similarities, it leads to something new because the whole becomes more than the sum of its parts. This feels like an important question to explore and far beyond the scope of the book. For now, we go on.

A Crossing: The Help Embraces the Harm

Here is a place where the crossing of help and harm come back to me. I ask the TAE question, "What does one term give back to the other that helps their interaction?"

I recall Bridgette from my women's group in Chapter 1. She is the young woman whose father raped her in the night and made her pancakes in the day. Bridgette survived through her capacity to numb, a dorsal vagus response, brought on by cutting her vagina. I pause and drop down inside, asking into the felt sense. I see cloud-like images. One cloud, the help, moves to embrace the other, the harm. This sentence comes: *The help embraces the harm.*

In an emotionally regulated (ventral vagal) *felt shift,* the help brings grounded, integrated healing. In an addictive (dorsal/sympathetic) felt shift, the help brings relief and harm simultaneously. Both shifts come from the body's "intrinsically motivated" tendency to seek survival. It becomes crucial to understand the harm (the addiction) in this context. This is the paradigm shift.

Hypothesis: Self-Organization is the Same as Self-Regulation

Thinking with consilience brings moments of pure joy. It is deeply satisfying when the brain makes exciting connections, linking together differentiated parts and creating more than the sum of those parts. Siegel (2012b) describes one of these moments when he links together the concept of self-organization, from complexity theory, with self-regulation. Self-regulation is the capacity to ground and maintain oneself in optimal ways. It is a central concept in the study of psychopathology. Are they related or perhaps the same?

Holding this concept of self-organization in mind, Siegel (2012b) describes picking up the *Diagnostic and Statistical Manual.* He begins to view the psychiatric disorders through the lens of chaos and rigidity. He realizes that they can all be understood as states of *disintegration,* with health being the state of integration/self-regulation. He offers the hypothesis that the use of complex systems theory to describe self-organization parallels the current psychopathological view of self-regulation as described in the DSM. For example, bipolar disorder can be seen as the oscillation from chaos to rigidity. Overlaying complexity theory, anxiety disorders can be viewed as a state of chaos and depression as a movement towards rigidity. The diagnostic categories can be understood as impairments to integration in the nervous system and in relationships. Understanding psychological problems as experiences of emotional dysregulation and disintegration makes an enormous amount of sense and is compatible with the FSPM of addiction. It has far-reaching implications that validate our paradigm shift.

Addiction is viewed as the nervous system's natural, self-organizing attempt to self-regulate in order to survive, offering a kind of respite when being present is too overwhelming. In focusing terms, perhaps another way of understanding the felt shift is to say that it is the body's way of self-organizing and/or self-regulating.

Complex Systems are Non-Linear, Challenging Twelve Steps

Complexity brings with it a non-linear quality. Changes to the system create unpredictable results. If small changes occur in one part of the system, it can have a large impact on the whole system. If those changes are positive this can be a good thing, but if they are stressful it means that the whole system can be challenged. For example, if a client recovers a traumatic memory, the whole system will be activated – flooded with painful thoughts, feelings, physical sensations and memories. If the change is positive it can have an equally large impact. Attempts at harm reduction are so vulnerable to the slightest challenge to the system, so fraught with the constant threat of relapse in the early stages. And yet, positive experiences can have such a profound impact on sustaining a more grounded existence. The unpredictability keeps our work as psychotherapists intriguing and alive.

Our current way of treating addiction, the twelve-step model, is based on a linear, top-down approach where everyone follows the same twelve steps and sets sobriety as their goal. In this binary system, the addicted person has to choose to either continue to use, or to completely stop. For some people this works. But if we look at the current relapse rates of addiction, it is clear that this approach is not working well for many. I believe that is because the actual experience of addiction follows a nonlinear pathway. This non-linear characteristic of addiction is part of what creates such an ongoing challenge. It is also the reason why going into the felt sense of experience can help us to access more information from our clients about their struggles to stop self-harming. Often my clients will describe their confusion in not understanding their behaviour. Their efforts at achieving sobriety do not make sense to them. They use when times are bad, to soothe, and they use when times are good, to celebrate. Many engage in the twelve steps, trying to stop "cold turkey" only to relapse over and over again. Then they feel the shame of failure. In addition, even when they have achieved sobriety, sometimes for many, many years, they can relapse. In the twelve-step model, this results in starting back at the beginning of their sobriety journey. Letting go of something that helps you, even when it harms you, usually needs to be titrated.

I recently worked with Jarred, who had been sober for 22 years. For more than two decades, he was able to live life without the need to drown his sorrows in alcohol and cocaine. When his mother died, he was triggered beyond anything he could ever have imagined. During the funeral, his brother disclosed to him that their mother had sexually abused him. Inconsolable and terrified, he returned to what he knew would block the pain and fear. He went on a huge binge. He did this in a completely dissociated way. Without any conscious awareness, his body went back to what it knew would work. Interestingly, the relapse stopped after one incident. As he sobered up he was able to access the alert part of his brain, the prefrontal cortex. He then came to see me and we began to process the trauma. His capacity to find his way back to sobriety resurfaced quickly. He had not lost all, he was not going back to the beginning of his healing journey. Rather, he understood that his nervous system shut down the most efficient way it knew how in that moment of hearing this shocking news from his brother. Both Jarred and his life partner were reassured by this knowing.

The Harm Reduction Model

The harm reduction model is advocated by the FSPM. It honours the complexity of the journey, and each individual's unique needs. In this model, the addicted person works on a pathway to reduce harm caused by the behaviour. Sometimes that involves sobriety, but often small steps of change are followed to decrease harm over time. Tatarsky (2002), one of the pioneers of harm reduction, puts it this way, "The therapist-guide offers validation and respect for each client, along with a willingness to meet the person where he or she "is at" on the journey and to help them achieve the next step toward their goal" (p. x).

Complex Systems have Emergent and Recursive Properties

Complex systems have both the emergent qualities of newness and fresh experiencing (bottom up) and the recursive qualities of familiar patterns of experience (top down). When we are integrated, we experience these qualities with a sense of harmony. We have a balance of novel and predictable that sits well in the body, creating a sense of grounding. When we are stressed, and possibly traumatized with new upsetting experiences, we may feel too much unpredictability, resulting in a chaotic state. If we cannot mobilize to help ourselves, the system will go into rigidity and then shut down.

Trauma can also create experiences where we perceive danger when we are in fact safe. When we get triggered, we experience old recursive patterns of behavior that can cause us to become dysregulated, resulting in chaos and/or rigidity. This is where, as therapists, we need to guide our clients into enough safety so that they can interrupt the recursive patterns.

Eyes-Wide-Open Presence

Addictive behaviours get activated with recursive patterns. Harm reduction often brings with it the emergence of wonderfully new, fresh awakenings. As wonderful as those experiences are, the profound hold that recursive patterns have on the traumatized brain cannot be underestimated. Remember how neuroplasticity works. The more the neurons in the recursive pathway have been firing and wiring together, the more rigid the pathway becomes, hence the more susceptible the addicted person is to relapse. The good news is that we can rewire and change the pathways with neural exercises, introducing emergent qualities of aliveness. Fostering and sharing the relational felt sense of what

I call *eyes-wide-open presence* with our clients is the best part of the work for me. Here we see the window of tolerance expanding as the person with whom we have shared so much suffering is awakening to their own life energy and presence. Amazing.

My client George, for example, became adept at recognizing these recursive patterns. He knew that the trigger started with a thick sensation in his chest. The felt sense would form into a state of flight, fight with feelings of panic and shame. Over time he learned to get the right amount of distance to be able to be with the trigger, without being swallowed up by it. Eventually he could notice, ride the wave of the trigger, and settle back into a ventral state. What surprised him though, was how freshly an old recursive pattern could get triggered after years. Its non-linear quality jarred him. He thought it had disappeared for good. However, all was not lost. Similar to Jarred's experience, he learned that while the trigger ignited just as quickly, it also settled quickly as his body remembered the emergent neuropathways. His daily practices helped him to understand what had been activated and he was able to stay sober. This was profoundly satisfying for both of us.

Bringing it all Together: The Triangle of Well-being and Resilience

Siegel describes the *triangle of wellbeing* as a metaphor for his idea that mind, brain, and relationships are three aspects of one reality. The image of the triangle represents the flow of energy and information across the system. Recall Siegel's definition of mind as, "An embodied and relational process that regulates the flow of energy and information" (2012b, p. 2).

The bottom point of the triangle is relationships. Siegel emphasizes the vital importance of relating as a sharing of the flow of energy and information between people. The top right is the brain, the term he uses for the nervous system, extending throughout the whole body. The top left of the triangle is mind, an emergent process that occurs from the system of energy and information flow. This flow is within and between people. In focusing language, I call this the *relational felt sense*. The mind is embodied and relational. Regulation of the mind involves monitoring and modifying energy and information flow.

Mindsight: Seeing the Mind

According to Siegel *mindsight* is "the ability to perceive the internal world of the self and others, not just to observe behavior; to have a perception of the inner world of minds" (2012a, pp. A1–52).

Siegel's drive to seek connection with other disciplines was inspired by more than intellectual curiosity. It was also a result of his experiences at medical school. He describes feeling deeply disturbed by the lack of empathy that he witnessed in the way that physicians were relating to their patients. He recognized early on that this capacity to block feeling, to treat patients like objects, was very dangerous. He vowed never to let this happen to him. In doing so, he began a journey of understanding and integrating presence of "mind" in his way of being with patients. He coined the word *mindsight* to describe this ability to perceive the internal world of the self and others, so as not to observe behavior only but rather to have a perception of the inner world of minds (2012a, pp. A1–A52). Once we become aware of the inner world of others, we connect in an embodied way. As a physician, he recognized this as a missing and essential aspect of medical practice.

The concept of mindsight was central to the development of IPNB. It provided a new approach to psychotherapy, weaving together the neurobiological, and the interpersonal realms leading to ideas and ways of working that can help clients develop more insight and empathy towards themselves and others. By engaging in neural exercises, therapists teach their clients how to monitor and modulate energy and information flow. Clients learn how to shift from states of chaos and rigidity into states of integration.

SNAG and SIFT

Engaging our clients in neural exercises is a central part of being a mindful therapist. SNAG is Siegel's acronym for stimulating neuronal activity and growth. An example of this would be mindfulness practices such as *the wheel of awareness*, a meditation practice that Siegel developed. Focusing practice also appears to be an example of SNAGing.

Tracking awareness of different aspects of experiencing is called SIFT. This stands for sensations, images, feelings, and thoughts. Here again we see a relationship between focusing practice in finding a felt sense (thoughts, feelings, physical sensations, memories) and SIFT in IPNB.

Practicing mindsight methods is a powerful way of interrupting the addiction cycle. Teaching our clients about the vital importance of developing new neuropathways helps to empower them, healing lifelong feelings of helplessness. It creates a powerful action step towards presence, towards showing up for life.

Attachment Theory: Holding and Letting Go

We will now look briefly at attachment theory since Chapter 7 will take us into an in-depth exploration of attachment and trauma as it relates to addiction. Attachment theory is a central framework in the development of IPNB. The theory, originally postulated by Ainsworth and Bowlby (1969), states that early relationships with our primary caretakers shape our capacity to self-regulate. The attachment system is innate in mammals and motivates us to seek proximity with our caregivers, particularly when we are distressed. How our caregivers respond to us shapes our sense of relationships and our world.

There are two broad patterns of attachment, secure/insecure and organized/disorganized. Secure speaks to a "good enough" level of emotional and physical safety for the child. Organized attachment patterns lead to the neuronal growth of a healthy developing brain, and a coherent life narrative.

Four Classifications of Attachment

I like to think of attachment relationships in an embodied way, in terms of how we are held in the world. We will go through the four classifications with the body in mind.

Secure: safely held in loving arms. Secure attachment allows the baby to be held with the right amount of closeness and distance. The caregiver/s move in when baby needs soothing and attending to and are sensitive to easing the hold as baby extends into the world. Closeness and distance are navigated with a "relaxed-enough" embodied presence. Baby feels seen, heard, understood and loved. Baby's body feels relaxed, leaning into the warm embrace.

Insecure-Avoidant: unsafely held with too much distance. The avoidant caregiver/s withhold from baby, creating distance and a sense of unease in baby's ability to rest into and be carried by the caregiver. The little body learns to be cautious in seeking closeness, not able to trust in their presence. Baby feels unseen, rejected, held so far away that it isn't safe to express the need for soothing. Baby's body remains vigilant.

Insecure-Ambivalent: Unpredictably held, too close and too far away. Ambivalent caregivers are unpredictable in their capacity to see and respond to baby's distress. When they do respond they often hold baby too close, projecting their own needs onto them. At other times, they are avoidant, not seeing baby's distress. Baby is never able to rest into the caregiver's availability. The inconsistency is very confusing resulting in an anxious, hyper-aroused state for the child.

Disorganized: Not safe, not held enough. Disorganized attachment is the most difficult pattern for baby. Caregivers in this pattern are either terrified or terrifying. They are not available enough to see or respond to baby in a safe way. Baby is living in an unresolvable paradox: The caregiver who is supposed to soothe them, and perhaps infrequently does, is the source of their pain. Unable to resolve this dilemma, baby may first become anxious, and then move into a state of shutting down. The body appears trancelike, dissociated. Baby embodies defeat.

Interestingly, this unresolvable paradox is mirrored in the state of addiction. "What helps you, harms you."

Mapping Attachment Styles and the Felt Sense Polyvagal Model of Addiction

Looking at the FSPM we see:

Integrated: Secure Attachment. Recall from chapter one, the ventral vagal state of integration depicted at the bottom of the model. Here we see secure attachment, with the social engagement system switched on. Baby is safely held in loving arms.

Chaos: Insecure Avoidant/Ambivalent. To the right is the sympathetic state of chaos. This is where baby is held too far away in avoidant and too close/too far in ambivalent.

Rigidity: Insecure/Disorganized. To the left is the dorsal vagal state of rigidity. This is the state of serious threat. Baby shuts down to survive, often dissociating.

Intertwining States. Sometimes these states are crossed with each other or overlapping. People can have different attachment styles depending on the situation and/or the people they are engaging with.

Play: Secure Attachment. This intertwined state is regulated by the ventral branch of the vagus and is therefore secure. While it is intertwined with the sympathetic branch and therefore an activated state, it maintains a sense of safety. It is activation under the influence of the ventral vagal state. Baby embodies a secure attachment pattern.

Stillness: Secure Attachment. This intertwined state is regulated by the ventral branch of the vagus and therefore enables a secure attachment. While it is intertwined with the dorsal branch of the vagus, it maintains a sense of safety. Baby feels safe in the stillness, enjoying the many hours of breast feeding.

Addicted: Insecure Attachment. The intertwining of the sympathetic and dorsal branches of the autonomic nervous system results in the most dysregulated state. *It is postulated that those who live in this state have often experienced a dysregulated attachment in childhood.* This can be a direct result of childhood trauma. However, one needs to be very careful in assessing early attachment patterns when working with addiction. It is a complex issue that is highly impacted by cultural norms. Sometimes it involves early history, and sometimes not. It may be that a growing number of people are developing addiction in adolescence and adulthood due to the highly addictive nature of our dislocated society.

Critiquing Attachment Theory: The Unclassifiable

Not everyone falls neatly into the above attachment categories. According to Siegel (2012b), "There are some patterns that are "unclassifiable", in that they do not meet criteria for any of the prior four categories" (p. 98). Traditional science works with the four patterns of attachment. In Chapter 7 we will explore attachment theory using a TAE approach. This will enable us to explore the areas that are "unclassifiable". Critiquing the theory helps us to reveal all that is left out. Being curious about what doesn't fit helps us to think beyond the "unit" model. We will think beyond the patterns to what emerges in a fresh way.

To sum up, we have covered a lot of terrain in this chapter. The importance of emotion regulation forms the basis of IPNB and our FSPM of addiction. In that spirit, it's a good time to pause, put down the book, and move the body. Let the terms digest inside as you move into a sweet spot of regulation.

References

Afford, P. (2020). *Therapy in the age of neuroscience*. New York: Routledge.

Alexander, B. (2008). *The globalization of addiction, A study in poverty of the spirit*. New York: Oxford University Press.

Badenoch, B. (2008). *Being a brain-wise therapist: A practical guide to interpersonal neurobiology*. New York: W.W. Norton & Company.

Bowlby, J. (1969). *Attachment and loss*. New York: Basic Books.

Gendlin, E. T. (1962/1997). Experiencing and the creation of meaning: A philosophical and psychological approach to the subjective. Evanston, IL: Northwestern University Press.

Gendlin, E. T. (1992). Thinking beyond patterns: Body, language and situations. In B. Den Ouden & M. Moen (Eds), *The presence of feeling in thought*. New York: Peter Lang.

Gendlin, E. T. (2017, March 26). *Crossing in TAE with Gene Gendlin*. Canada: Nada Lou Productions.

Schore, A. N. (2012). *The science of the art of psychotherapy*. New York: W. W. Norton & Co.

Siegel, D. J. (2012a). *Pocket guide to interpersonal neurobiology: An integrative handbook of the mind*. New York: Norton, Inc.

Siegel, D. J. (2012b). *The developing mind, second edition: How relationships and the brain interact to shape who we are*. New York: Guilford Publications.

Tatarsky, A. (2002). *Harm reduction psychotherapy: A new treatment for drug and alcohol problems*. Lanham: Rowman & Littlefield Publishers.

Wilson, E. O. (1998). *Consilience: The unity of knowledge*. New York: Alfred A. Knopf Inc.

Winhall, J. (2014). Understanding and treating addiction with the felt sense experience model. In G. Madison (Ed.), *Emerging practice in focusing-oriented psychotherapy*. London: Jessica Kingsley Publishers.

7   Creating a Safe Nest

First-Person Experiencing

As we begin Chapter 7, I settle myself inside. Bringing attention down into the centre of my body, I say the words, "attachment, trauma, addiction". I wait and see what comes ... I'm back with the young women, and the young me, in my incest group. An instance comes: a moment in time where we are all letting loose, struck by something funny.

Part of the wonder of being with our group of women are the times when we laugh uproariously together. Our joy is exquisite. Precious and victorious, it erupts in spite of everything. It is a defiant joy that cannot be denied or annihilated by the abusers. It comes up from the depths of despair and fatigue, bringing energy just when we are depleted, bringing love into and between us just as we are at a loss. We shift and surrender ourselves to each other as we settle into our safe nest.

My implicit memories take me to a felt sense of joy. Ah, yes, I remember these brief moments as we settle into our safe nest. Tears come and I welcome them. I take time to let my body enjoy the full felt sense of joy. It came now for a reason. I have somehow always known that keeping my eye on good energy lets me stay present and hopeful. My body knows to start this chapter with safety, connection and love. Carrying this felt sense into the work saves me. I breathe into the image of my cat Louie, his soft, elegant body cuddling close for comfort. I can be with the horror of trauma as I breathe into the felt sense handle of Louie, warm animal friend, asleep on my belly.

Instinctively Seeking Good Energy

As I stay with this felt sense, an image of newborn babies comes. I'm back at the hospital where I work with the women in group. I recall a very powerful experience during this time. I'm in the emergency department. I've been paged to come and assess a patient who has just attempted suicide with an overdose of aspirin. As I walk into this stark hospital room, I see an absolutely miserable young fellow having been given a hefty dose of charcoal and a stomach pump. His face is smeared in black vomit. Agh! I'm taken aback. Little did I know at the time that charcoal binds to unwanted substances which helps the body rid itself of toxins. Haunted eyes peer out at me. Long skinny limbs are shaking for dear life as his body is wracked with gagging and sobbing. I am learning how to be with all of this. I do know how to be kind. I'm not sure I know how to be calm.

At the time I have no conscious recall of my mother's suicide attempt when I was five, but my body remembers. I knew it had occurred, but through divided attention, I didn't make the connection between this fellow's suicide attempt and my mother's. It wasn't integrated as it is now. I completed the assessment and then without thinking consciously about where I was going, I literally found myself gazing at newborn babies in incubators on the maternity ward. I have no recollection of deciding to go there. I didn't consciously decide. My body took me to this place, sought out this fresh, innocent energy as a way of helping me to be with this horror. Realizing that my deeper self, my implicit bodily knowing, carries me to good energy is my source of strength. Without this source I could not be an effective trauma/addiction therapist. More than knowing any concept or theory, I have found that making contact with and trusting this body wisdom is the most important thing.

Sharing intensely painful experiences with our clients demands something of us. It awakens and grows a capacity to learn how to care for and contain ourselves and at the same time to be present for them. Similar to parenting, the role needs us to embrace leadership, to show a way, to create a safe nest for whatever comes into the room.

Focusing Practice

Let's pause and feel into what is happening for you inside. As we go deeper into the addiction/trauma work, I invite you to find your source of knowing, calm, safety, joy. Take your time, sifting down, deep into the body. Check into your breath, your belly, your limbs, welcoming whatever comes. I encourage you to pause and be with this place for however long you need. When you find a source of grounding, take time to find a handle for it. Say the handle inside and let it resonate so you can return to this comforting place when in need. If possible, find a listening partner. Create a caring *relational felt sense* between you.

Back in the Women's Group

Many traumatic experiences disrupt our safety. We share it together. Another instance comes…Bad things happen. News comes that one of the women in our group has hung herself. It all becomes too much for her and the terror of being pursued by her abusers is overwhelming. The professionals who were supposed to rescue her violated her, repeating a childhood trauma. Her addictive mechanisms aren't enough to bear this fearful pain. I feel collapsed inside, shattered and drenched in the horror. I try to be there for all of the women, to hold a space for all of us. But I am sinking. Her violent suicide cuts through our circle and terrifies us all. It shatters our sense of justice, even the little bit that existed. We are overwhelmed with a complicated grief.

All of the women in the group decide that they want to go to her funeral. We circle around her open coffin, holding each other close. While this is enormously painful it also solidifies our sense of "we". We will all carry this moment inside forever. We are creating a special kind of intimacy, a salve for the wounds that bind us together. This feels good, and I make a point of making eye contact with everyone to help them encode this moment of connection.

Vicarious Trauma, The Hot Potato

It's painful to talk about these stories. It brings back my own vicarious trauma, a trauma that comes from being overwhelmed by the horrific stories that we hear every day. Forty years ago, few spoke of how this work impacted us as healers. I felt very alone with it at the time, even though I had good colleagues. Who could show you how to deal with flashbacks to the trauma that our clients were sharing, and how it awakened our own? It's hard not to minimize our own trauma when clients are enduring sexual torture, police rapes, knifings, shootings, homelessness. And if we have known such horrors, it's hard to remain present without retraumatizing ourselves. At the time that I was leading the women's group, the concept of "vicarious" trauma wasn't acknowledged. Our suffering as therapists was unspeakable, yet it was screaming inside us. Eventually, it erupted and we were able to comfort each other for a time.

As healers, it's absolutely imperative that we learn to be with painful feelings. We must find a way to welcome what we hear, see, feel, and remember. It's hard to know what to do with the unspeakable. I remember a client saying that she needed to tell me something, but she didn't want to hurt me with the horror of it. Holding trauma is like holding a hot potato in your hands. Holding it hurts and passing it on hurts. It's easy to see how addictive behaviours become our friend. This is why the most important thing is to find our source of good energy, whatever form that takes for you, and connect it with the healing energy of body wisdom. Then we can bear the pain and show our clients how we bear it. If we are not up to this challenge, we have no business doing this work.

Pause and Find Your Body Wisdom

Practice bringing in your handle for healing energy, body wisdom, a word or phrase that evokes this comforting resource for you. Slowing down, feel into this felt sense.

Now, slowly say the words, *attachment, trauma, addiction.* What comes? What wants your attention now? Chances are that a lot comes for you. Ask into the felt sense: *What is this all about? How does my body carry this? What does it need?* As you hold your good energy, invite your body to make a caring relationship with uncomfortable feelings. Notice if a physical sense of release comes, a *felt shift* in how you are able to be with all of this. Maybe this is a time to write about it or find a listening partner.

Thinking at the Edge: Feeling into Thinking

As I begin to move back into the process of *thinking at the edge* (TAE), I suddenly have a felt shift, a physical release, as I become aware of the natural flow that I am experiencing in this process. TAE methodology takes us back to our natural way of thinking. When we are connected to the felt sense, we move back and forth from thinking about something to feeling into it, carrying it in the body, in a focusing process. It is only because we have been trained to separate thinking, and value it over feeling, that we have to train ourselves to go back to "feeling into thinking".

The six steps of focusing help us return to whole-body, integrated subjective experiencing, including thoughts. They help us with issues in our life. The 14 steps of TAE help us return to whole-body, integrated conceptualizing, including feelings. We have been trained to have contempt for our feelings in the academic world, to sacrifice subjective experiencing and the creation of meaning for the "objective truth". But when we use TAE to study addiction, then we are moving towards the "sweet spot" of integration.

I'm wondering if you are with me so far. It takes time to find our way back to our natural state of integration. It predates the mind/body split. I encourage you to do what I am doing on this journey. When I become confused, and this happens often while writing, I close my eyes, and breathe down into the felt sense of all of this, making a big space for whatever is there. Concepts are reorganizing as we discard well-known patterns of thinking. I have learned to welcome confusion and to trust that something fresh will emerge as I stay with the process.

Attachment, Trauma, Addiction: Making Vital Connections

This chapter takes us into the world of trauma, as it relates to attachment and addiction. How do these three areas of study relate to each other? When I take them down inside, they feel friendly, intimately connected, informing each other. They seem to relate to each other in a sequential way. Attachment wounds can lead to trauma, and trauma can lead to addiction. Many healers, including feminist therapists and body workers, have been making these connections for decades. Listening to the client's embodied experiences with non-pathologizing ears led to the understanding that early attachment trauma often leads to self-harm and addiction. However, it is only recently that trauma and attachment studies have begun to influence the mainstream way of thinking about and treating addiction.

The field of addiction has not focused on its psychological roots until recently. Perhaps this is because addiction has been viewed as a brain disease, a position that the dominant twelve-step approach adheres to. Since it has been assumed that the root cause is primarily genetic there is no reason to look at childhood development. Achieving sobriety is the main focus, and twelve-step programmes the treatment of choice. This view is changing. As we understand more about the brain's neuroplasticity, the field of trauma is developing quickly. We now appreciate the importance of looking to the past and to the impact of traumatic attachment relationships on brain development. We are discovering that traumatic experiences impair normal growth and development, creating emotional dysregulation, and setting the stage for addictive behaviours.

Addiction as an "Attachment Disorder"

There is a growing body of work that depicts addiction as a result of early traumatic attachment wounds. This work tends to focus on the individual and familial intrapsychic issues that create insecure attachment styles. It looks at parental styles of attachment and how they impact children's capacity to emotionally soothe themselves. Attachment theorists see clients turning to addictive behaviours because early parental relationships have let them down.

The *Adult Attachment Interview* (George, Kaplan & Main, 1996) was created to measure adult's early attachment relationships. This questionnaire helps therapists understand their clients' parenting styles, and how they can provide their children with a more secure attachment. This work is so important, and it is embedded in the felt sense polyvagal model (FSPM).

Recall that FSPM integrates attachment styles into the autonomic nervous system. The model illustrates the connection between attachment styles and the capacity to self-regulate. Looking at the model, we see how the vertical line illustrates the attachment dimension from integrated/secure to the opposite end of addicted/insecure. The horizontal line illustrates the arousal spectrum from chaos to rigidity. Here is the interplay: How securely attached we are with ourselves and in our relationships (vertical) influences how emotionally regulated we are able to be (horizontal). Note that addictions do not occur in a state of safety and secure attachment. I think even those who see addiction as primarily a brain disease would agree that children who grow up in a safe environment are less likely to struggle with addiction.

There is more, a bigger picture that we have explored in past chapters. Recall our anti-oppressive lens in the formulation of addiction. How do we bring this into the parent/child dyad? Herman's (2005) iconic book *Trauma and Recovery* was one of the first books to make the link between traumatic attachment, self-harm, and political trauma. Alexander's (2008) dislocation theory emphasizes the role of our alienated, narcissistically driven society in creating addiction. Morgan's (2019) book *Addiction, Attachment, Trauma and Recovery* integrates dislocation theory into the field of attachment. Both Felitti's (1998) work with the adverse childhood experiences study (ACES) and Hari's (2015) enlightening work in revealing the role of racism and poverty contribute to a larger, global understanding of the aetiology of addiction. Maté's (2008) seminal book *In the Realm of Hungry Ghosts: Close Encounters with Addiction* develops from his work with street involved people in Vancouver. Perhaps, more than any other theorist/practitioner, Maté shows us how to integrate attachment, trauma, and addiction into a coherent model.

First-Person Experiencing

As I write this, I sense a growing need to pause. Something again is niggling at me. The question isn't yet formulated, but something about "the whole" comes into my head. I find myself asking the question, does all addiction, or even most addiction, begin with early childhood attachment wounds? Some attachment theorists would say yes. How much do societal issues impact addiction? Aren't we underestimating the impact of cultural changes, and global trauma?

I feel irritable, uncomfortable in my body. I become grumpy, tired. I feel torn. I love this body of work on attachment, and yet, as I read about other ways of understanding addiction, like dislocation theory, I feel a sensation of being torn, confused. More comes. I take my time to feel into my body... I feel deeply agitated by the emphasis on maternal behaviours in attachment theory. It feels like mothers are being microscopically examined, and societal factors are being minimized. In this misogynistic culture, I feel distrust, concern with mother blaming. This sits in my chest, making me feel the need to protect my own mothering and all mothering. I feel myself moving into flight/fight, but I don't want to be defensive, I want to be curious.

I remind myself to return to my body: breathing, slowing down. Paying attention inside, I find my wise voice, going back to thinking at the edge. It tells me to go inside, back to the body, and to the felt sense of this moment. As I'm with this experience a lot of information comes. I go to the torn feeling. What does it need? I see an image of three concentric circles. The inner circle is micro (individual, family), the middle circle is mezzo (community) and the outer circle is macro (global).

This strikes me as funny. It's a surprise to find the implicit bodily knowing. This image comes from my graduate school training in social work practice forty years ago when I learned about the need to understand the client within the context of community and culture. We need to go back to the whole, not the parts. Yes! This process isn't dualistic, it's concentric. However, in my training long ago, there was a powerful split between those of us who were interested in clinical work with individuals and families, the micro level, and those who viewed the source of client's problems as a result of systemic oppression, at the macro level. While our professors presented a systems theory model that showed the individual within the micro, mezzo and macro levels, we students thought differently. The split was palpable. The individual/family group were considered to be middle class "do-gooders" who were only interested in prestige and serving the privileged. Psychotherapy was viewed as self-indulgent. The social workers who identified as activists, working with "the disadvantaged" (the language of the 70's) were perceived as rageful and too radical. Many of us, on both sides of the argument, felt deeply hurt by each other. I felt a split right down the middle. I knew the power of psychotherapy. It had rescued me from my own struggle with addiction. And, I loved the intellectual rigor and passionate radicalism of the activist group.

Thinking Systemically About Attachment: Bridging the Divide

My body still carries the experience of this deep divide. I now see that this book is partly about healing this split. That's what the torn feeling is about. We need to move away from binary thinking. We need to think systemically. For example, in addressing attachment theory, let's start with our three concentric circles. We can zoom in to the family. Then we can zoom out to study the community that this family lives in. Then we zoom out more to the global level of analysis. How are this family and community the same and different from each other? How are they impacted by the larger world? And how do they carry this impact in their bodies? Here we can look into each part from the experience of other, and in doing so we create something new. Then from this new vantage point, we can look back at the parts to see what each can bring to the other. A new crossing starts to emerge.

Making this connection creates a felt shift. I feel lighter, happier inside. Of course. When we go into the felt sense, we immediately know that bodies live in the big, wide world. Body/environment is one process. We have spent most of our time focusing on the micro level of analysis in the field of psychology and addiction studies. It's time to zoom out to the macro level. It's time to go global.

Understanding how our bodies carry cultural trauma is key to developing a more nuanced, sophisticated path. This requires a shift from top-down left brain, to bottom-up right-brain dominance. We need to open to fresh ways of exploring, challenging our old patterns of thinking. As we dig deeper, we come to a structural analysis of the issues. We need to pass the microphone to those who are working with global trauma and engage in compassionate dialogue. We need to find out more about marginalized groups of people and how attachment theory relates to their experiences across cultures.

But I knew this already. How did I lose it so quickly and feel the torn sense so deeply? The answer is that we are trained to think in tidy little ways that often involve an either or path. We are trained to confine our ideas to little boxes, units that hold information. Then we work with what fits, and what doesn't fit gets discarded. The torn feeling was what came when I went to either/or thinking, so it isn't surprising that I lost my embodied knowing for a time. This is a place that still carries some pain, so it came back to me in need of kind attention. This is a great reminder of the importance of paying attention to that feeling of discomfort and to welcome feelings, and felt sense, when we are thinking. Rather than viewing feeling as somehow contaminating our thinking, we find a structured way to invite a whole-body felt sense of the concept, letting it form from the bottom up. Then we can work with the thoughts to create new concepts. As we move through this chapter, let's be mindful of the ways that we can think beyond patterns, to a global analysis of attachment, trauma, addiction. Through an anti-oppressive lens, let's go to early days in attachment theory, noticing how research reflects issues in top-down and bottom-up processing.

Attachment Theory: Early Days

Recall from Chapter 6, Bowlby's (1969) theory that early relationships with our primary caretakers shape our capacity to self-regulate. He believed that the attachment system is innate in mammals and motivates us to seek proximity with our caregivers, particularly when we are distressed. Ainsworth, a psychologist and colleague of Bowlby's, initially tested his ideas through naturalistic observation. This is a qualitative research method often used by anthropologists that involves observing behaviour in the natural setting. This method invites an embodied presence to be curious about attachment relationships.

Ainsworth (1967) appreciated the importance of cultural sensitivity and conducted her first study in Uganda. She spent time there observing mother–infant relationships. How would babies respond when mother left them alone or with a stranger? She found the methodology difficult, particularly in controlling for the amount of stress that babies were exposed to (Gaskins, 2013). Babies in Uganda were cared for by several mother figures, so if the primary mother left the environment, the baby would still be able to see other mother figures (called allomothers), which could decrease the level of stress. Ainsworth then did a second study using naturalistic home observations with infants in Baltimore. Difficulties with these studies resulted in her changing to a quantitative methodology and a shift into the laboratory. From these experiences, she developed the *strange situation procedure* (SSP; Ainsworth, Behar, Waters & Wall, 2015).

Strange Situation Procedure

Ainsworth created the SSP, a laboratory-based method that measures infant's attachment styles based on their response to being separated from their mothers. There are eight three-minute episodes. In some of these episodes, the mother leaves the infant alone in the room, and in other episodes she leaves the infant with a stranger. The process is designed to mildly stress the infant in an escalating way. From this study, she established the three styles of attachment that we discussed in Chapter 6: *secure, insecure/ambivalent, insecure/avoidant.* The fourth attachment style, *disorganized,* was later created by Main and Solomon (1990).

As we discussed Chapter 6, addiction has been thought of as the result of an insecure attachment style. A high percentage of children with disorganized attachment have parents who struggled with addiction

(O'Connor, Sigman, & Brill, 1987). This category came about because of the group of children who did not fall within the three existing styles. What all of this research does is offer convincing evidence to support the notion that attachment difficulties and addiction are linked across the generations.

Thinking at the Edge of Attachment Theory: The Quantitative Shift

Recall Chapter 3 in which we explored the issue of bottom-up and top-down ways of knowing. Ainsworth's methodological shift from qualitative to quantitative research is important to explore. Here we return to thinking about how we think about and research addiction.

Quantitative research, a top-down approach of dividing concepts into categories, or units, like the four attachment styles, is the dominant approach in psychological research. Critics argue that by using a laboratory and thereby removing the study from its natural setting, researchers are missing the cultural context and meaning of the mother/dyad interaction. In addition, much of the research has been done in WEIRD (western, educated, industrialized, rich, developed) countries in North America and western Europe. How relatable are the findings with other cultures?

A good example of this discussion is described in a paper entitled, From Uganda to Baltimore to Alexandra Township: How far can Ainsworth's theory stretch? (Dawson, 2018). Researchers studied Ainsworth's (1969) construct of maternal sensitivity using the Maternal Behavioral Q-Sort-mini (MBQS-mini) at the Umdelezane parent-infant programmes in Johannesburg, South Africa. Maternal sensitivity, considered to be the main indicator of secure attachment, involves assessing the mother's responsiveness, her capacity for attunement with her infant's needs. Ainsworth developed this measure from both her Ugandan and American studies drawing the conclusion that all infants across cultures have a need for trusting and sensitive attachment figures. Since then, researchers have expanded this concept, reinforcing the universality of maternal sensitivity to include the centrality of parent-infant play, verbal responsiveness, the inclusion of learning in parent-infant interaction, and the inclusion of positive affect.

The South African study describes an emerging debate in the field of attachment theory. The researcher noted that during the study "mom has lost points on the MBQS for failing to facilitate learning in her interactions with baby, for her lack of animation, her general lack of proactiveness, and her use of objects and feeding to soothe" (Dawson, 2018, p. 2). It was reported that mom said she felt shy during the study, and the researcher wonders if mom feels scrutinized by the white professional researcher. The researcher also wondered if mother's level of literacy would enable her to feel comfortable to use the books and toys that were made available. "Although mom scored in the moderate range, it doesn't feel like the available items have captured her strengths" (p. 2). The authors make the point that many of the indicators of maternal sensitivity are not culturally sensitive and thereby miss the mark in assessing the attachment style. This argument is made time and again in relation to other cultural differences.

Qualitative research is much more prevalent in anthropology. It has a long tradition of using natural observation. Quinn and Mageo (2013) capture the tension in the field of attachment studies in the introduction to their edited collection, *Attachment Reconsidered*:

> It would be a shame if attachment theorists did not take this volume seriously. A primary reason they might not be disposed to do so is because of the ethnographic methodology herein. While in many quarters, "mixed methods" research is becoming acceptable and even desirable, attachment theory is still largely wedded to narrowly quantitative methods represented by the Strange Situation Procedure. Our suggestions are that attachment needs to be studied in the context of local meaning and child-rearing practices, along with cultural models of virtue and psychodynamics, all of which are best discovered through ethnography. (p. 25)

Ethnography involves researchers creating a qualitative description of a community after living in that community for a long period of time, observing and recording events in their natural setting. This is the main method used by many anthropologists. This method represents a bottom-up approach of first-person experiencing. Here the researcher embeds themselves in the culture and observes behaviours within the context of their cultural meaning.

The Wisdom of Mixed Methods

Quinn and Mageo (2013) suggest that one way of dealing with concerns that attachment theory is ethnocentric is to use the *mixed methods* approach. They suggest that while quantitative methods "squeeze out meaning", they reduce data so that they can be reliably compared. And while qualitative methods preserve meaning, they make comparing difficult. The authors' view is that meaning-preservation methods (qualitative) are better for developing theory, while data-reduction methods are best for testing hypotheses.

Here we see an opportunity to cross top-down and bottom-up methodology, enabling more unexpected, "out-of-the-box" experiences to be welcomed into theory building. The FSPM is an example of crossing quantitative neurobiological findings with qualitative focusing practice. This crossing honours the richness and complexity of experiences of attachment and how those experiences impact our understanding of addiction. Now is the time for innovative mixed methods. After all, it's not as if we are doing a good job of eradicating addiction. Rates are soaring; we are in a crisis. What better time to think outside of the box, to create theory and test it systematically?

A Feminist Lens on Attachment

It's easy to become defensive with so much intense scrutiny of maternal behaviours in the field of attachment. In a recent interview with Maté (personal communication, 2020), it was clear that he is frustrated by this attitude. "I spent two pages talking about my mother and her holocaust history in *In the Realm of Hungry Ghosts* and the *Toronto Star* still ran an article with a headline that said, "A Canadian says it's our mothers' fault."

Maté understands the oppressive lens of patriarchy. He stands out as a man who is able to fully acknowledge the deep structural problems that misogyny creates in our society. In an article on Canadian radio star Jian Ghomeshi regarding his charges of sexual aggression, Maté (2014) wrote:

> We live in a society steeped in male narcissism, one in which aggression towards women is deeply entrenched in the collective male psyche. Nor is male sexual predation confined to a few "sick" individuals: that we see it portrayed, relentlessly and voyeuristically, in movies, TV shows, and advertising is beyond obvious, except for those mired in denial.

All this attention on mothers begs the question, what about fathers? Of course, the irony is that in this patriarchal culture, how could fathers not have a profound impact? They impact by their presence, by their absence, and by the way that they hold space for their partners. Are they part of the patriarchy, or part of the quest for liberation? Are they oppressing their partners, or seeking liberation for all members of their family?

Father's presence is held in mother's body. Mother carries the felt sense of her partner in her attachment shape with baby. It's high time that we articulate the quality of father's presence as part of attachment theory, both in terms of honouring fathers, and in disarming the patriarchy. We know that children develop different attachment styles with mom and dad. Digging into this in relation to the development of addiction is important. Theories about the ethology of sex addiction in particular are deeply entrenched in misogyny.

Mother blaming is no fun. It creates a tearing of the soul, especially for mothers of addicted children. It needs to stop. It is clear from theorists like Maté and Siegel that this is not the intention, nor the belief. We know that bodies carry intergenerational trauma, and that trauma is passed down on a cellular level from parents to their children. Yet, mother blaming persists.

Blaming is rampant in our top-down culture. In this state of global trauma, we need to find kindness, deep embodied kindness, the kind of kindness that creates wisdom as it flourishes. Kindness feels so good in the body. Once you find it, it's hard to let it go. And yet, it can slip away so quickly when our blaming paradigm takes hold. Now, more than ever, we need to move to a more nuanced way of understanding how power and politics shapes culture, how culture shapes our bodies, and how this shaping impacts our capacity to emotionally regulate. Then we can fully appreciate how maternal care is an expression of all aspects of culture. To that end we are all responsible for how our children come into this world, how they are cared for, and how much addiction impacts their lives.

We must take the field of attachment further by examining different kinds of families and attachment styles. Much work is needed in honouring queer and trans families and being curious about all ways of attaching and raising children. By deconstructing our notion of "family", we open ourselves to honouring a multitude of ways of nurturing babies and the families that raise them. When concepts of mother and father become challenged, as in queer and trans families, we stretch to find new language and new ways of understanding. This bottom-up receptivity brings a creative edge to appreciating how addiction interacts with connection. Perhaps the universal predictor of addiction is not the early attachment with mother, but the quality of safe, loving connection with relationships and with the natural world.

Global Attachment Trauma

As we expand our awareness of trauma to the mezzo and macro levels, it appears that there is mass suffering from anxiety, depression, and addiction on a global scale. Is it too much to say that we are all suffering from an insecure global attachment trauma, a kind of trauma that comes from white body supremacy? I think not. We know white supremacy hurts us all. When we step on others to gain power and privilege, we hurt them, and we hurt ourselves.

The world is in crisis, pandemic crisis, climate crisis, and relational crisis. It is not possible to have a secure attachment with our global community. Our global community is insecure. Those who don't acknowledge this crisis are dissociating, understandably. We know that our bodies are designed to shut down in crisis. So, it shouldn't be surprising then that addiction is on the rise.

Remember the FSPM. When we go to shut down, the dorsal vagus, we often use addiction to propel us back and forth from flight/fight to fold. Remember that trauma moves us back into survival mode, into the triggered state. While shutdown helps us when we have no escape, it is tragic when we *can* act, but aren't aware of this. It takes a person who can hold the trauma and step beside it to see the crucial importance of acting. Sometimes these folks are young, less invested in the status quo, more invested in their future. A good example is a person like Greta Thunberg, the newest version of a teen idol, with a mass following of young people who are fighting for climate change. Here are two salient quotes from Thunberg (2018):

> This is a cry for help ... To all of you who have never treated this crisis as a crisis ... To all the politicians that ridicule us on social media, and have named and shamed me so that people tell me that I'm retarded, a bitch and a terrorist, and many other things. (p. 11)

> People are suffering. People are dying. Entire ecosystems are collapsing. We are in the beginning of a mass extinction. And all you can talk about is money and fairy tales of eternal economic growth. How dare you! (p. 127)

The Politics of Trauma

As we integrate our awareness of addiction, trauma, and attachment at the mezzo and macro levels, we need to create new models of healing that incorporate all three levels of analysis. Haines (2019) does this; she challenges us to think big, to integrate a model that addresses healing from a personal and a political lens. While she appreciates attachment theory's emphasis on the power of social bonds, Haines encourages us to expand our view:

> I'd like to challenge this work to look further – to the lack of dignified connection and belonging offered to many communities by the broader social norms. Attachment is not just to our primary caregivers or our family and children – while it is key there. We also need to belong within our communities. Our communities need to belong to the broader social fabric. There is a broader circle of belonging that also affects attachment, a sense of security, and real choices for connection and interdependence. (p. 143)

Haines (2019) goes on to invite the reader to consider what happens to attachment when children grow up in unsafe environments where they witness racist acts against family members. Perhaps they have a safe attachment with parents, but when they are targeted in their communities, they are not safe. She asks us to consider what happens to attachment when we live in a world where one in three women and one in six men experience some form of sexual violence in their lifetime. And, what happens when these facts are denied, and justice is never received? Perhaps the most important question is, what happens to people who, for whatever reasons, have never had enough safety to be able to settle their nervous systems? Then trauma isn't an event, it's life. We are in a vicious circle. We live in a world where addiction is pathologized, shamed, punished, and people are increasingly dying in the streets. How do we calm our bodies down and move out of addictive behaviours, when we are so intensely shamed?

Haines created a healing method called *generative somatics*, an integration of somatic therapy and social activism. It focuses on the importance of individual and systemic trauma. This integration intrigues me and takes me back to the torn feeling that I was connecting with in my experiences in my Master of Social Work programme: the strife between social justice students and psychotherapy students.

In a recent interview with Haines, we discussed our similar desire for the healing world to embrace both personal and systemic transformation. We were curious about how we both came to a place of understanding the vital importance of bringing these worlds together.

Haines explains that her experience in West Germany in her last year of high school helped to politicize her. She experienced a global view of the world, and at the same time had an opportunity to begin to connect with deep personal trauma as a result of child sexual abuse by her father and his friends. These two experiences happened together, enabling her to feel into the importance of both kinds of trauma.

Asked if she works directly with addiction, Haines replied that she refers out to others because the area is complex and requires a specific expertise. Given that generative somatics works so closely with the nervous system, she did identify the state of constriction that is present in the addicted body. A treatment approach that integrates somatic work with harm reduction psychotherapy offers a powerful healing path.

To sum up, in this chapter, we have explored the interconnectedness of addiction, trauma, and attachment from a systems theory perspective. While our current thinking isolates each area of study, our thinking at the edge process reveals a wholistic vision of profound linkages between all three areas. This sophisticated model enables us to perceive the deep systemic roots of addiction, trauma, and attachment and our way out of this vicious circle. While it isn't easy, the body carries us forward.

References

Afford, P. (2020). *Therapy in the age of neuroscience*. New York: Routledge.

Ainsworth M. D. S. (1967). *Infancy in Uganda: Infant care and the growth of love*. Baltimore, MD: The Johns Hopkins University Press.

Ainsworth M. D. S. (1969). Maternal sensitivity scales. *Power, 6*, 1379–1388.

Ainsworth, M. D., Behar, M. C., Waters, E, & Wall, S. N. (2015). *Patterns of attachment: A psychological study of the strange situation*. New York: Routledge.

Alexander, B. (2008). *The globalization of addiction, A study in poverty of the spirit*. New York, NY: Oxford University Press.

Bowlby, J. (1969). *Attachment and loss.* New York, NY: Basic Books.

Dawson, N. (2018). From Uganda to Baltimore to Alexandra Township: How far can Ainsworth's theory stretch? *South African Journal of Psychiatry, 24,* 1137.

Felitti, V. J., Anda, R. F., Nordenberg, D., Williamson, D. F., Spitz, A. M., Edwards, V., Koss, M. P., & Marks, J. S. (1998). Adverse childhood experiences. *American Journal of Preventive Medicine, 14*(4) 245–258.

Gaskins, S. (2013). The puzzle of attachment. In N. Quinn & J. M. Mageo (Eds.), *Attachment reconsidered: Cultural perspectives on a Western theory* (pp. 33–66). London, UK: Palgrave.

George, C., Kaplan, N. & Main, M. (1996). *Adult attachment interview* (3rd ed.). Unpublished manuscript. Berkeley: Department of Psychology, University of California.

Haines, S. (2019). *The politics of trauma.* Berkeley, CA: North Atlantic Books.

Hari, J. (2015). *Chasing the scream: The first and last days of the war on drugs.* New York: Bloomsbury.

Herman, J. (2015). *Trauma and recovery: The aftermath of violence—from domestic abuse to political terror.* New York: Basic Books.

Main, M., & Solomon, J. (1990). Procedures for identifying infants as disorganized/disoriented during the Ainsworth Strange Situation. In M. T. Greenberg, D. Cicchetti, & E. M. Cummings (Eds.), *Attachment in the preschool years: Theory, research, and intervention* (pp. 121–160). The John D. and Catherine T. MacArthur Foundation series on mental health and development. Chicago: University of Chicago Press.

Maté, G. (1999, April 4). Drugging the kids: The swelling rate of diagnosis and drug-oriented treatment of attention deficit hyperactivity disorder in our kids the focus of competing books—A Canadian says it's our mothers' fault. *Toronto Star.* Star April 14, 1999 Page: D2424 Edition: SU2.

Maté, G. (2014). Jian Ghomeshi and the problem of narcissistic male rage. *The Star,* A 15.

Maté, G. (2008). *In the realm of hungry ghosts: Close encounters with addiction.* Toronto, ON: Alfred A. Knopf Canada.

Morgan, O. J. (2019) *Addiction, attachment, trauma and recovery: The power of connection.* New York: W. W. Norton & Company Publishing.

O'Connor, M. J., Sigman, M., & Brill, N. (1987). Disorganization of attachment in relation to Matérnal alcohol consumption. *Journal of Consulting and Clinical Psychology, 55,* 831–836.

Quinn, N. & Mageo, J. M. (Eds.; 2013), *Attachment reconsidered: Cultural perspectives on a Western theory* (pp. 33–66). London, UK: Palgrave Books.

Thunberg, G. (2018). *No one is too small to make a difference.* New York: Penguin Books.

Winhall, J. (2014). Understanding and treating addiction with the felt sense experience model. In G. Madison, (Ed.), *Emerging practice in focusing-oriented psychotherapy.* London: Jessica Kingsley Publishers.

8 Bringing Polyvagal Theory into the World of Addiction

> Heroin was the only thing that really worked, the only thing that stopped him scampering around in a hamster's wheel of unanswerable questions. Heroin was the cavalry ... it landed purring at the base of his skull, and wrapped itself darkly around his nervous system, like a black cat curling up on its favourite cushion.
>
> *Edward St. Aubyn, Bad News.*

St. Aubyn's metaphor captures the powerful soothing sensations as his nervous system is warmly held by the enticing black cat: the black cat of heroin that helps him and hurts him. This chapter looks at a new way of understanding the autonomic nervous system (ANS), and a new way of understanding addiction as an adaptive attempt to regulate our autonomic state. In so doing, it brings the polyvagal theory into the world of addiction.

First-Person Experiencing: Resolving the Paradox, "What Helps you Hurts You"

I'm remembering the moment when it occurred to me that addiction belonged as an intertwining state in the polyvagal theory. I was reading Dana's (2018) book, *The Polyvagal Theory in Therapy* having just attended her two-day workshop. As I was reading about intertwining states, I looked up at my first version of the model. I didn't know about intertwining states then. I had ventral, sympathetic, dorsal and "addicted" between dorsal and sympathetic. I now realized that addiction was an intertwining of sympathetic and dorsal. If I added the two intertwining states that Porges described, stillness (flow in client version) and play (fun in client version), I had a beautiful mapping of the interplay between the three branches of the ANS.

Now I had found a home for this mysterious behavior we call addiction. A polyvagal-informed home for resolving the paradox that I started with: What helps you hurts you. The resolution came in understanding addiction as a propeller of neurophysiological state change in the ANS. Confirmation of this idea by Porges led to the development of the felt sense polyvagal model (FSPM). Crossing or intertwining top-down and bottom-up ways of knowing brings us to a better place in unravelling the mysteries of addictive behaviours. Polyvagal theory is a beautiful crossing of ways. It embraces a felt sense experience in its honouring of the body's wisdom, and it brings the best of neuroscience to help us understand the ANS. As I write this I have a deep felt sense stirring inside. I pause and find the handle, "sweet consolidation". I have arrived, after forty years of inquiry, at a place of consolidating all that I have been experiencing about this paradox. For now, it is such a sweet spot. And it is also a knowing that more will come to challenge this spot, and the more will be welcomed.

Porges' Vagal Paradox

Porges also started with a paradox. This is not surprising, as paradox often occurs with creative, right-brain thinking. Paradox has its own kind of logic, a non-linear kind of logic that is welcomed into the implicit, right brain world. In thinking at the edge, we cross concepts that don't make logical sense, being with the felt sense of each from inside the other.

In his own journey Porges talks about how he became more and more interested in how feelings and sensations impact the nervous system. The realization that 80% of the vagus nerve fibres are *afferent*, meaning they travel up to the brainstem from the viscera, helped Porges to appreciate the importance of the body, and the importance of integrating feelings and bodily sensations into our understanding of the nervous system.

Early on in his work, Porges published an article about heart rate patterns in human infants. This was when his understanding was still aligned with the traditional model of the ANS, which did not include the dorsal vagus. He received a letter from a neonatologist that challenged him to rethink his understanding of the autonomic nervous system. The letter pointed to the fact that premature babies in distress were experiencing bradycardia. This slowing of the heart rate is the opposite of what would be expected under activation of the sympathetic branch of the nervous system. He tucked the letter into his briefcase and spent the next two years trying to answer the following question: "How could the regulation of the heart be an index of resilience and health when it was represented in high-amplitude respiratory sinus arrhythmia and an index of risk when it was represented in bradycardia?" (Porges, 2011, p. 6). In other words, how could something that is supposed to be helping you (the vagus) be hurting you? This idea may sound familiar. It points to the same paradox that emerged in my women's group.

This question was resolved through understanding that there are in fact two branches of the vagus nerve, the ventral branch, or the "good vagus" and an ancient branch that Porges called the dorsal vagus. In the traditional model of the ANS, it was assumed that the parasympathetic branch was the "good guy" associated with health, growth and restoration. It clearly wasn't this branch that was causing bradycardia in these premature babies. The sympathetic branch would cause increased heart rate and this wasn't the case either, so what was going on here?

Porges solved the problem by studying the changes that occurred in the neural regulation of the nervous system through evolution. Our reptilian ancestors have an unmyelinated vagus that responds to threat with bradycardia and shutting down through feigning death. Porges called this ancient branch the dorsal vagus. As mammals evolved, a second pathway of the vagus emerged. This myelinated pathway is the "good guy".

Neonatologists knew about this unmyelinated dorsal branch instinctively because they worked with premature babies and saw the evidence of dorsal responses in these infants. Why? Because these babies are born before the myelinated ventral branch of the mammalian vagus is formed and so their little nervous systems have features that are reptile-like. They are not able to promote health and growth. When stressed their dorsal vagus responses can be deadly.

Recently, while presenting the FSPM at a focusing conference in Chile, I was approached by a woman who worked as a neonatal physiotherapist. She had never heard of polyvagal theory and was overcome with emotion as she explained to me that she finally understood why these premature infants were responding with a slowing of heart rate. When she handed these very sick babies to their mothers' she had not been able to explain to them what was happening. Now she could.

Linking Polyvagal Theory to Trauma and Addiction

This same dorsal response is evident in our traumatized clients. When Porges began to share his findings, the trauma world resonated, and many clinical applications emerged (Porges & Dana, 2018). We see this dissociated, shut-down response to trauma on a regular basis, and now, like the physiotherapist, we have a way of understanding how it works in the nervous system. Dissociated responses of numbing, fainting, trauma bonds, (repeating abusive relationships), and blocked memories can now be seen in this new light as dorsal vagal responses to threat. In this context addictions are helpful ways to activate dorsal or sympathetic responses when the body is under threat. While they may look bizarre, and they do indeed result in harm, they have a logic of their own that is oriented towards survival. This understanding is key to appreciating the importance of Porges' discovery.

Why is this so? Because it validates these behaviours as adaptive, and the folks who rely on them as, in a sense, normal. If our bodies are designed this way then the behaviours are not sick, they are in fact brilliantly adaptive. This is vitally important because we then see traumatic responses in a new light that calls for nothing less than a paradigm shift, a shift that honours the body's inherent knowing, healing shame and blame. We need to put new and more body-informed healing practices into the forefront.

Many other cultures and movements never lost their appreciation for the wisdom of the body. Our culture lost its way post-Descartes. We have much to learn and unlearn. My own understanding came from the feminist movement. We embraced body wisdom, and intuitively understood traumatic responses, including addiction, as inherently helpful. But our female voices were not respected, and we didn't have the significant piece of the puzzle that polyvagal theory provides. This sophisticated understanding of the autonomic nervous system provides a neurophysiological explanation for traumatic/addictive responses, and the power of a scientific language that speaks to, and challenges, our post-Descartes era.

Our Very Elegant Survival System

Polyvagal theory teaches us that we respond to threat in a very elegant and systematic way, first by activating the ventral branch of the vagus nerve, our "smart" vagus. If the situation cannot be resolved in this way, the sympathetic branch kicks in to empower us to mobilize. If mobilizing is not possible, we have a third option available to maximize our potential for survival, the dorsal branch of the vagus nerve that shuts us down, helping us to dissociate, to bear the unbearable.

Once we understand the three evolutionary responses, we see the elegance of the system. The body is not working against itself. It is not a system of paired antagonism, an either/or. The body is designed to work in harmony. The vagus nerve is busily carrying body sensation up to the brain stem, keeping us apprised of safety and danger. Based on the current appraisal, the body responds appropriately, like gears in a car. If you are driving on flat, safe conditions along a main roadway, third gear (ventral vagus) will do. If you need to go faster, shift into fourth (sympathetic). If you hit a bump, shift down to second gear (dorsal) to avoid too much impact. The dorsal vagus will maximize your potential to stay safe, but it will hamper your ability to reach your destination.

Addictive behaviours can quickly and efficiently shift flight/fight (sympathetic), and immobility (dorsal) states to enable survival. This is a good thing, because if you are about to be attacked you need an effective way to deal with it, especially if you cannot escape. Then you desperately need to dissociate. Of course, it can become highly problematic when the body becomes triggered or if the body is living in a sustained state of dysregulation. Then we need to work hard at reorienting to the present moment. We will discuss this further when we talk about safety.

The polyvagal theory is deep and complex. I am going to share with you my organic way of integrating what I have found to be important concepts that help us as psychotherapists. The following are two main points in the theory that inform the basis of the FSPM:

1. *Neural regulation of our physiological state influences our thoughts and behaviours, and this impacts our social interactions. How well we regulate our state in the presence of others is a core issue in mental well-being, and in our quality of our life.*

    Put simply, we view the world in very different ways depending upon which state we are experiencing in our autonomic nervous system. If we feel safe we will respond from the ventral, grounded state. Our thinking will be clear as the prefrontal cortex is online and helping us to problem-solve. We see people as essentially friendly and approachable. If, however, we feel threatened, we will move into systems of defense. And as we have described in discussions about trauma responses, when triggered we can misread the experience and go into defense when we are in fact safe. Hence, the FSPM is useful in helping us learn about and locate our current state. Then we can decode the trigger, creating more potential for emotional regulation.

    Before I knew anything about the polyvagal theory, I noticed these state changes in the young women in my incest survivor group. Their whole body would sometimes shift and change shape as they moved from one state to the next. For example, in Chapter 3, I described how Bridgette attacked Mary for wearing stiletto heels. As the attack came, Mary's body changed from a somewhat open stance to a closed, curled up shape with head down and feet tucked under her. This signalled her shift from a mildly sympathetic to a dorsal state. Understanding these shifts as physiological changes in the ANS is very important in tracking emotional regulation when we work with trauma and addiction. As Mary shifted into dorsal her attitude also changed. She no longer felt it useful to participate in the group because she said, "Life sucks and nothing changes." She pulled into herself and shut down.

    It is also important to notice state changes in predicting relapse in addictive clients. When people can make bright eye contact and are connected with us and the world around them, addictive behaviours are not needed. Recognizing the neurophysiological state changes in the women in my group led me to seek out training in a body-centred therapy. It was clear to me that we needed to go deeper into bodily-felt knowing because I could see the felt shift that came in the women's whole demeanour. Going deeper meant proceeding gently and slowly so as not to precipitate what we called "the emergency stage", when clients would get triggered and feel very unsafe.

As we learn how to assess neurophysiological state, we can map it on to the FSPM and teach clients how to do this for themselves. When clients learn what states they are experiencing, and how to facilitate more ventral presence, they feel empowered. Understanding addictions as effective state changers makes sense to people, and often decreases shame. The realization that you can change states with a healing felt sense experience, an embodied practice that brings soothing and relief, can be life changing. We can teach clients healing state changes, one step at a time.

2. *The autonomic nervous system is bidirectional.*

The traditional model of the ANS diminished the importance of attending to the body. It mostly focused on efferent information, i.e. from brain down to body. This is not surprising as we live in a culture that subjugates feelings. However, knowing that the majority of information carried by the vagus nerve is visceral (from the body up to the brain) led Porges to emphasize the importance of paying attention to bodily knowing.

The polyvagal theory is both a bottom-up and a top-down model. Our brain is continuously regulating our viscera and vice versa. Appreciating how vital it is to feel into the bidirectionality brings us into full aliveness. When we are connected to our bodies, we know that thoughts affect our physiology and physiology affects our thoughts. Integrating thoughts, feelings, physical sensations, and memories is the nature of felt sensing, and we use these four avenues to connect with this inner wisdom. Looking at the FSPM, we see these four aspects inside each of the states of the ANS. Felt sensing is bidirectional. Thinking at the edge brings this bidirectionality into conceptual thinking.

Emphasizing the bidirectional nature of our nervous system is key to understanding how we as humans orient to the world. In abandoning our bodies, we live in dysregulated states of flight/fight and fold. We are all suffering from global trauma that alienates us from ourselves, each other, and the natural world. It follows that we as a society have fallen into chronic states of dysregulation. Polyvagal theory can make a major contribution to this societal crisis by helping us understand our bodies' system of safety, our ANS, and how it works to help us in times of danger. As we become more aware of our bodies, we have more choice in how we respond. And choice is empowerment.

A Breath Practice

When we attend to our breath, we become instantly aware of the bidirectional nature of our existence. Porges describes an exercise that he does in his workshops in a lovely interview with Prengel (2016). Porges asks participants to pair up and practice inhalations and exhalations in a way that demonstrates how we can shift ANS states in our breathing patterns. I invite you to try this with a partner.

Sitting across from each other, first partner one takes 10 rapid inhalations, and 10 slow exhalations. After this, partner one checks to see how their partner's face looks to them. This pattern of breathing activates the ventral branch of the parasympathetic nervous system and as a result partner two appears friendly and safe.

Next partner one takes 10 long inhalations and 10 rapid exhalations and then checks to see how their partner's face looks now. This opposite breathing pattern activates the sympathetic branch of the ANS. As a result, partner two looks very critical and unsafe to partner one because in this state of sympathetic arousal, we experience threat.

Partners now change roles, taking turns doing this exercise. By shifting the inhalation/exhalation ratio, we are shifting ANS states. Once done, partners debrief. They are asked to notice how this was for them and take time to share.

This breath exercise clearly illustrates in an embodied way how our experiences change based on our ANS states. We can teach our clients how to shift into a ventral state, or at least to invite a ventral state to come. We can only invite, because the body will not shift from a top down place on command. We must be gentle in our coaxing, allowing time to re-educate our ANS.

These two fundamental concepts in the polyvagal theory, how state change impacts our perception of the world, and the bidirectional nature of mind-body connection, give us a solid basis from which to understand the nature of addictive behaviours as efficient state changers.

Thinking at the Edge with Polyvagal Theory

There are five concepts and lessons that stand out for me in working with the polyvagal theory and addiction:

Lesson 1: Safety First
Safety is the bedrock. None of us are safe unless all of us are safe.
Lesson 2: Interoception
Honour your mind-body connection.
Lesson 3: Neuroception
Our body's wisdom is designed to seek safety.
Lesson 4: The Social Engagement System
We need each other to survive and thrive.
Lesson 5: Co-regulation
Body/environments are alive and co-regulate.

Let's take each one and start by explaining the concept in terms of what we already know. Then, with Gendlin's thinking at the edge method, we are going to bring the concepts into the body, one at a time, by inviting a felt sense to come with each of them. Given the championing of the body in the polyvagal theory it is only fitting that we would take time to let our bodies inform our thoughts and vice versa.

I am going to share my felt sense of each concept as it relates to a powerful and unprecedented experience that we are all going through as I write this book. The date is March 22, 2020, and you and I and the whole world are in the grips of Covid-19, a global pandemic. By the time you read this, events will have unfolded in a way that is completely unknown at this moment. It feels like nothing will ever be the same again. Our systems of defense are raging and for some, shutting down, as we all make our way through the fear and sickness that has enveloped us.

After my turn, I will invite you to take each concept inside and allow a felt sense to form. That way, we are exploring the polyvagal theory in an experiential way, letting the bodily response speak to us as we cross concept with felt experience. This is how the theory comes alive for me, and my hope is that it will come alive for you. Once you have it in this bodily way, you can cross it as discussed in previous chapters, and challenge it, taking it further and making it yours. It will inform your work and your life in an extraordinary, and also deeply familiar way.

Lesson 1. Safety First: None of Us Is Safe Unless All of Us Are Safe

I believe the most important message that polyvagal theory conveys is the primacy of safety. When we feel safe, our bodies are emotionally regulated, our immune system is protecting us and our cognitive abilities are maximized. How do we understand safety in light of the polyvagal theory?

Safety is experienced when the "good vagus", the ventral branch of the parasympathetic nervous system is engaged. Systems of defense are resting, not needed when we feel the cozy state of safety. A favourite phrase that Porges uses is the importance of feeling safe in the arms of another. This is the place of immobilization without fear that is represented on the client model as flow, and the clinician model as stillness. This intertwining state involves the ventral and dorsal branches of the vagus nerve. The ventral branch of flock on the client model and integrated on the clinician model is the state of safety. It promotes health, growth, and restoration. When the ventral branch is present and dorsal is activated, it is safe to be still in the body.

To be able to surrender to another means that we trust the other. We trust the relationship to provide for us, and for the moment, we can let go and just be. If we are lucky we are born into this safety, in a secure and trusting environment. The capacity to ground ourselves, to feel safe and regulated inside our bodies, is the most fundamental skill we can achieve in a lifetime. Some of us learn these skills and the felt sense in our bodies from our loving caretakers. Some have this capacity early on in life but lose it with experiences of pain and suffering. Others spend the better part of their existence trying to create this safe nest in which to grow and heal.

Health, growth, and restoration are not possible without safety. This is the first place that we should be curious about with our clients. How safe a person is determines how emotionally and physically healthy they are. Without safety our bodies spend time in the sympathetic and dorsal branches of the ANS, where our immune systems are compromised. This is why trauma and addiction are so highly correlated with physical illness.

Creating a Safe Nest

The polyvagal theory reminds us to be aware of our physical surroundings as part of creating safety. In particular, sudden noises, especially low sounds, can trigger cues of danger. We need to create a warm, soothing environment. Soft colours, a warm blanket, a calm picture, and a cozy seat, all help our clients and ourselves to be able to go deeper when we need the comfort of a safe nest. Plants help too, and the soothing smell of lavender. They are healing agents that boost our immune system.

Often when people come to therapy in the late afternoon they are sleepy. We have a cup of tea and a biscuit, or piece of fruit, to help energize the body. Just as it is not possible to feel safe when our ANS is fired up in systems of defense, it isn't possible to feel energized to do the hard work of therapy when we are hungry. This is a very concrete way that working with the body shapes your practice. Bodies get hungry, bodies get sleepy, bodies speak to us. When we as healers validate these needs, we give so much and the sense of safety we create allows so much more healing to happen.

One of my young clients loves bananas, so I try to have one on hand for our Thursday appointment. I love the way her face lights up as she takes her first bite. In my groups, we have a break to connect with each other in a non-structured way, and I provide some food that I prepared for them. "Food is love," and I want the people who come to our centre to feel safe and loved. I invite this. I don't expect or require or need it. I simply invite it. In addition, eating together is a friendly connecting way to begin to build community. I encourage you to be creative and inviting in making your safe nest, in your own way. In our offices we can create the conditions of safety, hopefully "enough" safety, for the present moment.

What is Enough Safety?

Many of the people who we see in our offices are not and never have experienced "enough" safety. By offering my space, time, and heart to their process of healing, I am doing what I can to create safety in our time together. But, people's experience of safety differ a great deal as we have seen in our discussion of cultural aspects of trauma. Many people may feel safe at home, but they are simply not safe on the streets. In a culture of white body supremacy, some of us are more safe than others, and some of us have never known safety. This cannot be overstated.

And in an existential way, we all live with uncertainty all of the time. Safety is a moment by moment experience. Most of us deny this most of the time, and then something intense happens and we feel our vulnerablilty. If we have a lot of privilege, we can slip back into the cozy feeling of stability as the events fade. There is no slipping back for many of us. Our current models of "safety" reflect a reality of privilege. It is assumed that we all return to a ventral vagal state of safety after "an event" occurs. This is simply not true. What if the "event" is your life experience? What if, for example, as a trans person, you never experience safety?

Chronic States of Dysregulation

In a chronic state of ANS dysregulation, that is, in the absence of the ventral vagus calming down the body, it is difficult to imagine how the traumatized, addicted person can find their way to safety, or find their way *back* to safety. In a recent email exchange with Porges, I asked him the following: "I wonder how someone informed by the polyvagal theory views safety from the perspective of marginalized people who are not and have never been safe in our world. For them, the typical notion of returning to safety doesn't apply. How do their nervous systems calm down? Perhaps only in small groups, at minimal intervals?"

He replied, "If you have the mental image with an associated visceral feeling (physiological state), the therapist has something to work with. In this case, the top-down process triggers a bottom-up feeling and therapy expands on this" (Porges, personal communication, February 9, 2020).

Those of us who work in the body know this to be true because we see how our clients are able to find the felt sense of safety as they begin to access the ventral vagus. This is hopeful and helps us to imagine the future for our addicted clients as stable and secure as long as they maintain their grounding practices. It is more worrisome for those who have not had past experiences of safety. Then we are very challenged to create this neuropathway. But in this work, we never say never. I have an image of a tiny little flame, one that we breathe into in hopes of connecting with our client. The fact that the person shows up in our office indicates a desire for connection, and this is the place where we start. Polyvagal theory is about safety and connection. We need to listen to those who feel the least safe and connected. Marginalized communities are our teachers. As we turn outwards to hear from them, we can turn inwards to do our own work.

Global trauma is also creating chronic states of ANS dysregulation. We are creating a new generation of people who are developing addictions as a result of macro level experiences such as the current technological revolution, and global traumas such as the climate crisis and the Covid-19 pandemic. These experiences lead many of us to feel a constant sense of angst, and emotional dysregulation becomes the norm.

So how do we deal with this level of angst as psychotherapists? We dig in and learn as much as we can about safety and the body, and we advocate for clients. We start by consciously working on addressing safety, knowing that it is the bedrock of the healing process.

In our post-Descartes era, we focus on concrete ways to address safety. We create surveillance systems and fences to address our fears. We build walls and borders to keep out marginalized people in an attempt to be safe. But we forget the most important lesson when we do this. *None of us is safe enough, unless all of us are safe enough.* By dissociating from our bodily responses and feelings, we lose our compassionate connection with others. We don't address our deepest ways of knowing and needing safety. We scratch the surface, but don't provide enough safety to facilitate the systemic response that is urgently called for.

First-Person Experiencing

If I am honest with myself I know that I have been avoiding this moment of really pausing. Distraction is very helpful when times are tough. And these are very tough times. Bizarre times. Covid-19 has brought the world to its knees. It is teaching us the most important polyvagal lesson: we cannot be safe and healthy unless we help everyone in the world to be safe and healthy.

I feel safe in my home. In fact, there is a cozy, warm quality to my felt sense of being at home. It feels like shelter in a storm. I'm cooking more, writing more, and learning more about how to reach people on the internet. I'm appreciating my husband more since this all happened. I'm appreciating our abiding friendship and partnership as we weather the storm together.

But, as I drop down inside I feel a strange gripping sensation in my chest. Something to do with isolation, a scary word that takes me back to feeling so alone, not belonging, as a little girl. I wonder how it would be to live alone right now and face all the scary news on my own. I'm grateful for being able to share with my partner, and my children, and my community. Yesterday I was walking along a barren street and finally came across a couple of people approaching on the other side of the road. At first we just gazed at each other, and then my face broke out into a big smile. I didn't decide to smile. My body decided. And a wonderful thing happened. I took a risk, and engaged with these people, and they both responded with gorgeous smiles. As I walked on I felt tears come, and I thought about how much we have lost, and how much we have gained from Covid-19.

As I touch into my felt sense again, I feel a knowing come. The little girl needs to hear from me that she isn't alone. This will help her fear, help her to feel safe. And then I realize that we all seem to need this. "We are in this together," we say to each other. The power of safety and connection, the "good" vagus.

But wait. As I touch into my own fear, and feel the strength of my own grounding practices, I suddenly realize I've missed something so obvious, and so vital when it comes to safety and addiction. What happens when you touch into your fear and what helps you is no longer available to you? What if you are dependent on drugs and alcohol, or anything else that you may not have access to now? What a terrifying thought. I make a note to myself to check that out, and for now quietly return to my comforting felt sense.

Focusing Practice

Now I invite you to take "safety first" down into your body, being with whatever wants to come as you take the concept inside. Take a few deep breaths, follow your inside path as you turn your attention to a bodily knowing place. Ask the question, "How does my body carry all of this about safety?" Take time to pause and be with this. Maybe make a body card or write in your journal.

What is Essential for Safety?

It's very telling to see what our culture determines to be essential during the pandemic. I'm happy to say that as I search the internet I see that most places in North America have decided liquor stores are an essential service. This seems to be based on the fact that there is a recognition of people's vulnerability to physical withdrawal without the drugs and alcohol that they have become dependent on. Of course, this decision has aroused fury within the population who view addiction as a moral defect. I'm relieved to see that their disdain has not determined our approach.

What is essential is that we learn how much we need to be connected to and concerned for each other. We are told that our capacity to stop this virus from spreading is directly related to how much we can adhere to social distancing. It is up to us to think of others, to keep ourselves safe.

Lesson 2. Interoception: Honour Your Mind/Body Connection

Interoception is a sense that helps us to be aware of and to understand what is going on inside our bodies, our embodied awareness. It is an important process in the polyvagal theory because it addresses the bi-directionality of visceral and cognitive processes that are carried between the body and the brainstem. Porges (2011) has done a great deal of work on developing a new model for categorizing sensory information. In his model, he calls interoception the sixth sense. The scope of the work is beyond this book, but it is important to understand how interoception forms a key component of the the polyvagal theory as it relates to the functioning of the vagus nerve. Recall that 80% of the information carried by the vagal pathway is afferent, meaning it goes from body to brain, from the bottom up.

When we are able to feel into our bodily information and to read it accurately, we are more likely to maintain a ventral state of grounding. Those who experience difficulty with sensory awareness, such as people with autism, attention deficit hyperactivity, post traumatic stress, and/or addictions, have difficulty with interoceptive processes. They often struggle to connect with and read sensations and subsequent signals from the body. They live in chronic states of defense and addictions become a way to cope with the emotional dysregulation. Hence, practices that enhance interoceptive functioning are very helpful as they bring the body back to a ventral state. Body-based practices such as embodied psychotherapies, yoga, drumming, chanting, singing, focusing, mindfulness, all work on developing interoceptive skills. New and creative ways are developing such as Porges' (2017) *safe and sound* protocol.

First-Person Experiencing

> I breathe, going inside. I feel a surge of exhilaration in the centre of my body. Focusing is the act of interocepting. My wonderful practice crosses so beautifully with the concept. The felt sense of experience is the integration of embodied awareness. No wonder I feel so at home with the polyvagal theory. It comes together inside in an image: a warm bubbly, safe, cauldron. Cauldron? So funny what comes from the body. My body says I am a witch who mixes things together. A friendly, curious witch. This takes me back to our discussion of consilience in Chapter 6. Crossing and mixing and creating a brew, a model. A FSPM for treating addiction.
>
> The above is an example of how the body works. I had thought that I would ask my body how each of the concepts is carried in relation to the Covid-19 pandemic. When I went inside something else came, and that is just fine. The good energy of this image is helping me with my experience of the pandemic. The body knows and I listen.

Focusing Practice

Now I invite you to take time to go down inside with the concept of interoception and see what comes for you. What is the quality of your connection with your bodily knowing?

Lesson 3. Neuroception: Our Body's Wisdom is Designed to Seek Safety

Neuroception is a concept created by Porges for naming the innate ability of the nervous system to detect features in the environment that signal safety, danger, and life-threat. It happens in primitive parts of the brain and is not within our conscious awareness. This process is evident when we see two people meeting for the first time. If they feel safe they engage, smiling and greeting each other. If they feel a sense of threat, they may pull back, avoid eye contact, and may even start to flush or sweat. Interestingly, they may not have any conscious idea about why they feel the threat. But the nervous system knows. It leads the way in a bodily response. Our nervous system is continuously assessing risk, if the environment looks safe, it inhibits the defensive reactions of flight, fight, and shutdown. Research into this area shows that the temporal lobe of the cortex is involved in assessing face and body movements that indicate safety.

Crossing Felt Shift and Neuroception

The connection between neuroception and the felt shift in the body has been intriguing me for years. This is perhaps the heart of the model. I recognized my own felt shifts and how they radically changed my thoughts and feelings and the same physical release that I saw in the women in my early group. With the awareness of the autonomic nervous system, I began to understand that this was a shift in neurophysiological states. While I didn't call it neuroception, I thought of it as a knowing that comes from the felt sense. Here is an interesting crossing of concepts, the body's wisdom which leads to the felt shift, and neuroception. I have noticed that when I explain this point of connecting the felt sense with the ANS, many people shake their heads in agreement. "Yes," they say. "That makes sense." They appear to smile or be somehow satisfied as if this feels right in the body. From there it flows that addictions are propellors of these shifts. Again, I notice that people will nod and say, "Yes, that makes sense." I think of these moments as sweet spots of consilience because we are "feeling into thinking", our state of integration.

Focusing Practice

In our TAE crossing, we ask the question how is the body's wisdom that creates the physical release, the felt shift, related to, or the same as, neuroception? Be with one through the felt sense of the other. Let your body feel into the crossing of felt experiencing with neuroscience.

Neuroception and Triggers: A Retuning/Reframing Process

We can think of our neuroceptive abilities as a kind of protective overseer who is always there keeping an eye out for our safety. This sounds very helpful when we think of trauma, but as we know, it isn't that straightforward. Trauma creates triggers, and triggers distort the current moment. Our neuroceptive abilities become dysregulated, and we find ourselves detecting threat unnecessarily.

This dysregulation can explain many of the DSM diagnostic categories. As we begin to see these experiences as manifestations of emotional dysregulation, we can bring a new paradigm to the field of trauma and addiction. We drop the pathologizing model that carries the language of "disorders" and instead engage our learning model. Through this lens, we see these states as a result of overuse or overlearning of trauma responses. The neurophysiological states are neutral, not sick, carrying no judgement. They may however, require a retuning when trauma is involved.

This is enabled in part by neural exercises that facilitate the ventral vagus. Our job as therapists is to help our clients re-educate their nervous systems, to update the internal calendar, orienting to the present moment. This enables us to work through painful triggered states.

Triggers are our friends. Why? Because they come to us as reminders of wounded places that need our help. They are powerful parts of ourselves, lost experiences suspended in space and time, longing to be reclaimed and embodied. It is through embracing them that we find our whole, integrated self. When we reframe triggers in this way, we gradually tame the felt sense experience, reclaiming parts of ourselves. Only then can we make sense of our life story because we can be with the truth.

First-Person Experiencing

I take the word neuroception down inside. It feels warm in here. An image of a cozy lion comes. A lion who is watching and protecting me, detecting danger. Red and gold swirls of colour encircle my feet and spread up to wrap around my whole body and beyond into the distance. This part feels like another sense, or like an old friend that I have relied on all my life. It watches without me thinking about it. It knows when to go into high alert. Ah, yes, now an old, familiar image of a soldier comes, watching through the night to protect me while I am sleeping. He stands on guard, pistol cocked, surveying the horizon.

As I bring attention back to the room I am amazed at what came. I remember this soldier from an EMDR session I had about thirty years ago. It feels so right for this concept of neuroception. My conscious self is asleep in an army tent and my neuroceptor/soldier is standing on guard. This is how I grew up. I lived in flight/fight and fawn.

In my healing journey I had to connect with the soldier and work through triggered states. I learned to say to that soldier, "That was in the past. It isn't happening now." Over many years we have come together in my struggle to feel safe and to heal.

Now, with the pandemic, all is unsafe around the world. I have learned to surrender to the moment-by-moment sense of safety, using my interoceptive focusing practice to be with my neuroceptive soldier.

As I read this I realize that the soldier has become a lion. Is this what the healing journey does? Transforms rigid soldiers into cozy lions?

Focusing Practice

Now I invite you to bring your attention into the body, taking in the word neuroception. Give yourself some time here. I encourage you to find a listening partner. A good listener, especially a listener who hears your interoceptive experiences, will help you to deepen your process. We have covered a lot of terrain in this chapter, so take your time to enjoy a pause.

Lesson 4. Social Engagement System: We need each other to survive and thrive

The social engagement system is located on the FSPM clinician version in the part of the diagram that refers to the integrated state. It is part of the ventral vagal branch of the ANS that promotes safety, growth, and restoration. Brainstem areas that regulate the ventral vagal branch are also involved in regulating the muscles in the head and face, involving our eyes, ears, and voice. This branch of the vagus communicates with organs above the diaphragm and forms bidirectional neural communication between the heart and the face. This "safety circuit" (Dana, 2018, p. 27) begins at birth and regulates our behaviours that range from social engagement to surveillance. We invite people to come closer or to distance by our facial expression, the tilt of our head, and our tone of voice. Our bodies tell the story of our neuroceptive detector.

We are wired to socially engage (Cacioppo & Cacioppo, 2014). When we feel whole and integrated, we seek out connection in good times and bad times, flocking together to celebrate life and death.

Social Engagement and Addiction: No Thanks!

Looking at the clinician model, we see the opposite state of integrated is addicted. The graphic representation of these opposing states is a powerful visual cue for clients as a reminder of all they have lost. It reflects the reality that social engagement is avoided and feared for those struggling with addiction. This makes sense as we know that the social engagement system is not available when we are emotionally dysregulated. Seeing their behaviour as an intertwining of chaos and rigidity helps them to face the absence of integration and engagement with others. They begin to see how their addictive behaviours keep them isolated and safe from traumatic attachments, but also prevent the possibility of close warm connection.

Painful as that is, we must help our addicted clients face the truth about their lives. This is difficult in the beginning of treatment because the addicted state is one of self-deception and profound isolation. While it takes time to build connection, clients usually show up at first in crisis. This is our opportunity to begin the arduous, and at the same time, wondrous healing journey. As they develop a sense of grounding I encourage them to attend my FSPM groups. There they can begin to co-regulate with others, restoring their sense of dignity and connection. Group work is the treatment of choice, the path forward when clients are ready.

I'm remembering back to the first line of this book, "Eight pairs of eyes, gazing at me, but not with me." At the moment of beginning to write, I was recognizing the missing piece. And I knew it intuitively as I began working with these young women in my incest survivor group. While they appeared to be looking *at* me, they were not connecting *with* me. And I knew that connection was the key to my being able to help them. While I wouldn't have used the polyvagal language of social engagement, I knew that the source of healing would come from engaging, and coregulating with these young women, helping all of us to learn to feel safe in our bodies, and with each other. That was scary and wonderful.

I also knew intuitively that their wispy, floaty gaze was protecting them from contact with me. I was not an older, male doctor, keeping distance from them with my "otherness" and sometimes disdain. I was young, female, curious, and warm. While I was nervous, I was also eager to connect. Scary business for them. And so they dissociated for many weeks as we dug down into the mud and the blood of their trauma and addiction. I wouldn't have called this foggy gaze the dorsal vagus response. I didn't know about polyvagal theory and the discovery of the second branch of the vagus nerve. I didn't know anything about the term autonomic nervous system. But what we as feminist therapists knew and integrated into our work was indeed all about the ANS. We called these dysregulated states flooding (sympathetic) and numbing (dorsal). Now, with the creation of the polyvagal theory, we understand the lack of presence to be an absence of the social engagement system.

First-Person Experiencing: Feeling into Our Heart, Throat, Face Connection

Taking these three words, social engagement system, down into the body brings so much now in this time of the pandemic. All of our therapy work has moved online since we are practising social distancing to stop the spread of the virus. My body is humming after just finishing an online session with a client. We went deep into the body in this session, opening up a wounded place in the chest. We practiced placing one loving hand on our heart centre and the other on our cheek. We opened our eyes and looked at each other gently touching into our social engagement system, bringing soothing energy to the wounded place. Seeing each other doing this made all the difference. I found my body gently rocking back and forth to soothe this young woman. And without words her body answered back in a familiar rhythm. This was the second session that I ever had with her, both on-line. I am simply amazed at the depth we can go without ever having physically met.

Knowing that our voices can also be a very deep way of connecting brings another avenue for sensing into another person's presence. Sometimes phone calls are very rich experiences for listening and sharing. Some clients prefer or need this way of communicating. It opens another path for healing that can also be profound.

At the same time, I would not like to be working through a conflict, or triggered state with a client on the internet. While we can still see our faces for cues of safety, the subtlety of bodily movements is absent. Texting and phone calls are challenging when our nervous systems are in states of defense because of the absence of bodily information. Without cues of safety, we can misread each other and end up in a bad place. In this new experience we are making our way in learning what feels right in the body.

For now, the internet is a lifeline for our Covid-ridden world. While it has resulted in much too much social distancing, it is also bringing us the only opportunity to engage with each other's faces and bodies at a time when it isn't safe to be physically together. Online group meetings where we can see each other's faces are an essential part of healing in Covid times.

Focusing Practice

Now I invite you to take time to be with this concept, social engagement system. As we are all living through the pandemic, we are acutely aware of our social connections. You may be remembering, or we may still be experiencing, how the Covid-19 virus impacted your time with friends, family, lovers. Feel into your heart, throat, face connection. Don't be surprised if grief comes. Take time to be with it all.

Lesson 5. Co-regulation: Body/Environments are Alive and Co-regulate

In our current post-Descartes, hypermasculine world we emphasize the importance of the individual as a self-regulating being whose task is to learn how to be self-reliant. Too much support from others is perceived as hampering one's ability to fend for oneself. "Each man for himself" prevails as our motto. Domination and/or control is key – of self, others, and the natural world. This top-down approach includes a mechanistic view of body and environment.

Polyvagal theory suggests something quite different. In this bottom-up approach, we understand ourselves as living organisms deeply connected to and sustained by our relationship with the environment and each other. From the first breath we take, and our first embrace, we experience our interconnectedness. If all goes well, we begin to establish a safe-enough state of co-regulation with our caretakers. We have an innate understanding of the aliveness of the environment as it sustains our bodies and the natural world. "Once we define ourselves as an organism, whose survival is dependent on opportunities to successfully co-regulate, then we have moved into the life space of others" (Porges, 2016, p. 5).

In moving into others' life space, we appreciate the power of connection in contributing to our need for growth, health, and restoration, the vital functions of the ventral vagus. Rather than seeking separateness, we understand the need for safe and secure attachments to facilitate an eventual capacity for modulated autonomy. Porges points out that individuals who appear to be efficient in regulating themselves are in fact the ones who have had many opportunities to co-regulate with others. They have developed the neuropathways to promote resilience. In other words, if you started with "enough safety", chances are you will have developed the capacity to regulate when others aren't there for you.

In a world of white body supremacy, where misogyny prevails, we have become very fearful of our own vulnerability. Soft, open-hearted, vulnerable states are equated with femininity, and thus held in fear and contempt. Boys and men who are seen as co-regulating with their female relationships are viewed as weak. This is very sad.

Self Regulation and Addiction: Whatever Gets You Through the Night

For many of our clients, the absence of the ability to co-regulate neurophysiological state in the presence of others results in adaptively turning to objects or behaviours that bring comfort. I recall leading a workshop on the FSPM and asking participants who was there to comfort them when they were a child. Several people responded that they went to the tree in the back yard for comfort. How wonderful that the natural world provided this much needed haven.

The absence of co-regulation opportunities results in a myriad of ingenious ways to self-soothe. Porges emphasizes the importance of understanding that context defines what behaviours are appropriately adaptive to the environment. We can then interpret what is currently thought of as a behavioural "pathology" as a behavior that might be adaptive in one setting, but is not adaptive in another setting. For example, if there is no one to soothe you, to co-regulate with you, it is highly adaptive to use addictive behaviours such as sucking your thumb, masturbating, drinking alcohol, doing drugs, or eating large quantities of food to comfort and numb your pain.

When assessing our clients' capacity to co-regulate, we can turn to the FSPM and begin to formulate what state is driving what behaviours. This provides an opportunity to do some teaching about self and co-regulation and the nature of addiction. Sometimes, it is not clear whether a behaviour is addictive or not. For example, being addicted to a relationship can be very confusing. If you are relating to another person, surely you are co-regulating. Or are you?

It depends. Looking at our model, we can work with our client to assess how much of the time they are living in a ventral state, and how much of the time are they using the relationship to soothe discomfort. We can always go back to our three questions to assess addiction. Does the relationship help you in the short term? Does it hurt you in the long term? Can you end it if it is self-harming?

First-Person Experiencing

When I take co-regulation down inside I come to an old wounded place that I shared in Chapter 3. At this time I was not able to co-regulate because I didn't have enough of an integrated self. I lost myself in an addicted relationship. I remember hearing my therapist say, "You can be addicted to a person you know." The colour drained from me as I faced what was happening to my life.

I was very fortunate that I found John, this wise and loving therapist. I spent many years in his comforting chair. I learned how to welcome embodied awareness, and appreciate my grandparents for giving me the gift of co-regulation, the safe nest in which to grow and heal.

Focusing Practice

Polyvagal theory can be challenging to assimilate. In this chapter I have highlighted five main lessons that I feel are relevant to our understanding of the theory in psychotherapy. They can be summed up as follows: Seeking safety forms the bedrock of all that we do. As somatic practitioners we work in an embodied way to tap into our natural ability to assess safety. This ability, guided by the autonomic nervous system, is called neuroception. When we connect deeply with ourselves we enhance our capacity to deeply connect with others. This interconnectedness is essential for all living beings to thrive. As we take each lesson down into the body it becomes more clear and informs our practice. Now I invite you to take time to be with this down into the centre of your body. Listen to what your body knows about polyvagal theory.

References

Cacioppo, J. T. & Cacioppo, S. (2014). Older adults showing social or loneliness show poorer cognitive function 4 years later. *Evidence-Based Nursing, 17*(2), 59–60.

Dana, D. (2018). *The polyagal theory in therapy: Engaging the rhythm of regulation*. New York: W. W. Norton & Co.

Porges, S. (2011). *The polyvagal theory: Neurophysiological foundations of emotions, attachment, communication, self regulation*. New York. W. W. Norton & Company.

Porges, S. (2016, September). *Interview with Prengel, S.* [Mindfulness and co-egulation]. Retrieved from relationalimplicit.com/porges/.

Porges, S. (2017). *The pocket guide to the polyvagal theory: The transformative power of feeling safe*. New York: W. W. Norton & Company.

Porges, S. & Dana, D. (2018). *Clinical applications of the polyvagal theory: The emergence of polyvagal-informed therapies*. New York: W. W. Norton & Company.

9 Experiential Psychotherapy and Gendlin's Felt Sense: The Whole of a Situation

This chapter brings us to the heart of our journey together, the *felt sense* of all that we are exploring in the world of addiction. The felt sense contains the whole of our experiencing, including content *and* process, thinking *and* feeling: the sweet spot of integration that we discussed in Chapter 3. In the traditional top-down way of writing and reading a book, we would be concerned with the content, the words on the page. The author may occasionally refer to themselves or the reader, but only in passing, and it would not impact the content. In contrast, our journey of Gendlin's *thinking at the edge* methodology offers us a different way of being together. The process by which we explore addiction comes alive by sharing the felt sense of the concepts. As I write and you read we each interact with top-down content and bottom-up process, and our interaction deepens with first-person experiencing. We "carry each other forward", as Gendlin would say, with this interactional process.

By now, you know a lot about me and I imagine a lot about you. And I hope so much that you are enjoying yourself. While I have seldom worked as hard in my life, I am truly enjoying this process. I feel excited about sharing the following two experiences with you; meeting my first teacher, Mary Armstrong, and meeting her first teacher, Gene Gendlin. He would often say that he didn't invent focusing. Rather, he found it when he went searching for ways to understand how people change in this somewhat mysterious psychotherapy process and in life.

First-Person Experiencing: Meeting Mary Armstrong

"Your tears are welcome here," says Mary. It's the late 1980s and I am in my first session with a focusing-oriented trauma therapist. In her soft, eternally gentle way she makes a space for me to be fully open to all that I am experiencing. In a moment of being overwhelmed by the agony of my work, she is with me.

"How does your body carry all of this?" she asks. We pause. "What is happening down in the centre of the body?"

What new and curious questions. What is this way of being with me? As I slowly bring attention down into my body I feel the stirrings of what I learn is a felt sense. As she guides me deeper down I come to a new, fresh experience of calm. A calm that comes from connecting with the pain. A swirling calm that sits on my shoulders, helping me to settle inside. There are no words here, more a whole sense of heavy knowing, and a hint of something more, yet unknown. Even though that was over thirty years ago, I have never forgotten this experience. It was the beginning of my lifelong focusing journey.

Meeting Eugene Gendlin

My sessions with Armstrong led me to attend a focusing conference in the early 1990s held at Niagara Falls, Canada. I jump at the chance to meet Gendlin, leader of the focusing world, in a small group format for several days. Our group of thirty focusers from Canada and the United States are staying at an old convent that has been turned into a retreat centre on the banks of the majestic falls. Many experiences stand out for me. Gendlin himself is quite a surprise. I walk into the meeting room and see a group of people gathered around a slim, cross-legged man dressed in a plaid lumberjack shirt, old baggy pants, and mismatched socks. He is holding court and people are riveted. Later, someone says that they thought he was the janitor for the building, but no, he is the leader of the focusing movement. I like this about him right away: no putting on airs.

I find a seat in the circle as we each begin to settle into the first morning. People are very friendly, open, and curious. Many have known each other for some time and delight in reconnecting. The room is cozy and inviting, with soft couches and comfortable chairs. A leader invites us all to close our eyes and bring our awareness down into the centre of the body. We notice what is there that wants our attention. We notice the physical sensations in the body, and a soothing voice asks us to be with whatever wants to be heard. I feel a tingling sensation in my stomach, and as I stay with it, it becomes more like a tight knot. In time I recognize the anxiety and excitement I feel about being away from home, on my own after several years of intensive child rearing. I know that if I choose to connect in this focusing session, to really spend time listening inside, I may feel scared of what is stirring there. The soothing voice suggests that we be curious with all that comes. Hmmm, not sure about this. I give it time and listen to my inner stirrings. Waiting and being curious. Something changes and I feel a lovely physical releasing sensation where the tightness was. I welcome the felt shift. Acknowledging the heart of the issue brings relief and I feel compelled to return to this place that somehow signals a new and yet unclear direction. We are invited to begin to round off this experience and slowly bring ourselves back to the room. I open my eyes and am aware of a quiet, expansive feeling in the air. We have gone to a deeper place together and the difference in presence is palpable. Being with people in this still place is wonderful and I am drawn in more and more.

Gendlin's Safe Space: Do What is Right for You

Gene, as we all affectionately call him, begins by sharing about focusing ways of being together that may depart from the usual rules of engagement. He suggests that we do what is right for us. If our body tells us that we need to leave the room, we need to listen and honour that. He will not take it personally. Some of us are surprised by this. But Gendlin insists that it is true. He explains that in our focusing community, we welcome people taking good care of themselves and doing what they need to do. We are encouraged to say no whenever we need to, to pass when we don't want to speak, and to let our focusing partner know if they made a mistake in listening to us. He says he welcomes being wrong because then he has an opportunity to get it right. Gendlin motions with his arm as if he is throwing the mistake out the window.

This experience of feeling our power to choose what is right for us is exciting. If we know we can say no to something that doesn't feel right, then we can build enough safety to go to the murky edge of exploring our felt sense. We can show up more fully if we stand up for ourselves. We don't have to hide or explode in service of our needs. Gendlin encourages us to listen with respect to our own needs and the needs of our focusing partner. He emphasizes the vital importance of listening. As we take good care of ourselves, we become able to take good care of our relationships. I use this knowing as a benchmark for grounding myself in my work and building enough safety in my family and my focusing community.

Now, years later, as I have slowly and steadily integrated this empowered place, the voice that I call upon has become my own. But I know that I owe much to those who helped me to build this grounded, ventral capacity, and Gendlin is one of them. As I write this in April of 2020, I come across a video of Gendlin's (2007) presentation from a focusing conference entitled *Finding A Safe Place*. In it, he is being challenged to explain his notion of safety. He responds by saying that living is not safe, but we can find a safe place inside ourselves. Then he laughs and says that you may have to find it every morning. This is an interesting way of experiencing. Outside is unsafe, but we have the capacity to build inside safety, even if it is moment by moment. As I write this it feels helpful during these pandemic times.

The Dream: Lotte's Holocaust Story

First on the agenda of our day is Gendlin's dream workshop. It makes sense that he would be drawn to dreams since they are windows into our implicit world. In 1986 he published, *Let Your Body Interpret Your Dreams.* He explains that in focusing with dreams, we do not interpret them from a cognitive framework. We go inside to a focusing state and work with the dream from this deeper place where the body carries the knowing.

Gendlin asks if anyone would like to work with a dream. A small middle-aged woman comes forward. He asks her name and connects directly and openly with her. She gazes back and says her name is Lotte. In a beautiful moment, he reaches over, engaging her in an embodied way, a felt embrace without the touch. His gentle face wrinkles around the eyes as he softly says to her, "There are just the two of us here now. We will forget the others in the room." It's as if the lights go down as Gene and Lotte create their own space. The rest of us are now in the background awaiting.

He asks her to tell him about the dream. She gazes down. Her small body starts to fold up, long silvery grey hair falls forward on her shoulders as they slump. The body's bones pulling in to protect inside wounds. Gene waits and as he scans her body he notices a slight tremor in her hands. The room tightens as we take a collective breath. We are all moving in slow motion.

Lotte says that when she was a young girl she lived in Holland. As a Jewish family they hid during the war. In the dream she is back in the room in the attic. The dank smell of fear soaks the walls. She catches her breath as she tells the story. Very quickly, a feeling of dread comes, grabbing her by the throat. Gendlin tracks her body and catches her just as they reach the tip of the overwhelming wave. He backs her up by gently reaching in and inviting her to get some distance from the intensity. He explains that there is nothing good that comes from going to really uncomfortable places without help. We want to welcome these places because they offer so much information, but first we need to find some help in the dream.

Lotte's body settles with Gendlin's gentle guidance. He asks her more about her family life before the German invasion. We see her eyes scanning, searching for good memories in the gentleness of his face. She finds one and her eyes open wide letting Gendlin know that she feels the good energy of her close and loving family. He helps her to find this good energy in her body. She finds it in her chest area. They take time to ground it in the body, letting a felt sense form, finding a handle for this place of safety. Again, we all breathe, shifting and releasing tension.

They take this felt sense with them as they go back to the dream. He asks her to tell him about the characters. Any sense of good energy there? He is looking for anything they can use as a resource from the dream to continue with the uncomfortable place. She describes a kind and observant figure. A soft and airy presence that stands beside her and shares light and warmth. He invites Lotte to go down inside and find the airy place in her body. We wait.

She finds the felt sense in her belly. It contains strands of feelings, thoughts, physical sensations, and memories. It feels familiar, yet unknown at the same time. They take time to explore the whole of it. Something familiar about her mother comes and this feels nourishing to Lotte. Now that the help is here, Gendlin asks her if it would be all right to go back to the scary place in her throat with the airy warm part keeping them company. A very powerful thing happens. Lotte connects with something so strong that her body stands up and takes her into a crouching position under a nearby table. Gene immediately moves beside her and they're crouching together under cover from something yet to be revealed. We wait.

The whole room is counting on Gendlin. We are unsure, maybe a bit frightened and yet the sense of trusting the experience is very strong. Lotte breathes deeply, tears coming now. The tears reveal her shifting process. Gendlin follows, silently, allowing her lots of time and space.

Lotte whispers, "I was so small, so afraid."

"So small and afraid." Gene slowly drops a question down into the felt sense. "What does the small and afraid need?"

Together Gendlin helps Lotte bring the light and airy felt sense in her belly to be with the small and scared part in her throat. Light and airy encircles small and scared. They hold space for each other and in time, slowly make their way back to the chairs. Again, the room has been transformed. A still fullness prevails.

Gene explains how we can work with little pieces of a dream, coming back again and again as the felt sense calls to us. I remember him laughing and saying that the little people in our brain will continue mulling it over. He had an infectious laugh, childlike in its exuberance. We laugh with him, welcoming a felt shift of lightness as we all surface from a sacred experience, so appreciative of Gendlin and Lotte.

Focusing Practice

I invite you now to take time to go inside and notice what comes for you as you experience your own felt sense response to my shared experiences. You could ask into your dreams, following down inside and taking in your bodily knowing. If you feel lost in the steps you can always go back to the end of Chapter 2 to refresh, or find a focusing partner to exchange listening rounds. Notice what comes and perhaps drop the Gendlin question down into the felt sense. Ask, what does it need?

Gendlin's Holocaust Story

Many years later, I came upon an article about Gendlin's escape from Nazi-occupied Austria (Korbei, 1994). When I thought back to the dream workshop that I first witnessed, I was shocked. I had no idea that Gendlin and Lotte were both children of Jewish families fleeing from the Nazis.

His quality of presence was remarkable at the time. Now, after learning about their shared history, I realized that his capacity to keep his story out of it, while having been so much a part of it, was extraordinary.

In this same article, Gendlin describes an experience with his father that foreshadows his curiosity about feelings and intuition. During their escape 12-year-old Gene accompanies his father to visit a man in Cologne, Germany, who is supposed to be helping them. He waits as his father goes into a room. When he comes out his father is pale and says, "Let's go." He explains to Gendlin that he doesn't trust this man and will not follow him. Gendlin is confused by this because they are desperate and have no other help. Still, Gendlin says, his father follows his feeling:

> I was surprised then and also often asked myself later what kind of feeling it is which tells you something. Sometimes I tried to find such a feeling within myself, but I could not. But that I started to look for it had its effect in the end. Forty years later when I was asked how I could discover focusing, I remembered these circumstances. (In Korbei, 1994, p. 6)

Gendin the Philosopher

During the 1950s, Gendlin was a philosophy student at the University of Chicago. He began his academic career studying the phenomenological philosophers including Merleau-Ponty, Wittgenschtein, and Heidegger. He had this wonderful capacity to see beyond theories, to the place where we remain curious about *how* we are thinking about *what* we are thinking. He would often talk about different kinds of theories, or different ways of knowing and experiencing. While he welcomed them all, he challenged us to open more and more to the freshness of something new. He wanted us to fully appreciate that the process by which one came to a conclusion was key to understanding the content. He would remark that he could go to any department of the university, and while he didn't know as much about the content of the subject, he could see where they were stuck in the process they were following in their attempting to solve the problem.

While Gendlin went on in his career to develop focusing and applications of the practice, he identified as a philosopher. Gendlin (2007) said, "Philosophy works with ... not *even* concepts. It doesn't have *any* content. It's not about anything." This drew laughter from the crowd of trauma therapists, but I wonder to this day, how many people really took in the scope of what he was saying. He wanted them to think philosophically, to stand beside theory and embrace the process. He loved to be iconoclastic and playfully expose flaws in conventions. Sometimes exhuberant laughter would follow, and a beautiful opening into something new would shift the room to an exciting place. Other times his challenging of our patterned ways of thinking would create an uncomfortable space. Such is life for the iconoclast.

The Primacy of Human Presence

In 1962 Gendlin published *Experiencing and the Creation of Meaning*. The title reflects the heart of Gendlin's work. As a phenomenologist, he starts with the process of experiencing, and then follows that process as it leads us to the creation of meaning. By integrating philosophical and psychological methods, he broadens and deepens the quest for integration of conceptualizing and feeling. Gendlin was intrigued by the space between our lived experience and our conceptual understandings. Recall from Chapter 2 what he wrote about the primacy of human presence. He expressed his sense of how important it is to be a fellow human being first and foremost in using focusing in the process of psychotherapy: "What matters is to be a human being with another human being, to recognize the other person as another being in there" (1990, p. 205). It highlights the essence of what shone through in his presence with Lotte as they explored the space between the dream and the present moment. And it illustrates the essence of Gendlin's focusing-oriented psychotherapy (Gendlin, 1996). In his sessions and in his writing, he demonstrates deep experiencing, weaving together content and process by systematically naming already known top-down theories, placing them on one side of him, and bottom-up, first-person experiences on the other side. This creates a cleared space where he is ready to be in a fresh process. He encourages us to move back and forth from bottom-up to top-down to see if we have already-known theory that may help the client. But, the crucial difference is that he does not interpret the client's experience to fit into a box. He *suggests* it, and the client checks it against the bodily felt sense to see if it fits. The body then guides the process of change. If it fits, he works with it through the six steps of focusing, or other methods. If it doesn't fit, he lets it go.

This deep experiencing can be part of anything that we do and are; psychotherapy, thinking at the edge, living our lives. I see it in three movements. First we clear space, moving to the side preconceived concepts, then we clear our own agenda, and then we allow deep felt sense to come.

Focusing Practice: Honouring Your Shaky Being

Let's pause. Notice what happens inside. I feel a profound sense of awe whenever I read this piece from Gendlin. Not idealized awe. Instead a very grounded feeling of appreciation for his openness, his willingness to share his shaky being. How is your shaky being? Do you take good care of this part of you? Can you love this part of you? Do you ever explicitly share it with your clients? We are taught not to do this. But, the deeper we work with our own process, the more is revealed without language. I think Gendlin is saying, "This is all right. It is life." Of course too much shaky being is scary, but a nod to this part makes us real. Learning to love this part of ourselves *is* the healing journey. When we love our shaky being we do not hurt others or ourselves.

Three Ways of Knowing

As a philosopher, Gendlin emphasized the importance of understanding different kinds of theories. While there are many, he describes three ways of knowing that we will briefly review. This helps us to appreciate the new concepts that he brings to experiential therapy. The first one is the top-down scientific method that we have been discussing. One starts by looking for patterns and dividing up the subject into parts, or units, that fit into that pattern. Gendlin called this the *unit model*. The following passage illustrates his way of being with the scientific method. He welcomed it, yet stressed the importance of understanding science within the context of human interaction.

1. *The Traditional Unit Model: Our current model of addiction*
    Gendlin (1998) spoke the following about traditional scientific approaches:

    > Some theories, and there are many .. work by chopping things up into little units and then reconstructing whatever you're thinking about in those little units. *That's a wonderful thing because it gives clarity.* And what we call science in this society is based on that way of proceeding. You take whatever it is you're studying and you chop it up into units, as carefully as you can, and whatever is left over gets lost. Sorry we can't deal with that. But the units are extremely valuable because what you reconstruct out of them is clear. And with that model you can build airplanes. And with that model you can build automobiles, and you can build computers, and you can build microphones that carry over there. So don't say that that's no good.

2. *The Holistic Model: Utilized by the Ecology Movement*
    This holistic approach is the opposite of the unit model because according to this theory, everything is one big whole. There are no units or parts. Everything is connected to everything. This holistic approach is used by the modern ecology movement. The idea is that all parts are interlocked and cannot be understood as separate entities. In the natural world, this approach emphasizes the interconnectedness of

ecosystems, and the belief that you cannot study discrete ecosystems alone because they function together.

3.   *Functional Wholes: Interactional Systems Theory Model*
The approach called *functional wholes* is used in family systems therapy. Recall in Chapter 6 we discussed systems theory in relation to interpersonal neurobiology. Each whole, a person, a relationship, a family is seen as a whole within a whole system. And each whole is impacted by the interactional process between them. This interactional process takes precedence because it shapes the relationships, family, and subsystems. A person may function well outside of the family system, but once in the system the interaction of family members often determines their capacity to regulate.

In summary, Gendlin is careful to point out that *we need all three models* to help us create theories. This relates back to our discussion of mixed methods in Chapter 7. What is crucial is that we understand which model we are using and why. And that we are clear about theory being just that, theory. We need to have a new appreciation for what constitutes "truth". It depends on the lens you use to view it. It makes sense that the traditional model would be employed to help with physical illness that results from addiction. At this point, however, this "unit model" dominates our approach. Human suffering calls for an embodied interactional way of seeing.

Gendlin's View of Neurobiology

I have often wondered what Gendlin would think of the felt sense polyvagal model (FSPM). I was intrigued when I heard him speak about the advances in neurobiology. He felt that a neurobiological understanding of the body as cells and neurons was an important way to help advance all kinds of medical treatments, and as such these concepts need to stand alone. However, he welcomed the idea of building theories that could integrate the scientific method with subjective experiencing. He encouraged us to bring in neurobiological concepts that create patterned ways of organizing reality, (polyvagal theory) and overlay it with patterns of human interaction (felt sense experiencing). Then we can explore the shadows that emerge through applying the model with our clients (Gendlin, 2008). The FSPM is my attempt at this crossing.

Recently, I came across an article by Gendlin (1961a) entitled, "Galvanic skin response correlates of different modes of experiencing." He was crossing the traditional method of studying the body's autonomic nervous system through monitoring galvanic skin response, with the focusing process. That same year (1961b), he also studied the autonomic response to different qualities of therapist-client relationship. Think back to Chapter 2 where I described how Gendlin noticed clients' periods of continuous direct reference to experiencing, followed by periods of silence (which he later named focusing) in the early research. He discovered that this process of deep experiencing was a major predictor of success in psychotherapy. Galvanic skin response (GSR) measures activation of the sympathetic branch of the nervous system. The study found that silent, continuous reference to experiencing produced significantly fewer GSRs than periods involving speech. They concluded that allowing oneself to be immersed in a feeling process appears to be adaptive, even when the content is somewhat stressful. In other words, focusing appears to facilitate a ventral vagal response.

Experiential Psychotherapy: The Birth of Gendlin's Felt Sense and Felt Shift

In today's cognitively oriented world, it's no surprise that most psychotherapy models focus on the content of what the client shares, while the process by which it is being experienced is not addressed. Cognitive behavioural and insight-oriented therapies dominate. The therapist is seen as the expert who interprets the client's experience based on theoretical constructs. Our theories of personality focus on content too. We conceptualize pathological traits by developing diagnostic categories reflected in the *Diagnostic and Statistical Manual*. This traditional unit model discards information that doesn't fit into the category.

Gendlin saw the shortcomings in this top-down model. During the 1950s at the University of Chicago, he was lucky enough to meet Rogers, father of an experiential psychotherapy called *client-centred* therapy. They both shared a belief in the primacy of process over content. Experiential psychotherapy emphasizes the importance of honouring the client's inner capacity to heal through attending to moment-by-moment process in the safety of a non-judgemental therapeutic relationship. The therapist's role of listening and mirroring back the client's experiences was a radical departure from both the cognitive/behavioural and the psychoanalytic approaches.

While Rogers was aware of the importance of therapeutic relationship, Gendlin had a growing sense that the client's inner experience was key in facilitating change. He talked about a "moment of movement" that he noticed occurring in clients. He could see that deep experiencing was leading to a physical release in the body. These moments foreshadow what became known as the *felt shift*. Gendlin took Rogers' work further. By naming this deep experiencing focusing, he defined the importance of referencing the body directly. He created the six steps to help people find this process if they didn't yet know it.

Gendlin's Felt Shift as a "Motor of Personality Change"

By identifying the felt shift as a physical marker for personality change, Gendlin (1964) led the way in our awakening to embodied practices. He wrote, "Direct reference, as well as the resulting symbolizations, involves bodily felt tension relief" (p. 13). His pioneering work underlies the growing movement in the field of trauma towards embodiment. We owe much to him for this. Now, I want us to take this knowing into the field of addiction.

Once we are connected inside, we feel into the physical release that points us in the direction of healing. In new theories, such as the polyvagal theory, we see these felt shifts described as neurophysiological state changes. Porges points out that these state changes involve a significant shift in how we view the world. Gendlin (1964) describes this as the whole scene changing as clients contact the felt sense. Using the FSPM, we can teach clients both the six steps of focusing, and the states of the autonomic nervous system, enabling them to use the model as a map for healing.

The Experiencing Scale: Tracking the Felt Sense

The Experiencing Scale (EXP; 1986) is a powerful tool that measures seven stages of experiencing involving emotional and cognitive awareness of one's ongoing experience. During the first three stages, the speaker is primarily focused on external events. During stage four there is a growing sense of inward connecting to feelings about the situation. Stage five, six, and seven include the speaker's direct reference to the felt sense and the felt shift. Reliability and validity were developed for the scale, and judges were trained through standardized materials. Several versions of the scale are available. Here is a simple one:

1. The client simply talks about events, ideas, or others
2. Refers to self but without expressing emotions
3. Expresses emotions but only as they relate to external circumstances
4. The client focuses directly on emotions and thoughts about self
5. Engages in an exploration of their inner experience (felt sense)
6. Gains awareness of previously implicit feelings and meanings (felt shift)
7. On-going process of in-depth self-understanding, which provides new perspectives to solve significant problems

The Experiencing Scale provides a wonderfully clear way to track the powerful change that happens in the body. I use it all the time in explaining to clients and students the importance of embodied work. We rate sessions as a way of discussing process and outcomes, noticing where low and high experiencing occurs, and where felt shifts happen. The EXP can also be related to Siegel's window of tolerance and Porges' polyvagal theory. Low experiencing indicates a rigid window of tolerance, a dorsal response. High experiencing indicates a state of integration, a ventral response. In the clinical example in Chapter 12, I will show you how you can use the scale in conjunction with the FSPM to enhance your assessment and treatment.

We know what produces change. It isn't insight. Insight is stimulating, but we all know that we can have all the insight in the world and it won't necessarily change behaviour. *What changes behaviour is connecting with our bodies.* And now we have a way of tracking our capacity to connect deeply. I've often wondered how clients who report positive outcomes from cognitive behavioural therapy would rate on the EXP. I wonder if the ones who did well were rating above a level four on the EXP, meaning that they were already connected to their body's wisdom.

A Process Model: Gendlin's Major Philosophical Work

Let's go back to Gendlin's comments about his father's knowing something from a feeling, this feeling that may well have saved them from the Nazis. Gendlin tells us that this comment influenced his life. So, it isn't surprizing that he felt Descartes was wrong. How could he follow a way that prized cognition and subjugated feelings? In Gendlin's master philosophical work *A Process Model* (1997), he presents an alternative to Descartes' mind/body duality. Offering an alternative to the body as machine-like, Gendlin's way invites us to consider our natural state as a living organism where life begins as an interaction with environment.

A process model is a journey into the felt sense. As we read we go inside and experience it all: physical sensations, feelings, thoughts, and memories. *A process model* is a very challenging piece of work, and I am no philosopher. When I feel totally overwhelmed with the reading I remember my teacher's advice: Ask your body for the felt sense of the concept. It will show the way. The following concepts will resonate with you because we have been experiencing them as we think at the edge of addiction. Now we will name a few of them. As we take them in, you will see how they are already shaped by the felt sense.

Body/Environment is One

In his talk at the Boston trauma conference, Gendlin (2007) helps us to understand what he means by this in terms of how we are able to speak our thoughts as we have them.

> We have to both use, respect and also change the notion that we have of the body. It's *not* a structure that fills space and time. We need to *consider* it that way, so that we can analyse it and have medicine and chemistry and neurology and all these very important things. But the body is *not* a structure that just "is" in the environment, in space, like you see me sit here. The body is where I am out here talking to you, where I'm all the way out there, and without this, (gestures) my body

wouldn't be the way it is right now. The words wouldn't come out right, if I weren't body-environment unity, and if I weren't implying forward. So my words come. Sometimes you can wonder where your words come from, and how they come. People don't wonder enough. They open their mouth and the words come out.

In this talk, we see how Gendlin nods to the traditional way of understanding body as a machine-like structure, shows us how that way can be helpful, and then goes on to show us how in fact our bodies are not separate from the environment.

Focusing Practice

Let's try a practice to illustrate this. I invite you to turn your attention inside and down into the centre of your body. Inhale slowly and notice how, as you breathe in, your lungs expand at the same time. *Air coming in happens at the same time as lungs expanding.* When we are connected to our felt sense, we know we are one with the environment. Do you feel this profound shift from the mind/body split?

Interaction First

We are not computers or tables. We are mammals. We breathe and move and desire and struggle, and in so doing we interact with the world from the beginning of consciousness. We *are* interaction.

Once we close our eyes and feel into our body's aliveness we know that we live in interaction and connection with all living beings including plants and animals. We are not a discrete unit. We flow. Our interacting occurs in a myriad of ways, from breathing, to experiencing events, to symbolizing in words or images those events. This interacting brings forth growth and change. Focusing and polyvagal theory characterize the body/environment as one.

First-Person Experiencing: Implicit Intricacy – We Are More Than We Can Say

I gently take Gendlin's phrase down inside ... implicit intricacy ... I love how it sounds. This is the place of "more than words can ever say". In focusing we go deep inside to the implicit world. This preconceptual space between awareness and sleep. Here we delight in the intricacy, the complexity of everything. As I stay with this place I find a felt sense and many intricate strands come from it. An image of little me standing at the kitchen door of our next door neighbours house. It is early morning and I am waiting for my friend to finish breakfast so we can walk to school together. Through my little eyes I see her perfect world. Mom and dad and three children around the table. I watch my friend slather strawberry jam on her warm buttery toast. She asks if I want some. "No thank you." My little eight-year-old self wants to disappear. Painful to feel so deeply "not fitting" into the box. The nuclear "family unit box". More pain than I can hold. No dad for me. No "stay-at-home" mom for me. Not me, this unit model.

I stay with this felt sense of "not me" and more and more strands fall from it. The day I stole a dollar from my friend. I lied and said I didn't take it, but I did. Sinking into sorry to hurt my friend. So jealous of her unit. Her simple perfect unit. My messy misfit non unit.

Another strand. One I follow that finds my grandma and my poppy "family unit". Feels good in my body to find them. I belong in this misfit unit. I follow it to a memory of little me skipping in my red coat; the day I leave my grandparent's house to move back with mom. Sinking into strands of grief.

I am implicit intricacy. I am more than I can say. I am more than I can know. I carry myself forward freshly to new places. I find me in these fresh places that are more than I can say. We are more than we can say. More than any part, or particle or unit will ever know.

Focusing Practice

Where lies your deep complexity? Explore the strands that come from the felt sense of all of that. When we go inside we know that we are much more than words can say. Please pause here.

Implicit intricacy and Words

In implicit intricacy we learn to play with words freshly. The old way that we use words is as though there is one definition that everyone already knows. But words, like experience, happen within a context. And the meaning of those words changes depending on the context. If you already know it, how can you say anything new? Gendlin urges us to think and experience freshly. That means that we have to use words from the felt sense to create something new that opens as we stay with it. And often these words make no logical sense when we share them from the top down. But formed from the body they have their own way of creating something new that carries forward. For example, as a descriptor of the felt sense "flowing stillness" makes no logical sense, but when it comes from a focusing practice, then we see it as an opening to be curious. Recall how we worked with "what helps you harms you". Much like a dream, the implying is beyond what is already there. Something fresh opens and then carries forward to new implying.

Implying and Carrying Forward

Life forms freshly inside all living beings. Unlike machines, every living process occurs in its own new way. We see this in plants. When we give a plant water we set off a whole process that is implied in its capacity to carry forward its own direction of growth. Implying is a kind of body wisdom. The body knows what needs to carry forward. This fresh process is very important for us as psychotherapists. We need to take care to put our already known theory beside us and allow whatever wants to come to surprise us. Akira Akemi (2017), a focusing oriented psychotherapist and scholar, puts it this way,

> It alarms me when people, both clients and therapists, impose certain contents or concepts on experience, without staying in the openness of *not knowing*. In this openness, ... the client's experiencing carries forward, and they look backward together to discover freshly how they got here. (p. 33)

First-Person Experiencing: A Dreamy Carrying Forward

> I'm in a dream I had twenty years ago. I am swimming through the river, arms swooshing backwards over my head, each backstroke carries me forward to freshly new waters. I am moving backwards, carrying forwards.

> There is another woman swimming beside me. She is me and not me. She is black and I am white. I remember Gendlin saying that often when we dream in opposites we are searching for parts of self that are lost. She is the part of me that I lost in my marriage. She comes with me as she carries me forward in a way that is only understood as I look back now through the felt sense.

Focusing Practice

How does your body imply a carrying forward? Perhaps in how it knows to heal a wounded place, or how to take you to a new experience that you did not think about visiting, you just found your way there. Appreciate your body's knowing.

Addiction as Process Skipping

How do we understand addiction through Gendlin's process model? In his discussion about *manner of experiencing*, Gendlin (1964) outlines different terms that describe the manner, or quality of experiencing. While he didn't speak of addiction specifically, he did speak of ways in which we stop or block process, inhibiting the body's capacity to carry forward. He called this stoppage *structure bound*. This means that experiencing is limited by old fixed patterns of thinking and feeling. We all know people like this. You tell them something new and you see them fitting it into stale patterns that block the freshness of your experience. And in their own experiencing you can see how they get stuck in what Gendlin calls dead ends. In this structure-bound state, they tend to deaden feeling, a state of rigidity (dorsal) on our FSPM or they flood with too much feeling, chaos (sympathetic) on the FSPM. Dead ends lack the presence of the ventral branch of the vagus nerve, the sweet spot of grounded aliveness.

Structure-bound processes block experiencing, hence Gendlin called this *process skipping*. When the process is structure-bound it remains the same, it doesn't interact with the environment. Addiction is then seen as an attempt to either numb the overwhelming chaotic state or to enliven the rigid state of numbness. Either way it results in a blocked process and the neurophysiological shift that happens in the body with the addictive shift has no meaning, it doesn't carry forward with health, growth, or restoration. Instead, it propels back and forth in a state of increasing oblivion. The challenge in working with people in addiction is that what has kept them safe now becomes the very thing that they need to let go of, isolation. Sometimes we have to crawl into the cage of the trauma survivor and respectfully pull them out. The addicted survivor must be coaxed. It is an active stance that we take as therapists and it is very demanding work.

So where to begin the healing journey? In order to help facilitate a ventral vagal state of fresh processing and integration we need to begin our interaction gently, yet firmly. It is a long road from seeking oblivion to embracing aliveness in the company of others. We are literally willing our clients back into a living process, building a loving, trusting connection with us, their first harbour of safety. We honour what helped in the past. We offer a firm and soft container in the present. We welcome flowing aliveness in the future.

References

Akemi, A. (2017). The radical impact of experiencing on psychotherapy theory: an examination of two kinds of crossings. *Person-Centered & Experiential Psychotherapies, 16*(2) 159–172.

Gendlin, E. T. (1961a). Galvanic skin response correlates of different modes of experiencing. *Journal of Clinical Psychology, 17,* 73–77.

Gendlin, E. T. & Berlin, J. I. (1961b). Autonomic correlates of inter-action process. Unpublished manuscript. http://previous.focusing.org/gendlin/docs/gol_2227.html.

Gendlin, E. T. (1962). *Experiencing and the creation of meaning: A philosophical and psychological approach to the subjective.* Evanston, IL: Northwestern University Press.

Gendlin, E. T. (1964). Theory of personality change. In P. Worchel & D. Byrne (Eds.), *Personality change.* New York: Wiley.

Gendlin, E. T. (1986). *Let your body interpret your dreams.* Wilmette, IL: Chiron Publications.

Gendlin, E. T. (1990). The small steps of the therapy process: How they come and how to help them come. In G. Lietaer, J. Rombauts & R. Van Balen (Eds.), *Client-centred and experiential psychotherapy in the nineties.* Leuven: Leuven University Press (pp. 205–224).

Gendlin, E. T. (1994). The story of gene's escape from Nazi-Occupied Austria, Korbei, L. In O. Frischenschlager (Ed.), *Wien, wo sonst! Die Entstehung der Psychoanalyse und ihrer Schulen* [Vienna where else! The origin of psychonanlysis and its schools]. Wien/Koln/Weimar: Bohlau (pp. 174–181).

Gendlin, E. T. (1996). *Focusing oriented psychotherapy: A manual of the experiential method.* New York: Guilford Press.

Gendlin, E. T. (1997). *A process model.* Evanston, IL: Northwestern University Press.

Gendlin, E. T. (1998). Keynote address: Coming home through focusing. In *Focusing international conference,* Lake Geneva, Wisconsin, U.S.A. May 1998. Retrieved from www.nadalou.com.

Gendlin, E. T. (2006). *Focusing international conference.* New York: Garrison Institute. Presentation from a focusing conference entitled *Finding a safe place.* Nada Lou Productions, 2019.

Gendlin, E. T. (2007). Focusing: The body speaks from the inside. *18th annual international trauma conference. Psychological trauma: neuroscience, attachment and therapeutic interventions,* Boston, June 2007.

Gendlin, E. T. (2008). *Philosophy, profiles, overlays, shadows.* Presentation at the Garrison Institute, New York, NY. Retrieved from https://www.youtube.com/watch?v=rECq34USK5k.

Korbei, L. & Eugene, G. (1994). *Wien, Wo Sonst. Die Entstehungder Psychoanalyse und ihrer Schulen* [Vienna, where else. The emergence of psychoanalysis and their schools]. In O. Frischenschlager, (pp. 174–181).

10 Bringing the Model to Life: Going Deep and Thinking Big

Our job as therapists is like no other. To do it well we must be our own instrument. Healing work comes through our capacity to co-regulate with our clients, showing them a way to create a secure attachment with themselves. Then they don't need addictions. As we learn to listen to and love our own "shaky being", we bring that energy to them. This is really the crux of the work. The idea is simple, but the work is very hard. It requires a lot from us. Surely we must love what we do, and learn to love ourselves, to thrive in this very demanding job.

In our top-down world, we emphasize *what* to do as therapists. We worry a lot about content, finding the right theory and techniques. It's understandable, especially when we are new to the work, but it misses the mark. As experiential embodied therapists, our focus starts with *how* to be with this person. Of course, what and how interconnect, but the starting point makes all the difference. While techniques and tools are part of our work, our energy needs to start with and return to the process of embodied interaction.

The good news is that we don't have to be perfect, and we don't have to be certified in all the latest myriad of ways to be a good psychotherapist. The last decade has created a very distasteful aura of therapeutic capitalism whereby all the latest therapy modalities are competing for our money and our time. To new therapists I suggest the cliché: trust the process. The most important thing is to create a relational felt sense, gently coaxing the client to engage with life. Then, as the body settles into a ventral state, enough safety emerges for both of you to flourish. You will at times be exhausted, but you will not burn out.

The Paradigm Shift – From a Medical Model to an Embodied Emotion Regulation Model

In Chapter 1, I shared with you the profound shift that happened for me while listening freshly to the young women in my first group. Now we are going to explore how this shift impacts our practice. We no longer think in terms of sickness, or maladaptive behaviours. The medical doctor is not the expert. Precisely the opposite. We think in polyvagal terms: the body's nervous system adapts to its context. In Brigette's dissociated state, she would cut her vagina, a behaviour that was seen as bizarre, and maladaptive. We see it as an embodied gesture that revealed her wounded place, while simultaneously releasing endogenous opioids to numb the pain. These adaptive behaviours are signals of alarm, not pathology. This way of seeing changes everything.

In our current medicalized paradigm, we are top heavy with professionals who want to hold on to a powerful role in the psychiatric system. Making this shift requires professionals to let go of status and control, humbly accepting the true partner in our work, the human body. It will require a lot of work to transform the system.

First-Person Experiencing: Moments of Liberation

I take these words inside: "It's not about sickness, it's about survival." My breath expands and deepens. It feels joyous to affirm the body's inherent wisdom. An image of Bridgette comes. I am back in the sacred space of our group, and she is sharing how she would awaken from a dissociated state to find herself cutting her vagina. How she couldn't stop it, no matter how much she tried. It had become an addictive behavior.

Her body heaves as she cries out, "I am a freak!" I move in close to her, reminding her to slow her breathing down. She looks up and I gently place my hand on her back to ground her. As she begins to settle, I look around the group. We all lean in to our shared felt sense and begin to connect to the edges of a ventral state. I wait so they will be able to take in what I am about to share.

My attention goes back to Bridgette as I offer a new way of understanding her behaviour. While I don't have the felt sense polyvagal model (FSPM) yet, I know how to validate and celebrate her body's adaptive dissociated response. As I explain this new way of understanding, her face opens. She looks around and sees the women in group riveted by her journey. It is their journey too. Looking incredulous, her jaw drops, and she lights up. Bridgette moves from feeling like a disordered person to a hero who made it through living hell. It is a moment of liberation, a profound felt shift that changes everything. These moments of liberation, arising out of a system that shames and pathologizes, are the heart of transformational healing. I pause here inside. It is these moments that I live for in the work.

Focusing Practice

I invite you now to take Brigette's moment of liberation down inside. Notice what comes as you feel into this paradigm shift, from sickness to survival. How could a little girl endure such unimaginable pain without the body's ability to dissociate? How does this change your way of being with your clients when you see their addictive behaviours as part of their body's wisdom? This is such an important question to explore in detail. The paradigm shift is a big one. We are all so trained to see our clients through the eyes of disease.

The Embodied Emotion Regulation Paradigm: A Bigger Picture

The FSPM to treat addiction is part of an embodied emotion regulation paradigm, a bottom-up approach. This strength-based paradigm shift not only helps us to understand addiction as a way to manage emotion regulation but it also provides an alternative theoretical framework for understanding all aspects of psychological distress as a function of emotion dysregulation. As we shift paradigms, we need a new language and treatment models.

The FSPM provides a new way of seeing and working with addiction. The autonomic nervous system becomes our map as we orient to the continuum from chaos to rigidity. The visual model reveals the way in which trauma, and its subsequent emotional dysregulation, relates to addiction and addiction to trauma. The link between the two is revealed in the propelling action that is depicted in the model, the swinging from chaos to rigidity. We see the true limitations in the current medical model as it lacks the interactional quality of experiencing in its discrete diagnostic categories. Treatment typically focuses on trauma or addiction, missing the underlying systemic precursors to both.

The Trauma of Addiction: The Bidirectional Link

While we are focusing on treating addiction it's clear that we cannot limit our discussion to addiction. We have seen how addiction and trauma are bidirectionally linked. When we understand that addictions function as neurophysiological state regulators in light of traumatic experiences, *it follows that they need to be addressed and treated together.* And, regardless of whether you believe that trauma underlies all addiction, the state of addiction is a traumatizing experience in itself. Trauma is present either as a precursor and/or a consequence of addiction.

Tragically, the fields have developed separately and in different ways.

Those struggling with addiction have made a significant contribution to the field by becoming counsellors and sponsors in the twelve-step programme. One such contribution is called *recovery focusing*. This model, created by Noel (2010), integrates the twelve steps and focusing practice. The field of trauma has developed more in the academic world, experiencing a sharp increase in status over the past ten years. Not so for addiction. Addiction is trauma's unnamed, second class sidekick.

Why is that exactly? Well, it's nasty business. People do horrific things to themselves and others. Are we trying to avoid the shame of addiction? After all, when we attach ourselves to a field, we take on its cultural shape. I am well aware of this when I tell strangers that I work with addiction, particularly sex addiction. They look at me with horror and disgust. I understand that it is frightening for people. If we want to do trauma work, it is incumbent upon us to acknowledge the prevalence of addiction and to find a grounded response to the shame and fear that accompanies it.

As addiction/trauma therapists, we must navigate our way through extremely complex feelings. When we think of our clients as trauma victims, it's easy to feel compassion, but when we see how they do crazy things to themselves and others in the name of feeding a need, it becomes very challenging to stay with compassionate responses. How do we continue to like them, and even love them, when they do these things – especially when they hurt others? Let's pause here and take some time to go inside.

Focusing Practice: To Judge and Not to Judge

I invite you to drop down inside with me now. Three deep breaths together, and then we sit quietly. As you read my story about Joe, whom we met in Chapter 3, notice what comes in your chest, throat, shoulders, jaw, and down into your belly ....

Two Different Versions of Joe

Remember young, creative, and quirky Joe? For a long time, his careful pattern of only drinking on weekends enabled him to maintain his other addiction, to work. By switching back and forth from one addiction to another he prolonged his ability to perform. But gradually he lost control and ended up crashing his car in a drunken state. After six months of sobriety, he comes in for his weekly appointment. His whole body is fired up with adrenaline, a telltale sympathetic response. He tells me that he got drunk last weekend after a bad fight with his wife.

As we sit together he becomes quiet, his body slumping into itself. He shifts to a foggy dorsal state and gazes down, disappearing into another place and time. We stay here as I carefully monitor the quality of his presence. I don't want him to fall too far. He has good colour in his face, and his breathing is slow but steady, so I let him be with this dissociated experience.

As he surfaces he says, "I haven't told you this. I went back to a massage place I used to go to a lot and hooked up with a woman. She was young, like 18, and I feel bad about that, and I feel bad about cheating on 'Caroline'." His body recoils in disgust with himself. I see the muscles in his face seize up as tears fall down his cheeks. "I started going to prostitutes when I was 16. My brother took me. I didn't tell you because I didn't think about it, until now. Something changed in me over the past six months of not drinking. I remember more now. I'm scared Jan, because when I start doing this, I can't stop. Last time Caroline almost caught me so I stopped, but now I'm back at it again."

As I listen to Joe, I feel a thud in my chest. His story resonates with a trauma place in me and I realize that I need time to work through these powerful feelings. A strong wave of judgement comes over me. I feel a push and pull with this person that I knew and didn't know. Two very different Joes.

I breathe and bring my attention to the intense pain in Joe's face. As he explores the edges of a felt sense something shifts in both of us. We pass through the shame and Joe's little boy part emerges. We touch into a wounded place as it begins to surface underneath the addictions. A great felt shift of compassion comes into my body as we sit with this delicate part of Joe, his little shaky being. He is like a newborn emerging, and we share this silent awakening. I sit very still. If I move he may recede.

After a time, I surface and glance at the clock. Twenty minutes left. I slowly whisper to the little boy that we will return to be with him. He is not alone anymore. Joe begins to orient to the room and walks over at the $2' \times 3'$ display of the FSPM. We often stand by the big poster and move our bodies around the different states as we make sense of the session. The movement of the whole body helps Joe to contact the felt sense of each state as he learns to identify what is happening in his body.

"When I came in today I was here," he says, his hand splayed over the ball of chaos, "I was so scared to tell you about the sexual stuff. Then I think I went over here," and he slides his hand over the addicted spot settling on rigidity. "Now I feel a big shift in the centre of my body. A settling, like a huge relief because I told you and it is okay. I'm here in the integrated place. I was afraid but I kept hearing what you said, that I did what I did to survive. That gave me the courage to tell you. I know I am responsible for what I did, but I thought of how you explained the way the autonomic nervous system works. I can feel the addictive shift, how it helps in the short term, but it doesn't feel calm like this, (placing his hand on integration). I didn't know how to get to this calm place before we started working together. I didn't know there was another way."

I sigh, feeling the joy of one of Joe's moments of liberation. "Yes," I say. "It's so important that you told me. Now we can bring in more of your story. It's great that you can see how you shut down as you became flooded with sympathetic energy. And as you stayed with the dissociated place a new part came. A little boy part. I'm looking forward to getting to know him more."

Joe flushes as I reveal the little boy. He is finding lost parts of himself. As the session ends, Joe's eyes search my face. We look at each other and I tell him that we will figure this out together. As he gazes back at me, I know that I can be with him through this process. Yet I wonder if he knows how much I have to figure out in myself to be able to do this work? I hope he doesn't think about that. Our work as therapists pulls on us in deep and disturbing ways. I am committed to showing up for both of us. Sharing Joe's pain invites compassion. Compassion eases judgement.

Over the years, I have unravelled my own trauma mystery. Now I can be with the many Joes that I help without the thud in my chest. We must listen and learn about our own journey so we can do the same for our clients.

Focusing Practice

I wonder what pulls on you in the work? It is vital that you take time to be with the felt sense of all of this. Then as you do your own inner healing you can provide enough ventral energy to create a solid relational space.

Where Do We Start?

Many clients will present with traumatic symptoms, but will not disclose addictive behaviours. And many others will present with addiction issues but will not disclose trauma. As we have seen, not only do our clients often misunderstand the connection between the two, we as professionals miss this link as well. It's not surprising really. After all, we are a product of our unit model paradigm. Thinking in polarities and distinct diagnostic categories, rather than systems that impact each other, can be very unproductive when it comes to human experiencing.

I start the healing process by asking myself, "How was this person wounded and how do they cope with the pain?" This question addresses both the trauma and the possible addictions. We dance back and forth between the story of the wound and the way that people survive. We saw the beginnings of this titrated dance with Joe. As we watch our clients' movements and listen to their stories, we see how bodies hold the deep secrets of the initial trauma. They also often hold the deep secrets of addiction. Our job is to help them find words, not just for what happened to them, but also for how they coped with it. Just as the initial wounds hold shame, so do the addictions.

These questions lie at the heart of the FSPM. As we explore them, we are assessing the dimensions of chaos and rigidity. How emotionally dysregulated is your client? What are their default states, and how do they move around the model? If you see a lot of chaos and rigidity, indicating trauma, how are they managing that level of dysregulation? It is likely either through living in a chronic dorsal state of dissociated rigidity and/ or propelling back and forth between chaos and rigidity with addictions.

Safe and Secret: The Hidden Faces of Addiction

Chances are much greater than we may think that traumatized clients are engaged in addictive behaviours that they shamefully hide. In my experience there is often more than one addiction, but like Joe, they tell you about them one at a time. You can ask, and I do, but the stories often dribble out. Or the client is caught red-handed. Sometimes the behaviours are dissociated as a result of trauma, and they cannot be named, but many times clients will initially lie to keep these ways safe and secret.

For some people, particularly when the addictions have been around for many years, the worst part of healing is not about their underlying trauma, it is about the damage they have done to others. In my experience, people who develop addictions are highly sensitive. As they begin to heal, intense feelings emerge. Facing behaviours that violate their value system and hurt other people often brings self-hate and unbearable remorse. It is very important as therapists that we understand this and address it head on. In doing so, it helps us, and our clients, to remember that the addicted brain doesn't care about anything other than what brings the hit of dopamine. The striatum doesn't know about integrity.

While our prefrontal cortex understands this, these behaviours are very tough to be with. Like family members, we become intricately linked with the struggle. It is painful to witness and experience the carnage of addiction. It requires immense courage for our clients to face these feelings, and it demands a capacity to hold these moments of liberation in the forefront of our experiencing. It is very helpful to think in terms of the FSPM at this point. It enables us to see the bad habit of addiction, as the autonomic nervous system doing precisely what it is designed to do: keep us alive.

The Big Mistake: Never Engage in a Power Struggle With the Addict Part

There is one main agenda that I have as a somatic psychotherapist. I am committed to helping my client engage in a life-enhancing process. The main agenda for the addicted part of the person is to shut down life process. This creates an interesting intersection of energies, one that can result in a power struggle if we are not careful. Often therapists fall into the bind of trying to woo their client back to life with strict sobriety protocols, while the client is obsessively shutting down their aliveness. Clients may be hiding these behaviours and then we are in even more of a bind. We want them to connect with the body, and they are actively engaged in *not* connecting with their body. This can become a terrible pitfall that needs to be monitored over time. We can easily be working at cross purposes if we don't have a clear agreement with the parts of the person that want to gain control of their behaviour. An important note here: It is vital that we be clear about a harm reduction approach because clients are reluctant to disclose if they believe that the only path forward is sobriety. Those with addictions have one foot on the brake (dorsal), and one foot on the gas (sympathetic), languishing in a stopped process. They only move when they are able to release the brake through stopping or decreasing the addictive behaviours.

The way to avoid these struggles is to align with the body and to teach our clients to understand addiction as the body's attempt to help. For sure, it can become an unhelpful response when we are triggered by past trauma. When we explain that the body needs help to learn new neuro-pathways that are more adaptive now, clients begin to befriend their body. Here is an example of how Lily, a client who we will meet again in Chapter 14, worked with this struggle.

Lily has been seeing me for nine months. She started her sobriety in a twelve-step programme one year prior. She came to see me because as a dancer, she wanted to learn more about an embodied approach to healing. She has made great progress in connecting with her bodily felt sense. One morning she comes into my office frightened and in despair because she had one sip, yes *one sip*, of wine at a party on the weekend. She feels that she is sabotaging herself, since the horrible addict in her is bound and determined to undermine her. She feels the presence of the "addict in the corner doing pushups", a concept that we discussed in Chapter 3, from the twelve-step programme. She just can't understand how she could be so impulsive. She didn't think about it at all. Before she knew it, the wine was to her lips. Only after she drank it did she become aware of what she had just done. Deep shame reddens her face and neck, and I see her body recoil in self- disgust. Lily is pumped full of adrenaline, in flight/fight mode.

First-Person Experiencing

> Hearing Lily's story shifts me from a ventral vagal state to a sympathetic response. I take a deep breath, slowly extending my exhalation, calming my nervous system. Seeing how she is twisting herself up into little knots of fear and disgust is so sad. In this triggered state, she has lost her capacity to befriend her body. She is caught up in the metaphor of the devil addict, afraid of her very own internalized bogey man. Through the deep shame that she is experiencing, I remind her to slow down, take a moment to turn her attention inward, to listen to how things are inside. Together we find our way down into a familiar, shared space. Calming our bodies down, feeling the relational felt sense, the space between us that allows us to settle our nervous systems together. Ah. Yes. Here we are together quietly noticing what comes.

I ask Lily about her felt sense of this whole situation. Can she find the addict part? Does it feel devilish? Where does she feel this in the body? She quietly searches for the felt sense. It is swirly inside. It doesn't feel like a devil. It is before words, a shape just beginning to come. A tightness forms at the base of her throat. We wait a while. It remains the same so I decide to ask into it.

I suggest that maybe there was a good reason why the body reverted back to wanting to numb. If we can find the connection, perhaps the dissociated trigger, we can begin to unravel the mystery behind this seemingly self-sabotaging addictive behaviour. I ask her to start back at the beginning of the week. She pauses, searching. She finds herself in her theatre class. A woman shared a painful story about being sexually harassed. Lily felt upset by this. I notice that she becomes distant. Her eyes fog over, and her face flattens as she drops into a dorsal state. Now I get the connection. This woman's story triggers Lily's early sexual trauma that we have just begun to explore. I don't want to deepen this felt sense today given that she was tempted with alcohol. Her drop into the dorsal vagus is telling us to back up from the intensity for a while. I respect this. I want to help her to ground, so I bring her back to the room by gently calling her name and we breathe. I wonder if she will make the connection, or if it will remain dissociated, so I wait to see.

As her body resonates with the felt sense of her response to the woman's story, she begins to make the connection with her own sexual history. She understands how she got triggered and addictive habits became tempting as a way to numb the pain. I explain how her body's nervous system gets stuck in old pathways that need updating when we get triggered. This makes sense to her and she feels relieved. I ask her about the devil, and she smiles. "No devil here," she says, "Just my body's old habits that once protected me." Together we map out the session's journey on the FSPM. She traces her fingers from chaos to rigidity to stillness and integration. She takes out her picture of the client model on her phone and says out loud, "From flight to fold to flow to flock."

Of course, there is not always a clear connection between cravings and triggers. That would be far too easy. Sometimes it is just the brain waltzing down old familiar trails. But too often we can miss these triggered places when we do not work in an embodied way. It is through the felt sense that the body reveals the source of the trauma as well as its adaptive impulses.

The Importance of Asking

It's so important that we find out as soon as we can how the client orients to the FSPM. Then we can join with their autonomic nervous system, respecting the states the body is utilizing in an attempt to regulate emotionally. We start the process by aligning with the client's pattern of neurophysiological activation. I believe that asking about addictions is essential in assessing this process. It's similar to taking the body's temperature. The presence of addictive behaviours reveals so much, so quickly, about our client's need to detach from body aliveness.

When I sit with clients I watch and listen to their bodies. Where is there life, and where is the body dying, or stuck? The story of the wounded place often emerges over time, and the way of coping will come to life if I welcome it. If I don't ask, they may not tell. So I ask, gently and very respectfully, normalizing the answers. I might say, "I hope you found some good ways to cope with all of that pain. Most folks will use whatever works. Like drugs or alcohol, or cutting the body. We have to be inventive to survive. We often don't understand our coping behaviours, but they tell a story if we listen closely." When I ask in this way people will usually open up and share. As I connect with their neuroceptive system, they know they are deeply understood.

The Trauma of Addiction Needs to be Named

So often I hear trauma therapists say that they don't work with addiction. I want to say, "Well, I bet you do!" When I suggest that addiction is present for many traumatized people, they say that by working on the trauma the addiction will stop. This may be true for some clients, some of the time. It is hard to imagine that without specifically naming these entrenched behaviours, particularly in the area of sex addiction, which is so deeply laden with shame, they will resolve on their own. Too much excrutiating pain and struggle is present in addiction work to think that it can, or would quietly retreat. Much of the time the behaviour is dissociated, and therefore needs to be named and reprocessed. And what about all the damage done to family members? Without naming it, far too much is left unspoken for them. In fact, for many it is precisely the naming of addiction that begins the healing journey.

When clients give words to their addictions, especially those with serious drug, alcohol and process addictions, a doorway of connection opens with us. Naming the struggle deepens our level of experiencing with them. Shame heals as it comes out of the dark. As clients become more present with us they begin to understand how absent they have been in their lives. They often do not understand in their conscious mind the relationship between stopping the addiction and becoming more present. It sounds obvious to us in our clear-headed thinking, but addiction involves numbing. As the brain rewires, harm reduction brings connection, a moment of liberation from the chains of dissociation. The person experiences a precious kind of reawakening. When people ask me why I do addiction work, these moments come to mind. They are truly amazing.

Yet some therapists prefer not to work with addiction, so it's important to know when and how to refer out. It's important to understand that if you work with trauma, chances are, you are also working with addiction at some level. In a polyvagal-informed model, addictions are the body's way of regulating traumatic material through activating dissociation when ventral pathways are not available. Seen in this light, it behoves us as trauma therapists to gain understanding of and capacity to assess the presence of addictive behaviours. Then we can treat the addiction directly, or, refer to an addiction coach who has a trauma-informed perspective. Together we monitor client progress as we attend to the felt sense of the trauma, and the current use of addictions. We communicate with each other about the work, which is based on a truly integrated model that takes into consideration the related neuropathways of trauma, addiction and dissociation.

The FSPM is generic in nature. It is an embodied way of healing through the wisdom of the autonomic nervous system. As such, it is easy to cross with other modalities of psychotherapy. A number of approaches have already been integrated into the model, for example, focusing-oriented therapy, interpersonal neurobiology, imago therapy, and polyvagal-informed therapy. The model is compatible with other modalities such as somatic experiencing, internal family systems, and sensorimotor psychotherapy. It is my hope that more integrations will ensue.

Three Process Movements: The Three D's

As we deepen our exploration of the psychotherapy journey, I start off in my head thinking about how to systematically explain the process of applying the FSPM. I quickly realize that this top-down way feels too linear, too focused on content, and it isn't the way I practice. I remember thinking at the edge and I drop down inside, inviting a sense of the overall healing journey to come.

As I go inside I sense how the process meanders and pauses as we explore the issues. Three process movements in the journey take shape: first, *deepening our experience*; second, *discovering and de-pathologizing the felt-sense story*; and third, *daily practices*. I'll call them the three D's. These movements help to bring some definition to the client's progress. We will go through each of them.

1. ***Deepening Our Experience: The Experiencing Scale***

Our first task with clients is to begin to make a relationship that is shaped by trust and enjoyment of each other's process. Interaction comes first as we build a relational felt sense. By creating this sacred space, we invite our client to very gently begin to come back into their body. The process of deepening is a lifelong journey that must evolve over time. *I can't stress this enough.* When we work with addiction and trauma, we must remember that the autonomic nervous system is engaged in disconnecting from embodied experience. Addiction is a guard dog, keeping deep feeling at bay. So, we work slowly and gently, awakening a vagal presence. Like Gendlin in the dream work, we help clients learn how to titrate experience. It's a dance and it's wonderful to be part of such a delicate process.

As an experiential, embodied psychotherapist I know that the greatest source of healing lies in my clients' capacity to engage with their felt sense, their body's natural way of knowing. I look for physical shifts in the body, what Gendlin (1964) calls a motor for change. These felt shifts indicate movement forward in the healing process. Over time, I teach my clients about the importance of the Experiencing Scale to help us assess where we are and where we need to go to access the healing power of the body. Together we use the scale to assess depth of experiencing. This guides us in the progress. In addition, I incorporate Siegel (2012) concept of the *window of tolerance* (discussed in Chapter 6). Clients learn how expanding their capacity to stay with challenging emotion allows for deepening of the felt sense experience. It is both very reassuring, and sometimes terrifying for clients to know that the deepening of their capacity to feel into their life is the path forward.

2. ***Discovering The Depathologizing Felt Sense Story***

We humans search for meaning in our lives. We love stories that have a beginning, a middle, and a satisfying end. Trauma tends to shatter meaning, robbing us of a way of understanding and making sense of our lives. We lose the cohesive narrative of our story through dissociating much of our experience. When we numb we hide from the truth. The healing journey is about facing the truth, piecing together the strands of experience through tracking the felt sense. While this can be very painful for our clients, it can be painful for us too. As we see what our clients must face, we can easily resist the truth. We must learn to face the unbearable so they can follow our lead. While we don't go digging for the horror, we follow what comes from the body. It's worth repeating: our job is like no other.

As we follow the body's wisdom, we learn that riding the painful wave is inevitable for healing. And we will be right there with them, keeping our eye on where we are going, helping them to find the sense of grounding as they keep moving through the experience. They must learn that painful feelings will not kill them. Through the lens of the FSPM we depathologize the story, welcoming moments of liberation from years of shame.

The journey can be thought of in parts that mirror Herman's (2015) stages of healing from trauma. The first stage is to establish some measure of safety and harm reduction – enough that the person can begin to feel into their body. We work on grounding and beginning to build a support system. Together we find the right path to let go of old hurtful ways. Then we move into stage two, remembering and mourning the trauma. This uncovering process helps clients to connect with the places that have been dissociated for so long, constructing a narrative that brings integration. Stage three is about reconnecting with the world, helping clients make a new life that is grounded in co-regulation with others.

3. **Daily Practices**

Healing occurs in a series of daily practices that one intentionally commits to. Each practice offers an opportunity to rewire old traumatic and addicted neuropathways. We engage our neuroplastic brain to learn new ways of healing and enjoying life. Together we develop a set of practices that are tailored to each client. I emphasize to clients that I believe it is possible to achieve and maintain sobriety by doing daily practices as a life long commitment. This brings hope and comfort to people who have been taught that they will always be "addicts".

These practices include anything that brings activation with the ventral branch of the ANS, states of flock, fun and flow. Examples include yoga, breath practices, exercise, music, journaling, focusing, meditation, prayer, being with family and friends, as well as some therapeutic tools that will be described in case examples. There are many wonderful practices that are part of other approaches within somatic experiencing, generative somatics, gestalt, internal family systems, and interpersonal neurobiology that can be integrated into the model. In the next chapter, we will look at how these three process movements are embedded in our healing journey.

References

Gendlin, E. T. (1964). Theory of personality change. In P. Worchel & D. Byrne (Eds.), *Personality change.* New York: Wiley (pp. 100–148.).

Herman, J. (2015). *Trauma and recovery: The aftermath of violence – from domestic abuse to political terror.* New York: Basic Books.

Noel, S. (2010). Loving at the edge: Recovery emerging. (Unpublished article.)

Siegel, D. J. (2012). *The developing mind, second edition: How relationships and the brain interact to shape who we are.* New York: Guilford Publications.

11 Nuts and Bolts: Embodied Assessment and Treatment Tool (EATT) and Focusing Oriented Therapy Strategies

As I began to apply the *felt sense polyvagal model* (FSPM), I realized that I would need to create a new assessment tool that reflects the strength-based, experiential nature of the therapeutic work. In therapy settings that use the typical bio-psycho-social model, a formal client assessment is completed within the beginning stages of therapy. It consists of taking a detailed history, and it often includes both a diagnosis and a bio-psycho-social formulation. The initial sessions are content-driven, with the therapist asking many questions to complete the formal assessment and diagnosis.

Using EATT: Allowing the Story to Unfold

In sharp contrast, the *embodied assessment and treatment tool* (EATT) integrates assessment and treatment as the process unfolds over many sessions. In keeping with the experiential nature of our work, and our attention to embodied process, the client's history unfolds as the body reveals its wounded places. With the FSPM as our map, we begin to track our client's autonomic nervous system, our anchor in this model.

The tool is currently being developed by our team at my clinic in Toronto, Canada. It has eight components that the therapist can use as they relate to each individual client. The components include the following:

1. The felt sense polyvagal model
2. The Experiencing Scale
3. The felt sense polyvagal dialogue
4. The three circles
5. The trauma egg
6. The nine domains of integration
7. The privilege wheel
8. Specific concerns

I think of these components as the model, the scale, the dialogue, the circles, the egg, the domains, and the wheel. In a top-down way, we would likely use all of them in the same order. Working in an experiential embodied way, I may use some or all of them as they seem helpful during the process. Over many months, we develop a comprehensive assessment package that documents ongoing progress and acts as a vehicle for the healing journey. Clients enjoy having the material as a resource to return to. New components are added if there are specific issues that arise. Screening tools can enhance your exploration of issues. Our job is to become keenly aware of what to look for, and when appropriate, to refer on to an expert in that area.

As we move through the healing journey we keep progress notes to document our work. Documenting the process by referring to the three D's (deepening experience, developing and depathologizing the story, and daily practices) is a helpful way to evaluate each session.

Let's look at each of the eight components of the EATT in more detail:

The Felt Sense Polyvagal Model

By now you are familiar with the FSPM. I have a large 2′ × 3′ poster of both the client and the clinician version in my office. I usually introduce the client version first, since many are initially overwhelmed with the clinician version. I often move to the clinician version over time as they begin to learn about the nervous system. I introduce the practice of "orienting to the model" to help clients learn to map their states. Many clients take pictures of the model on their phones and refer to it as they are map their current state. In introducing the model, I wait for an instance where I see the client's body clearly responding, and if I feel that we have enough safety, I gently begin to help them notice what they are feeling. This becomes a way into the model where much psycho-education takes place. Over time we document the current states and common pathways using our felt sense to guide us. For some clients the FSPM is not relatable. When this happens I don't refer directly to it, but it always informs my assessment process.

The Experiencing Scale (EXP)

We explored the Experiencing Scale (EXP; 1970) in Chapter 10. I keep copies of the simple version in my office and when I feel the time is right, I introduce clients to the importance of connecting with themselves in a deeper way than by discussing what we already know about the problem. It helps a lot to demystify the therapy process for clients when we explain Gendlin's research on effective outcomes in psychotherapy. He found that those who succeeded in therapy were able to let themselves feel deeply. I explain how this creates the felt shift, the motor of neurophysiological change. If they are interested, I explain more about focusing practice and the creation of the EXP. I refer to it to guide the process of encouraging them to go deeper. I relate it back to the FSPM by explaining that deep felt experiencing occurs along the ventral vagal pathway. For those with addictions, it helps to keep coming back to the importance of deepening our capacity to feel into life in an embodied way. By connecting with the felt sense, they begin to open to moments of liberation.

I find the EXP and the FSPM very helpful as a grounding point when clients come in feeling emotionally dysregulated. Using both as visual cues helps to orient to a more ventral state. I remind them that living in the top half of the model, the addictive cycle, represents very low levels, a one or two on the EXP. We note the levels that occur over the session, using the scale as a way of tracking client's progress. As noted previously, Siegel's (2012b) concept of the *window of tolerance* integrates well into this discussion. The higher the scores on the EXP, the wider the window of tolerance. Many clients enjoy learning how different theories relate and cross. They like the image of a river with chaos on one side, rigidity on the other, and deeper levels of experiencing in the middle.

The Felt Sense Polyvagal Dialogue

The FSPD is a communication tool that I created to help clients communicate more effectively. In working with addiction, it is essential that clients learn effective ways to heal in relationship. This Chapter 14 is devoted to it.

The Three Circles

The three circles is a tool that was developed by Carnes (2001). The three concentric circles provide a map that helps to shape the harm reduction journey. I use this with all of my addiction clients as soon as they say that they would like to change their behaviour. It is a very effective way to both document and manage the behaviours since it provides a map for healing and accountability. I relate each of the circles to the FSPM client version so people can see how they interact in the autonomic nervous system (Figure 11.1).

The Inner Circle: Fixate

Here we focus on the behaviours that the client wants to change, placing these in the inner circle. I use a harm reduction model, encouraging each person to find the path that works for them. Harm reduction aims to reduce the damage caused by the addiction without insisting on sobriety. It fits well with the polyvagal perspective. Letting go of addictive behaviours that have helped to bring a feeling of "safety" triggers defensive systems in the body, so we go slowly, honouring the need for stability. I listen to what the client wants and feels they can do to find a sense of

THREE CIRCLES

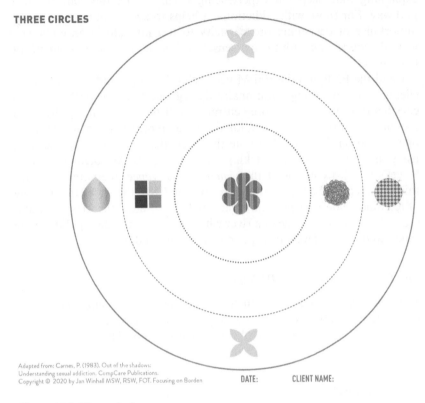

DATE: CLIENT NAME:

Figure 11.1 Three circles.

grounding in their lives. The autonomic nervous system needs to be on board with our plan.

Some clients choose sobriety, but often they are afraid to stop completely. Others want to learn how to manage their addictions. Some addictions, such as food and sex, require a harm reduction model since we cannot survive without eating, and grounded sexuality is an important part of life process. We start by making some boundaries around the behaviours to begin to establish a sense of structure and empowerment. For example, Joe decided to put "no alcohol consumption" in his inner circle, but he was not ready at that point to commit to "no paying for sex" because he didn't feel that he could commit to it at that time. Honouring the client's choice in inner circle behaviours is a crucial part of this model. Often people will not be able to let go of the behaviour completely at the beginning, and even if I feel strongly that they may need to, I respect the fear. I do insist however (and this is important) that if they truly want to liberate themselves from dependency, they must know that they can contain the behaviour. Discussing the concept of neuroplasticity is important here. Recall the "plastic paradox". Clients need to understand that their brain has become hardwired to go down the addictive pathway. They need to develop new neuropathways to reduce harm.

As we build the inner circle we align with the body, listening intently to what clients are feeling, welcoming fear and shame. This takes time, as we monitor both the adherence to boundaries and the client's neurophysiological states. This is where working with a trauma-informed addiction coach can be very helpful if you don't want to take on this aspect of the work.

Accountability and responsibility are crucial in the process of letting go of addictions. The three circles model provides a path of accountability as it reveals the inner circle behaviours that are being monitored and that can only be changed in consultation with the therapist and/or coach. Honesty is the most important thing here. I believe that clients become honest as they feel safe to engage in harm-reducing behaviours. Titrating is very important. Our job is to hold our clients accountable while listening deeply to the body's ANS. As we develop trusting connections, the body will engage. Bodies are designed to thrive and with time and our caring presence, they will often do just that.

The Middle Circle: Fight/Flight, Fold

These are the triggers that activate the inner circle behaviours. As we discuss stressors, clients begin to make the essential connections between their feelings and their addictions. We touch into these stressors as lightly as possible at the beginning of treatment. The process here is like *clearing space*, step one in focusing. We name the issues, but we don't go deeply into them. We teach clients to contain them and put them aside for the moment. Once they gain more sobriety we begin the uncovering work. Of course, this is the ideal process, and sometimes deep triggers emerge in the beginning of treatment. We honour their presence and gently teach clients grounding techniques to contain the intensity while we establish more stability with inner circle behaviours.

The Outer Circle: Flow, Flock, Fun

The outer circle is the pathway to a connected and empowered life. Here we find the activities that bring ventral activation: flow, flock, and fun on our model. At first clients may have very few of these resources. We tread gently so as not to shame or frighten them. This work is about building the life that they hope for. Connecting with a support group is key in working on this area. Activating the social engagement system is essential in healing from addiction. Healthy diet and exercise, building some close relationships, creative activities and daily practices such as mindfulness, focusing in partnerships, cultivating meaningful work and interests all contribute to a life free from addictive behaviours. If clients pray or meditate alone I encourage them to find a community in which to share the practice.

Mapping one's location in the three circles becomes a daily practice. As clients become aware of middle circle triggers, they can reach out to the outer circle grounding behaviours that bring them into connection with others, instead of pulling inwards to self-harm and self-soothe.

The Trauma Egg and The Background Wallpaper

The trauma egg was created by Murray (2012) over thirty years ago. It is a powerful way of taking an inventory of traumatic life experiences as your client works towards integration. You start by drawing a large egg shape on a large piece of paper. Starting at the bottom of the page you draw little bubbles inside the egg. Inside each bubble you put a drawing (no words), that symbolizes the experience. Felt-sense experiences held in the body reveal themselves over time and are depicted inside each bubble facilitating the creation of the trauma egg. I usually introduce this practice as the client begins to build a capacity to reduce harm, and we being to uncover underlying issues. Sometimes triggers to the trauma emerge in the beginning of treatment, as we are working on the middle circle. If so, we make a note of them as we start to build the egg, but I don't go into them at this point.

It is essential to remember that for some people, particularly marginalized groups, trauma is not one event, but rather an overall experience that colours all others. In focusing practice we call this the *background* part of the felt sense. Gendlin describes it as the wallpaper on the walls of the inside space. It is always present, creating a quality or flavour to one's experiencing. Perhaps it reflects one's default neurophysiological state. Recall our discussion about how neurophysiological state dictates how we view the world. For example, if our client lives in a chronic state of flight/fight, the background feeling would be one of fear or anger. Events are then interpreted through this lens and can distort the fresh experience. Likewise if we are lucky, and we have lived in and continue to thrive in a ventral state, our background wallpaper will be calm and balanced.

Background felt-sense stories of intergenerational trauma, global trauma, such as world wars, or what we may see in the future with children born into the current Covid-19 pandemic may surface. Race, class, and gender oppression are part of this background felt sense. Because these experiences are vital in our understanding of trauma, I add a place for them to be written around the wall of the egg, symbolizing their all-encompassing presence, the wallpaper of our lived experiences.

In the corners of the trauma egg you put five or ten words that you associate with each of your parents, the roles that you played in the family, rules that the family lived by, and themes that emerge from the traumatic events. Clients grow to understand how they became emotionally dysregulated, and begin to construct a cohesive narrative of their lives. This practice provides an avenue to achieve a ventral state of integration.

The Nine Domains of Integration

This way of conceptualizing integration was developed by Siegel (2012b) and its categories fit well within our model.

Integration of Consciousness: Does this person have an inner observing compassionate voice? Can they stand beside their experiencing?

Can we differentiate conscious awareness and if so, how? We can separate our subjective experience of awareness, our knowing, with that which is known, the object of awareness. When we practice gently observing ourselves we are aware of differentiated parts of our consciousness and the capacity to link or connect those parts. Without the capacity to differentiate awareness, we can become lost in a foggy or dissociated state. Once differentiated, we help our clients to link these parts together to seek integration.

I often tell my clients that I see healing as very much about what we choose to pay attention to. If we give all of our attention to the critical inside voice, we lose the capacity to find a gentle part of ourselves that can be with us with compassion. A very important starting point in therapy is to begin to build a differentiated sense of awareness that can be with our experience with some distance. In focusing practice, we call this being with the *felt sense* without falling into it and we practice it with clearing space. Siegel created a practice that facilitates this mindfulness skill called the *wheel of awareness*. It teaches you how to be aware of being aware. Learning how to be with experience with the right amount of closeness and distance is key to self-regulation. Mindfulness meditation exercises are powerful ways for our addicted clients to build new integrated neuropathways. Working on this domain is key to beginning to heal from addictive behaviours.

Vertical Integration: How connected is this person with their bodily-felt knowing?

Vertical integration involves the connecting pathways of energy and information flowing from the body up into the brainstem, limbic region of the brain, and up to the cortex. Recall that 80% of the information that the vagus nerve carries moves bottom-up *from* the body *up* to the brain, and only 20% moves in a top-down fashion from brain to body.

(We acknowledge that the brain is also *in* the body, but for now we are speaking of the part of the brain that is in the head.)

The nervous system has extensive innervation throughout the whole body, reaching into our muscles and bones, heart, lungs, and intestines. For clients who are well integrated, all of this bodily wisdom flows freely from the toes to the head. *Interoception*, the capacity to perceive the interior of the body, is well developed in clients who have good vertical integration. Put simply, this state is evident with clients who are connected to embodied knowing. This is assessed by noticing how able clients are to access their felt sense of a situation. Impaired integration in flow is often a result of trauma, resulting in dissociated body parts, feelings, and/or memories. Identifying blockages helps us to locate differentiated parts and link them together.

Bilateral Integration. Can this person think logically (using their left hemisphere)? Can they describe their felt-sense embodied knowing (right hemisphere)? How well can they move back and forth between both hemispheres?

Bilateral integration is concerned with how much integration there is between the left and right hemispheres. The relationship and functioning of the hemispheres is a controversial area. Siegel draws on the work of McGilchrist (2009) who views the hemispheres as mediating very different ways of being in the world, albeit with plenty of overlap and complexity. In talking about the brain, it is important not to oversimplify. However, in general, McGilchrist describes the left hemisphere as being concerned with discernment, logical, linear thinking, and making use of information while the right is more concerned with metaphor, the whole picture, and attending to bodily-felt knowing.

Linkage of the left and right hemispheres happens naturally for most people, allowing the brain to work as a whole. For some, however, this doesn't happen. For example, impaired bilateral integration occurs with clients who experienced avoidant attachment. They present as very rational and reasonable, but are disconnected from the feeling aspect of experiencing. They describe their problem in a detached way. This demonstrates their left hemisphere dominant orientation, a lack of bilateral integration. These clients are often frightened by the vulnerability of embodied presence.

Other clients present their issues with excessive flooding of the right hemisphere. Their capacity for clear-headed thinking is diminished. We see these examples manifested in relationships. The cliché "opposites attract" exists for a reason. How often do we see couples engaged in a power struggle between too much rationality and too much emotionality? The impairment of integration envelopes the couple. The struggle to find the sweet spot is both internal and relational.

The collaboration of both important ways of knowing is crucial for a state of integration. McGilchrist points out that our society has become left hemisphere dominated. He states that this top-down approach is threatening to obliterate the planet:

> There are it seems to me four main pathways to the truth: science, reason, intuition, and imagination. I also believe strongly that any worldview that tries to get by without paying due respect to all four of these is bound to fail. Each on its own has virtues and vices, its gifts, and inherent dangers: only by respecting each and all together can we learn to act wisely. And each is a blend of elements contributed by either hemisphere. (2009, p. xxvi)

Memory Integration: Is this person able to connect with the memory part of the felt sense experience in a coherent way?

In our top-down approach, we think of time in a linear way, dividing it up into little units of seconds, minutes, and hours. This is valuable and helps us to create an efficient way to live. Yet, it is only one way of experiencing time. We think of our memories as being behind us, separate from our current experiencing. From an embodied perspective, there is no clear demarcation of units of time. Our memories of times past flow into the present informing our current way of experiencing.

This definition brings memory into the present and the future. It helps us to see how past events can affect present experiences without our conscious awareness. Those of us who live and work with trauma and addiction know that events from the past not only bleed into the present but also continue to emerge in future experiencing.

Focusing Practice

The body knows a different way of experiencing time. The felt-sense experience of memory lives in our moment-by-moment processing. I invite you to close your eyes, breathing down into your belly. Recall an experience that feels intense. Let your body chose what wants to come ... feeling your feet on the floor and welcoming all that comes, thoughts, feelings, physical sensations, and memories about this experience. Stay with this moment and slowly allow a felt sense to form. Ask if there is a *handle* for this felt sense, a word, or phrase, or picture that captures the essence of all of this.

As you bring your awareness back to the room, notice how the felt sense sits in your body now, in this present moment. The body carries a process on into this moment and the next and the next. In the presence of trauma and addiction, we often block events. Triggers distort the present moment, giving us the sensation of fresh/frozen experiencing. Our past traumas live in our felt sense and come

---

crashing into the present moment without conscious awareness of the link to our past. A blockage occurs, and we are not able to connect our experiences in an integrated way. Our work as addiction/trauma therapists is to help the client link these differentiated aspects of the felt sense: thoughts, feelings, physical sensations, and memories, to develop integration of one's life narrative.

How do triggers work neurobiologically? Let's turn our attention to learning about implicit, explicit, and narrative memory.

Implicit and explicit memory.

Before 18 months of age, we have only *implicit memory*. We have a laying down of interconnections of neurons that include perception, emotion, sensation, and behaviour. We develop mental models that help us to remember. For example, a child sees a dog and over repeated visits with the dog the child lays down a mental model of what DOG is. Remember from our discussion about neuroplasticity, what fires together wires together. "Playing with my friend and his dog is fun." Good associations with DOG form a *schema* in the child's brain. Seeing a dog primes the brain for a good experience. *Priming* involves patterns of activation that form and are likely to reactivate with similar experiences. From these priming experiences *mental models*, generalizations of repeated experiences, develop over time.

Implicit memory is non-integrated, and therefore it can emerge without our knowing that it is from the past. We do not need to pay conscious attention with implicit memory. Therefore, we can experience emotions, body sensations, and behaviours without understanding that they are linked to past experiences. In working with addiction, we are often tapping into implicit memory. The addicted person is sometimes driven by intense mental models that are shaping present experiences and creating emotional dysregulation. Without the capacity to link these experiences to the past, chaos and/or rigidity reign.

Between 18 and 24 months of age, the hippocampus develops and we begin to form the more common kind of memory that we call *explicit memory*. Explicit memory requires focal attention. We are aware of attending. We use the hippocampus to encode and store two facets of explicit memory, factual information, and autobiographical memory. Autobiographical memory includes an awareness of self over time. We are conscious of events from the past. As we continue to grow over time, we develop a narrative form of memory that builds on implicit and explicit memories.

Divided Attention: Dissociation.

While the hippocampus is an integrative agent, it can also be impaired in the presence of overwhelming experiences including trauma. If a traumatic event occurs, our clients can divide attention, or dissociate, and focus only on one non-traumatizing aspect of the experience in order to survive. For example, one client shared that during a sexual assault she focused on a small figurine in the room and let her imagination take her to a place of comfort. Because the hippocampus requires focal attention to encode explicit memory, it was bypassed, and the assault was encoded only in implicit memory.

The presence of the stress hormone cortisol can also block hippocampal functioning. In addition, the body excretes adrenaline under stress and this increases the implicit encoding of fear by way of the amygdala. So we have a heightened response of blocked explicit and increased implicit memory encoding. No wonder we are challenged in our work in helping clients understand and heal their trauma experiences. And now we can begin to make sense of the process of being triggered by past trauma. *Triggers are blocked implicit memories.* They are the experience of *implicit* memories, stored freshly in the body, but frozen in *explicit* awareness, beginning to thaw when activated by resonating stimuli. Without the integrative work of linking differentiated experiences, healing cannot occur.

Narrative Integration: Can this person make sense of their life?

As we begin to integrate autobiographical memory, a coherent sense of our history emerges, and we understand the flow of our lives. Finding meaning in our experiences and the choices that we make in our lives is crucial to living an integrated life.

Trauma shatters meaning. This often forms an underlying basis for addiction. Without meaning, we live in chaos and rigidity. We are designed to move towards growth, yet, in the face of such painful times, we struggle to know the way. Meaning arises from following the felt sense. It is beautiful to witness addicted clients begin to heal and find meaning in helping others with their journey. Living a fully present life then becomes very rewarding.

State Integration: How well integrated are all the parts of this person?

How often do we sit with clients who are struggling with inner conflict? One part of them wants to eat, the other part wants to be skinny. One part wants to have lots of random sex, the other part wants to be monogamous. One part likes to be alone, the other part loves to party. We all have different parts. They develop as we experience life. In our culture, we are taught that we are one person with one identity. But in the felt sense of life we know that we often hold two or more felt sense experiences within us, and they all seek recognition.

If we are lucky, our differentiated parts get along well most of the time. If we suffered a great deal, we will have become emotionally dysregulated and will have developed a number of dissociated parts. Likely an addicted part will be present. In some cases, we will be completely dissociated from some of the parts. In the *Diagnostic and Statistical Manual* this is called *dissociative identity disorder*. I call this *multiple personality adaptation*. In this non-pathologizing way of viewing the highly dissociative client, we work with all the parts to welcome whatever comes and move the system towards integration. Linking the addicted part with the others is key to harm reduction.

Interpersonal Integration: Can this person feel close to others and hold on to self in relationship?

Interpersonal integration involves the capacity to create a secure attachment in relationships. If we are emotionally dysregulated because of early trauma, we will have a hard time establishing the right amount of closeness and distance in relationships. We will swing from chaos to rigidity and back, perhaps slipping into the isolation of addiction. These states of disintegration prevent a regulated attachment with others. Working on presence, grounding, and harm reduction will help to facilitate interpersonal integration. Focusing partnerships are an excellent path to connection and community.

Temporal Integration: Can this person accept life's uncertainty and impermanence?

A therapist asks, "My client tells me that she will never feel safe because no one can guarantee that she won't be raped again. What do I tell her?"

Forty years ago I attended a conference in Toronto called No More Secrets, about the secrets of sexual abuse. I listened intently while Butler (1978), my amazing teacher, replied to the above question. She said that while her client is right, there are no guarantees, right here and right now, we are safe. That is all the certainty that exists. We have to be with that. Carrying this wisdom has helped me enormously in my work and in my life.

We all long for certainty, permanence, and immortality. (In particular, our left hemisphere craves certainty and definitive answers.) Yet, we know in an embodied way that this is not possible. In order to integrate this knowing, we must welcome the uncomfortable and the unknown. By learning how to embrace the longing and the knowing, we integrate these differentiated parts.

Transpirational Integration: Does this person feel deeply interconnected with a wider sense of self, including the natural world?

Siegel created transpirational integration as an outcome of working through the previous eight domains. "Breathing across" the other domains creates a shift in clients as they integrate the work. Living deeply connected to an experiential, embodied knowing creates profound life changes. In our focusing practice, we savor step six, welcoming all that comes. From this place of integration, we are naturally motivated to heal a very wounded world. We understand that our bodies are one with our environment. Energy and information flow beyond the skin envelope. We are truly one with the world.

As I work with the nine domains of integration, I am struck by how beautifully they fit with the FSPM. This is because the idea of understanding human suffering in terms of the capacity to regulate our emotional state forms the basis of both interpersonal neurobiology and FSPM. The quest for integration of states of chaos and rigidity aligns well with focusing-oriented psychotherapy. Gendlin was very aware of these dysregulated states. He called them dead ends in the therapy process because clients were either too close to experience or too far away from experience, functioning at low levels on the Experiencing Scale.

While the quest is for a fully integrated felt-sense experience, I noticed that as I tracked my addiction clients, large pieces of experience were not integrated into their awareness. I began to delineate four aspects of the felt sense: thinking, feeling, physical sensation, and memory. I needed to track the dissociation in order to facilitate the integration. In the case with Margarita that follows, you will see how she initially blocked physical sensation as she began to uncover sexual trauma.

My overall assessment includes all of the domains of integration as aspects of the felt sense experience. In keeping with the EATT assessment protocol, we address aspects of each of the eight components as they appear in the client's process. For example, Margarita struggles with a sense of very disparate parts, or states of self, reflected in the sixth domain, state integration. Much of my assessment is focused on this domain as parts of her emerge, rather abruptly, after ten months of working together.

The Privilege Wheel

At the time of writing, this the world is facing unprecedented challenges by marginalized groups to address our place in terms of privilege. Our planet is suffering a pandemic that propels every human being into the same experience. This is extraordinary and the implications are staggering. One welcomed consequence of this is the rising up of peoples who have been beaten down by structural systems of oppression. We as psychotherapists need to rise up and honour these voices. There is no excuse for remaining unaware of our place in relation to how privileged we are.

To help us with this process, we use an exercise called the *power flower*. This activity is described in a toolkit that is available to the general public at https://www.oise.utoronto.ca/edactivism/Activist_Resources/The_Power_Flower.html. We start by drawing a flower with many petals. Each of the petals contains an inner and outer part. The outer petal represents the privileged identity. The inner petal represents the marginalized identity. The process describes our social identities and the ways that we experience privilege, power, and oppression in intersecting ways. Following along with the instructions we complete the petals of the flower in such a way that the intersection of our power and privilege are revealed. I encourage all of us to complete the wheel and encourage those clients who want to do so. Bringing this reality into the therapy office is vital for building trust, respect, and dignity from whatever place we hold in terms of privilege.

Specific Concerns

As we become more familiar with our clients, specific concerns may arise. Sometimes, they present with high levels of anxiety and/or depression, and our healing journey is hampered by the severity of emotional dysregulation. It becomes impossible for them to bring the attention and energy to the task of healing from addiction and trauma. A neurophysiological reset of the body can be profound and may include the carefully monitored use of medications. I don't hesitate to refer to a trusted colleague when I feel that my client may be helped with a course of medication.

The other common complaint that I hear from clients is their inability to concentrate and subsequent disruption in staying on task. This can seriously disrupt their ability to manage their addiction. Attention difficulties need to be noted and assessed if they persist over the course of treatment.

Focusing Practice

Let's pause for a moment and ask into the body. How is all of this about a new embodied assessment tool feeling in my body? Are there components that you are intrigued by? How would it be to document the healing journey over time, making the body's system of regulation our guide?

Focusing-Oriented Psychotherapy Strategies

While focusing can be integrated into all modalities, focusing-oriented therapists have developed strategies that shape the work. In my clinic, we use body cards that were created by focusing trainer Annette Dubreil. Clients draw on the cards with coloured pencils as a way of expressing the felt sense experiences. In each of the four corners of the card is a place to describe feelings, thoughts, physical sensations, and memories. Across the top of the card, we write the handle for the felt sense. We then orient the body cards to the FSPM noting what state is symbolized on the body card. As the work progresses clients accumulate many body cards that they use to track their healing journey. Diagram 10.1 is an example of a felt-sense experience in flight/fight. As the process evolves, the focuser often has a felt shift from this flight/fight state to a ventral state (Figure 11.2).

The following are examples of ten focusing strategies used in the FSPM. Each of the steps open opportunities to explore the implicit world of the felt sense more deeply. We ask open-ended questions to enliven the process. For example, we might drop a question into the body about how

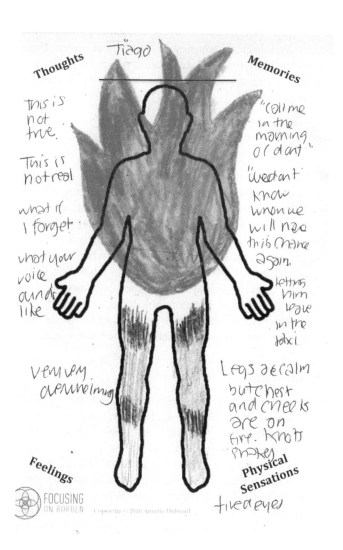

Figure 11.2 Body card.

all of this feels inside. Expansive questions create curiosity. Examples are: What is the worst of this? What does it need? What calls to it? How would it feel without all of it? As we progress through the focusing session, we note the steps and the quality of the felt shift if one occurs. We can do many rounds of focusing steps if the process leads us there. Asking for a handle (word or phrase that describes the felt sense) helps to symbolize the process, carrying it forward to the next step.

Orienting to the FSPM

We check in with the body's neurophysiological state and map it onto the model, tracking the pathways from state to state. The body cards help to document the neurophysiological journey as we heal over time. Experiences that once brought dysregulated states begin to settle into more ventral activation. An example of orienting to the model was described with Joe in Chapter 9.

Resourcing: Evoking Felt Sense Experiences of Grounding and Good Energy

When the client is ready to touch into the body, we teach grounding practices by going through the six steps of focusing and evoking specific felt sense experiences. For example, we invite ventral activation by exploring a sense of calm or safety either in real-life experience or through imagining such a state. I might say, "Can you find a time in your life or in your imagination where you felt calm or settled – a time when things felt all right?" As an experience comes into the body, we find a handle for this resourceful felt sense and then document it using the body card.

I have found that some clients are much more able to find a place of good energy than calm. They recall a time when they were having fun. We use this as a resource as we develop more capacity to settle the nervous system.

Finding the Right Distance from the Felt Sense

This strategy is one of the most commonly used in focusing-oriented therapy and when we think in terms of polyvagal theory, this comes as no surprise. Gendlin's "dead ends" of experiencing describe the dysregulated ANS states of flight/fight (sympathetic) and fold (dorsal).

In a flight/fight state, we are too close to our survival impulses to be able to calmly stay with our felt sense. We help our clients to back up a bit to be able to connect with the body. We can ask, "Would it be all right to take three deep breaths to step back from the intensity?" Or we can invite them to orient to the room, feeling their feet on the floor. Often I use clearing space as a way to ground.

Alternatively, in a fold or immobiilized state we are too far away from feeling, at very low levels of experiencing. When our clients are in states of dorsal shut-down, we must be very active in helping them to orient to the room. If there is enough ventral presence for the client to maintain grounding, we can gently ask questions like, "What is the worst of this?" to invite more intensity. An example of titrating closeness and distance was illustrated in Chapter 9 where Gendlin helps Lotte to back up from a chaotic state so she can develop the capacity to be with the experience and not overwhelmed by it.

Clearing Space Forward and Backward

Clearing space is step one in focusing. We are creating an inner relationship that is about *being with* experience. We are developing awareness of awareness. It is often used as a stand-alone practice. We start by naming and then gently setting aside issues in one's life that need to be cleared so we can find our way to a quiet space inside.

This is a different process than traditional mindfulness practice. In mindfulness, issues are not named. Attention is drawn to the senses and to letting go of content, whereas in focusing practice we are addressing issues in our life directly. We clear space first to invite a ventral state of calm. This enhances our capacity to be with one problem at a time and in an emotionally regulated way.

There are times, however, when clients are too distraught to clear space in the common way. Asking what is coming between you and feeling fine when you are in crisis can seem insensitive, drawing attention to the very issues you are trying to distance from. At these times, we can ask, "Is there any place in your life, or in your body, that feels okay right now?" It might be a brief moment with a favourite friend, or you may find it at the tip of your nose, or your earlobes. Any little experience, or place on the body, will help if we bring our attention there. From that place we can practice enlarging the area that feels okay, imagining that it is expanding as a way of increasing our capacity for calm. Clearing space backwards like this also works well for emotional and physical pain.

Grounded Aware Presence

The practice of *grounded aware presence* (GAP), created by Rome (2014), integrates mindful meditation practice with focusing. It works well to utilize both mindfulness and focusing as a way of activating a more ventral state. GAP brings us into the present moment by bringing awareness to both the immediate environment and our bodies. It differs from the classic clearing space process in that it does not ask us to take an inventory of our current troubles. Both ways can be helpful; we can choose which form of clearing space feels right at the time of our practice.

Engaging the Relational Felt Sense

Building a shared felt sense space with our clients takes time. As therapists we know the power of connection. Polyvagal theory confirms the need to activate the social engagement system in healing from addiction. Much pain and disappointment may have come from relating, so we are careful in our invitation to partner with us. Over time, an embodied sense of our interconnection carries the life energy forward for both of us. This energy deepens the capacity for experiencing as the window of tolerance widens and interpersonal integration deepens. When we are in shared presence, we are greater than the sum of our parts and capable of more than we would be on our own. I work more and more in groups now as a result of appreciating the power of the relational felt sense.

The Revolutionary Pause

Hendricks, a major contributor to the focusing world, and Gendlin's wife, named the revolutionary pause. At a focusing conference, Hendricks Gendlin (2003) said,

> Focusing is a force for peace because it frees people from being manipulated by external authority, cultural roles, ideologies, and the internal oppression of self attacking and shame. This freeing has to do with an ability to pause the on-going situation and create a space in which a felt sense can form.

Pausing in our culture is suspect. We are trained to fill it with words. Slowing down and welcoming silence gives voice to the body's wisdom. Slowing down means valuing process over content. As we deepen our experiencing, the language of the felt sense emerges. Prengel, a focusing-oriented psychotherapist, (www.active pause.com) has developed the practice of the pause and continues the work through his online community.

The Focusing Attitude: Welcoming the Uncomfortable

Everything is welcomed into the room as long as it is contained in a respectful way. When we think at the edge, we invite all of the bits that don't fit, and all of the feelings and thoughts that are not usually welcomed. This is true in the therapy office too. We must make a space that invites tremendous discomfort when we work with addiction. This is not easy to do when our own values and emotions are challenged. But this is addiction work, and we must be prepared to honour whatever comes, whatever needs to be named.

Working With Parts

Working with parts of self is a very natural process in focusing. When we clear space, we develop the capacity to be with something inside. Often that appears as a part of the self that is in conflict with another part. A striking ambivalence is usually present in the struggle between parts that want to continue using the bad habits and parts that want to stop. We stand beside the struggle and teach our clients to do so as they work towards integration.

Working With Dreams

It is no surprise that Gendlin was drawn to the metaphorical world of dreams. This is the space where we explore the implicit knowing, the world that thinks at the edge of our consciousness. Ellis' (2019) book, *A Clinician's Guide to Dream Therapy* provides an excellent resource to bring our clients' dream life into the therapy room. Often I find that clients are delighted by their deeper understanding of themselves as we work with a dream. The stuck places come alive and move forward when we listen to the dreaming world. Our dreams give us access to deeper levels of experiencing, and thus deeper levels of integration. Dreamwork accelerates transpersonal integration, the capacity to be with all of life's complexity.

Focusing Partnerships, Experiential Listening

In chapter two, I discussed the partnership model that we use in focusing practice. We learn and live focusing in listening partnerships, as we accompany each other down into our deeper process. It is the only contemplative practice I am aware of that activates the social engagement system so intensely during the practice. The relational felt sense that creates our safe nest is embedded in social engagement. This supports the work of healing from addiction immensely. I encourage clients to join groups as soon as they can. The connection with community is invaluable. Many moments of transpersonal integration occur in and because of the group process. These are moments of liberation.

Summary

This chapter offers a lot of details about ways to assess and treat addiction integrating EATT, the FSPM model, and the steps of focusing. It may seem unwieldy if you try to use them all or to follow a specific order. As ever, in this responsive and open-ended approach, the idea is to sense what is needed in the present moment and pick up the tool that the client's process seems to be asking for. In practice, once you have integrated these tools and this way of working, the process will feel fluid and as if you have many resources that can overlap and work seamlessly together. In the next chapter, you will see how all of this applies in a complex case study that shows the meandering and miraculous path towards trauma recovery.

References

Butler, S. (1978/1985). *The conspiracy of silence: The trauma of incest*. San Fransisco, CA: Volcano Press.

Carnes, P. (2001). *Out of the shadows: Understanding sexual addiction*. Center City, Minnesota: Hazelden.

Ellis, L. (2019). *A clinician's guide to dream therapy: Implementing simple and effective dream work*. New York: Routledge.

Hendricks Gendlin, M. (2003). Focusing as a force for peace. *Keynote address to the 15th focusing international conference*, Pforzeim, Germany.

Klein, M., Mathieu-Coghlan, P. L., Gendlin, E. T., & Keisler, D. (1970). *The experiencing scale: A research and training manual* (Vol. 1). Madison, WI: Wisconsin Psychiatric Institute.

McGilchrist, I. (2009). *The master and his emissary: The divided brain and the making of the Western world*. New Haven: Yale University Press.

Murray, M. (2012). *The Murray method: Creating a wholeness beyond trauma, abuse, neglect and addiction*. Vivo Publications. Date of publication Nov 30th 2017, ISBN-10 0985509317.

Rome, David. (2014). *Your body knows the answer*. Boulder, CO: Shambala Publications.

Siegel, D. J. (2012b). *The developing mind, second edition: How relationships and the brain interact to shape who we are*. New York: Guilford Publications.

12 An Embodied Experiential Assessment: The Margaritas

The first day I met Margarita I was struck by how much she needed to hide and how much she needed to be seen. She embodied a paradoxical state, and I could sense her struggle. Looking back on it now, I had a felt sense of her very disparate parts, although I had no idea just how separate these were. She came to me because her family doctor had just diagnosed her with fibromyalgia. It was suggested that therapy may help her high stress levels. Knowing that this diagnosis is often associated with dorsal activation of the autonomic nervous system, I was immediately curious about a trauma/addiction history. But something in my sense of her held me back from too much exploring on this first visit.

The first time I sit with this quietly contained Latino woman, I notice a quality about her appearance that feels lifeless. She is wearing a simple t-shirt and jeans, old running shoes. Her body folds into itself. It's as if she is saying, "Please don't notice me." As she tells me about moving to Canada from her native Costa Rica when she was eight years old, I notice a slight jerking of her head. It feels like a veiled sense of excitement and fear enters the room, but I can't quite sense into it. Even though she holds back from sharing content, there is a mysterious lurking, almost formidable energy that fills the room. I notice a tightening in my upper chest as my relational felt sense begins to form.

As we continue on for several weeks, Margarita keeps the level of experiencing low, hovering at a one or two, by focusing on physical complaints. If I ask her how this feels for her emotionally, she answers with detailed descriptions of doctor's appointments and sleepless nights. I know how important sleep is, so I offer some help with this issue. It is also related to her physical complaints, so she is keen to share information. After some exploring we decide to refer her to a sleep clinic for further investigation. She seems pleased with this, but remains guarded in her connection with me.

Orienting to the Felt Sense Polyvagal Model (FSPM)

The FSPM begins to take shape as I see this woman's need to hold tight to her dorsal, rigid state. While it is too soon to share it with her, the model reminds me that building a relational connection is challenging when clients are deeply embedded in rigidity. It is easy to feel uncomfortable as we sit with a client that pushes us away. I know that the most important thing in this process is to show up for Margarita with my ventral and vulnerable presence. I keep my mantra with me, "The primacy of human presence", Gendlin's (1990, p. 205) gift to the world.

Although much of her energy is shutting me out, her mere physical presence demonstrates a need for help. Remembering this helps me to clear space, putting my theories on one side of me and my own issues on the other. Now I am just here with Margarita, using my focusing-oriented strategy of getting the right closeness and distance. This defensive stance has protected her from things I have yet to learn about. I am patient as I track her autonomic nervous system, honouring her neuroceptive process and her need for distance.

The Three D's

Over several weeks I reflect on the three D's: deepening experience, developing the story, and daily practices. Margarita's capacity for deepening experience is reined in by her strong need for self-containment. It is very hard for her to feel into her body in this dorsal state. While I make no invitation for her to connect with the body, my own embodiment creates an energy between us. Trauma lurks around the room as we circle back and forth from physical complaint to sleepy dorsal activation. I look for signs of addiction as I wonder how she manages her emotional regulation.

About five weeks into our work, I offer her tea at the beginning of our session. This opens a door. Her face lights up as she sips the Bengal spice tea, a favourite at the clinic. I see a little girl's face peep out at me from behind the flat affect. Such a cute little face. Just as quickly as this part emerges, it is overshadowed by a furrowed brow and a sharp jerk of her head. I wait. Her expression shuts down, back to contained rigidity. But I am hopeful. A spark of life emerged for a brief instant. I begin to see different parts of Margarita. I sense a lack of integration that needs tending to.

Next session I make spice tea again and she lights up. This time, she stays lively with me as we begin to explore more about her life. She describes her childhood in San Jose, a city I have visited several times. We share in our love of this beautiful country, and I begin to feel like we are building a good connection. Over the next couple of sessions, she starts to explore feelings about her early family life. Some hints of an overly involved, controlling father emerge. In my session notes, I document a level 4 on the Experiencing Scale for the first time. Margarita is able to focus directly on her feelings and thoughts about herself. As we deepen the experience, we are beginning to develop her life story.

Privilege Wheel

We continue over the weeks and I learn more about her family. She has three older brothers who she says she doesn't feel any connection with. She describes her family as working class. Mom and dad sometimes struggle to provide for four children. When Margarita was eight years old, the family emigrated to Canada, reuniting with her father's brother. She tells me these stories maintaining a level 4 on the Experiencing Scale, sometimes a level five, indicating that she is deepening her window of tolerance. I decide that next session I will invite her to bring her attention down into the centre of her body.

Before I can say anything, our session begins with Margarita in full sympathetic surge. Her flight/fight response fills the room. "Wow," I say, "Tell me all about it." I have never seen her in such distress. I am glad to see a shift from flat affect, but I wonder how she will be able to calibrate the process. I stay with her distress as she tells me about a horrible experience with a government official regarding immigration issues. She is very angry, and her head is jerking as she tells me how disgusted she is with the racist attitudes of White Canadians.

I watch her whole body as she describes intense feelings of rage and humiliation. She is coming to life, finding her voice. I listen and reflect on my own Whiteness as Margarita shares her pain. This leads to an honest and revealing dialogue. I share with her my learning from the privilege wheel, and she is curious. She works on her wheel over the week and starts the next session by saying that it is very important for us to talk more about this. Paradoxically, for the first time I feel a strong sense of stable connection with her as I acknowledge my race and class privilege. This leads to a lively discussion of our common experiences of gender oppression. The conversation seems to release a block between us as we both learn more about our life stories. This proves to be right, as the next session reveals.

The Emergence of Parts

I'm settling into my office, watering my plants and getting some spice tea when I see Margarita, but not Margarita, approaching my door. My brain is trying to organize this image. I recognize her face, barely. The Margarita I know is shy, dresses in drab clothes, trying to maintain as neutral an appearance as possible so she can be safely invisible from unwanted attention. This woman is bold in her demeanour. She is wearing a bright red dress, high heels, beautifully applied makeup, and her long black hair is done up to perfection. I am floored.

She begins talking to me as if everything is normal. I listen and hear this Margarita explaining things to me that are new and very revealing about her life, in a way that her other self would never disclose. I'm riveted, engaging with her stories and asking questions that are eagerly answered. She is describing her early childhood memories of camping in the backyard with her brothers. A memory comes that stops her immediately, and for a moment I see the other Margarita as her whole body slumps into hiding.

A subtle shift, and again I see her head jerk a couple of times. It's as if she is listening to someone talking to her. She switches back into the new Margarita, poised, upright, and sassy. We continue with a lively conversation about how bored she gets with the others. The others? She wants to have fun. She loves to drink and party and they spoil everything. I feel my heart beating in my chest as I ask, "Who spoils everything?"

"Margarita and the little ones," she says. Even though I am shocked by what is happening, I note the presence of this new part as another dimension of my client that probably helps her to manage her emotional states by using alcohol and sex. I must go back to this when the time is right.

As she is talking I have a dawning realization. I am thinking about the conference I attended with Putnam, author of *Diagnosis and Treatment of Multiple Personality Disorder* (1989). The current model for working with parts is called internal family systems therapy, and the diagnosis is now called *dissociative identity disorder* (DID). It has become very popular recently. I first came upon parts work seen through the lens of multiple personality disorder. I remember Putnam describing how "multiples", as he called them, can switch from one personality to another without awareness of different parts taking over. So Margarita wouldn't necessarily know that this other self, the party girl, would be visiting me. I ask this part what her name is as casually as possible. "Dolores," she says, eyes sparkling. I take a breath, reminding myself that the land of trauma is indeed often stranger than fiction. I listen with curiosity and respect as Dolores shares with me her frustration about being controlled by boring old Margarita. As the session comes to an end I'm not sure how to wrap up. I say, "See you next week Dolores."

"Absolutely," she says, tossing her long black hair as she swooshes by me.

The first time one encounters a person with multiple personalities is, in our culture, an extraordinary experience. In fact, many people don't believe that it exists. I struggle to make sense out of what I have just experienced with Margarita and Dolores. I seek out my colleague who has more experience than I do, and share what I just witnessed. Yes, she is aware of the initial shock. I am not crazy. At the time that this was happening I was five years into practice. Luckily my colleague has twenty years of trauma work experience and she helped me to process what just happened.

That night as I try to fall asleep, I remember Bridgette and the pancakes. Daddy who makes her pancakes and drives her to school is daddy who pokes and stabs her little body leaving sticky white glue between her legs. How does she hold both Daddies? She makes them two separate daddies, and she splits herself into two: the good, safe little girl with the good daddy, and the bad little girl with the bad scary daddy. And she makes a huge wall between the two so she can keep the good daddy good. I can now sleep because I start to understand. We have so much work to do, my wondrous Margarita and I. I am growing wiser and tougher by the day.

Deepening and Developing the Process

Time passes in our work together and other parts of Margarita emerge. Child parts who were sexually abused by her brothers peer out at me. They were attacked in the tent in the backyard. When they emerge, Margarita's whole self becomes small, her voice and gestures childlike. Teenage parts come to tell wild tales of drinking and using lots of drugs to numb the pain. They come out at night when Margarita is sleeping. I love these parts. They remind me of my own sassy teenager part, and it is easy to relate to them. They carry a lot of pain though, and occasionally it surfaces. I'm aware that we haven't begun to work on the addictive behaviours, so I note, but don't process the trauma now. Usually, Margarita comes back, and if she is slow, I call on her. She comes and takes over for now. Amazing. It's different at night though. That's when the acting out occurs. We will work on that when we have started the three circles.

Dolores comes to visit from time to time, complaining about the boredom. She is a big critical presence in the group, complaining when the little ones make too much noise, but also playing with them when she feels like it. As I become acquainted with the parts I realize that most of them are dissociated from each other at this point. I still don't know about this part that jerks her head. That comes later.

Margarita Orients to the Model

While I want to tread carefully, I am eager to bring more embodied awareness into the therapy. I know that it will help us move out of the dead end neuropathway of addiction where she is stuck. I need to help Margarita access her felt sense so she can start living in flow, flock, and fun. I look over at my large FSPM on the wall and decide that it's time to introduce it. Margarita comes into our session looking very stressed and tells me that she knows about the teenagers and Dolores, the 20-year-old, because she finds bottles of wine and pills on her coffee table most mornings. She is so distraught about this behaviour. This is great, I think to myself. The addicted teenagers and Dolores are coming into awareness, although Margarita is adamant that they are not part of her. Margarita isn't an addict, she tells me. She is a serious, responsible teacher.

It occurs to me that this process of helping her integrate addicted parts is really not so different than working with addicted folks who aren't multiple. At first, nobody wants to accept the addict part. I begin to appreciate how much I am learning about the psyche through my work with Margarita. We are all made up of parts, or experiences. In our top-down world, we like to think of ourselves as being one consistent person, a unitary self. But when we live through the felt sense, we know that our implicit world is intricate and full of different and disparate parts. Our embodied living is full of paradox and complexity.

We see this most clearly in our work with addiction and trauma. When we are traumatized these parts remain frozen. Addicted parts stagnate when they are not seen and welcomed by the whole self. With this understanding, my job is to help Margarita acknowledge her trauma and the way in which her multiplicity helped her to carry the pain through dissociating each part. She needs to know that her addicted parts are just some of her parts, not the whole of who she is as a human being. She can integrate these parts to come into her whole being in a new way.

As I explain the model and how addiction serves to help her she listens intently. Her eyes follow my hand as I trace the neurophysiological pathway from flight/fight to fixate to fold. I then trace the new pathway from fun to flock to flow as I explain how we will discover this together. I see Margarita taking this all in and I wonder if other parts are listening. I hear her sigh a lot, and I decide to invite her to notice this as we begin to take in the new learning. I share my flow practice of focusing, a way to connect into the "sigh" in her body. I introduce the idea that her body can be a helpful guide instead of a source of pain. This is hard for her to imagine.

Tracking the Six Steps of Focusing and the Shift

Over the next several weeks, Margarita and I begin to practice focusing. I show her the circle in the middle of the model with the four pathways into the felt sense: feelings, physical sensations, thoughts, and memories. She learns to go inside and we begin by looking for a grounded or good energy felt sense to anchor as a resource. She finds a fun place and the body shift as the handle "roly poly" comes. I show her how to create a body card. Her face lights up as the little ones, Carmela, Carmelita, and Maria grab the crayons. The session ends with me describing the importance of daily practice. She agrees to take time to focus on "roly poly". Over the weeks Margarita becomes practiced at finding good energy felt senses and we begin to build a felt sense of grounding as she connects with her body. This practice of resourcing is shared by many somatic therapies today. It speaks to our shared understanding of the power of embodied knowing.

The Three Circles

We are making inroads with her integration of the addicted parts as I explain the nature and function of these behaviours in polyvagal language. It is easier for her to accept when she understands that it is her body's natural response to the trauma. I decide that now is the time to introduce the three circles as a way to manage the harm of her addictive behaviours. While Margarita shows interest in creating the circles, I see this head jerking emerge from the past as we begin to discuss the inner circle. It is a lot to manage here, with the parts that want to drink, the parts that don't, and the parts yet to be revealed. Yet, this is the nature of addiction work, and Margarita and I are committed.

We begin to build her inner circle. She wants to start by committing to no alcohol or drugs kept in the house so step one is to go home and get rid of it all. This feels huge to both of us. We stay away from the middle circle for now, and place her focusing practice and her work as a teacher in the outer circle. She adds her cat to the outer circle the next week. We continue to build, and she has some success over the months with diminishing the addictive behaviours.

Trauma Egg and Body Cards

Over time she becomes expert at mapping different neurophysiological states that she is experiencing. As she begins to make gains in applying her three circle practice, it feels like the right time to build her trauma egg. Margarita and I forge a powerful alliance as she grows to understand and integrate more of her trauma. She identifies as an "inner self helper" a name given by Putnam (1989) for the part of the inner system that can see more of the whole. As the "host" of the inner system, she helps me to navigate our healing journey. She is the part that most closely embodies the state of integration.

We venture into trauma memories now that we have resources to draw upon. She finds a piece of a memory. Something about her brother Todd. I ask her to pause and see if she can explore more. Nothing comes and she seems restless. I push a little and ask into the beginnings of the felt sense, "How does this Todd memory sit in your body?" She opens her eyes, and says emphatically, "I feel nothing in my body." We know we have work to do.

As we build the trauma egg, the little ones enjoy drawing and colouring the body cards, but they quickly disappear as we work through the sexual trauma. Because there are so many parts she develops an array of body cards. Sometimes, we lay them out on the floor and see how they relate to each other. Margarita is learning how to feel the little ones and to listen for them. She is learning how to protect them when they feel scared. This is wonderful and heartbreaking to witness.

The parts that are addicted are now being integrated into the FSPM as we highlight their pathway from flight/fight to fold, hovering over fixate. It helps Margarita to accept that they exist, even though they don't feel real to her. I don't find this surprising at all. It is quite common for many who are addicted to continue to feel estranged from the actual addictive behaviour. It feels like a "not-me" part of themselves because it is dissociated and re-enacted in a trance state.

Over the years that we work together, Margarita develops several daily practices. She has a focusing partnership, writes in a journal, uses her FSPM and her three circles to map her journey, and she is working on a daily exercise programme.

The Final Stage

Ours is not a straight path. We make progress as we move through the uncharted waters, deepening the window of tolerance. As we go deeper, the final part surfaces, unannounced. I'm listening to Margarita as she finds a tattered piece of memory, a smell that frightens her. Suddenly, she jerks her head violently and starts to growl as if to warn me to stay away. She stands up and shouts at me to stop! I try to breathe and remain still. I don't want her to sense that I am afraid.

She turns her back and after several seconds, faces me. So this is the part that jerks the head. At last she comes. This part swaggers around, filling the room with sexual energy. Tossing her hips, but wait, it feels like a male part. Big, masculine energy that wants to command the space. She/he tells me that he is Frankie and I better stay away. As quickly as Frankie comes, they go. Margarita feels exhausted and doesn't appear to know who just came for a visit. We say goodbye and I sink into my chair, shaken.

I know I have my work cut out for me in finding the right closeness and distance from Frankie. I take time to be with myself. I too am exhausted after this session. What now? Just when we were getting somewhere. But, although we were making progress with the drinking and the pills, Margarita just disclosed to me that she finds cuts on her breasts and legs. Since she has been decreasing the inner circle behaviours, the cuts have increased. Is this connected to Frankie?

The High Flyers

While I don't have a Frankie, I do have a teenage part that loves to party. I ask her if she has any suggestions about connecting with Frankie. Indeed she does.

"Wow," says Frankie, trying to remain cool and hide their excitement. I open the door to my convertible, and in they hop. We are off, flying down the road with the wind in our hair, Stevie Wonder blasting. I know instantly that this was a good call. I have won Frankie over with this moment of liberation.

In the months that pass Frankie reveals many experiences of traumatic re-enactment with unsafe sexual partners. After these episodes, she/he cuts the body. While it is a real worry, we are making progress as Margarita reluctantly listens in on my sessions with Frankie. Over time Margarita builds strength and insists on adding "no cutting" to the inner circle. While Frankie doesn't like it, she/he slowly diminishes in energy, seemingly settling in to the contained space. I still see flashes of their haughtiness, but now it is infused with a softer presence. A Frankie that is more fun and less scary emerges. Margarita now has an embodied experiential toolkit to draw upon as our precious journey evolves.

This clinical example illustrates how the process of healing from trauma does not follow a straight path, but calls upon the sensitive and well-timed use of a number of the elements of our model. It is less important to slavishly follow the steps, and much more important to track the client as they progress in a circular fashion, sometimes two steps forward, one step back, toward wholeness. If ever, as a therapist witnessing such incredible processes such as those described in this case, you feel disoriented, the way home is through the body – through tracking the nervous system and the felt senses carried by the client in response to you and your calm accompaniment. The more you can trust the process, the more you allow the client's body to find its right path toward integration and wholeness. And the tools in this and the previous chapter can be like guideposts lighting the way. What at first may seem wild and crazy begins to make perfect sense.

References

Gendlin, E. T. (1990). The small steps of the therapy process: How they come and how to help them come. In G. Lietaer, J. Rombauts & R. Van Balen (Eds.), *Client centred and experiential psychotherapy in the nineties* (pp. 205–224). Leuven: Leuven University Press.

Putnam, F.W. (1989). *Diagnosis and treatment of multiple personality disorder.* New York: Guilford Press.

13 Hailstorms and Turtles: The Felt Sense Polyvagal Dialogue

Working with addiction means working with relationships. As healers we stress the importance of seeking connection with others as a source of nourishment, but the addicted brain has another agenda. It seeks oblivion. We need to teach our clients that activating the social engagement system is key to managing addiction. It helps to explain this so they begin to appreciate the importance of relationships. When working with the *felt sense polyvagal model* (FSPM), I point out that flock is opposite fixate on our map. It's a long journey from oblivion to showing up and being present for ourselves and others.

In my work with couples and groups, I have created an integration of the felt sense polyvagal dialogue (FSPD) and imago therapy. I came upon imago therapy in the 1990s when Hendrix and LaKelly Hunt (2019) published their bestseller, *Getting the love you want.* Imago is the word the authors use to describe the unconscious image that we carry of our parents, and powerful others, from early on in life. This image or patterning shapes our choice of subsequent partners. They believe that while the relationship is often a re-enactment of childhood wounds, it also provides a vehicle for healing. They created the *imago dialogue*, a step-by-step process that offers couples a concrete way to explore conflicts and improve communication.

Meeting Harville and Helen

The first time I met Hendrix and LaKelly Hunt was at an international focusing conference in (2017). Talk about crossings!

What were Hendix and LaKelly Hunt doing there? It turns out that Hendrix was a student of Gendlin's at the University of Chicago in the 1960s. He tells a great story about how they met. Hendrix was doing a PhD in theology and struggling to find the right path to follow in his career. The ministry wasn't where he belonged. He felt quite lost. So he decided to read the publications of professors at the university and as he was searching through the list, he came upon Gendlin's thesis, which became his first book *Experiencing and the creation of meaning* (1962/1997).

Hendrix describes reading Gendlin as life changing. While he studied only briefly with the founder of focusing, Hendrix began to read philosophers like Heidegger and Merleau Ponty, who had so deeply influenced Gendlin. This opened up a new world for Hendrix, the beginnings of a path that led to the development of imago therapy. Years later, in 2000, Gendlin reached out to Hendrix and LaKelly Hunt. As the focusing community was growing he was curious to know more about how the imago community had developed. That was the last time that Hendrix saw Gendlin. When he learned of his death in 2017 he sent his condolences and this led to him presenting at the focusing conference.

My introduction to imago therapy in action came when I met Bierman, an expert in working with violence in relationships (1999) and a focusing-oriented psychotherapist. I was looking for an approach that incorporated deep listening to help couples communicate better. Bierman was running groups for couples where he was starting to integrate focusing into the imago dialogue process. When he suggested that I could assist him I jumped at the chance. During that time, I wrote *The Focusing Dialogue* that I presented at the first Felt Sense Conference in New York (Winhall, 2018) and have since incorporated this into my FSPM.

First-Person Experiencing

I'm letting my mind wonder back to my first interview with Harville and Helen. The plane lands and I get a cab to the hotel across the street from their home. I'm in the outskirts of Dallas, Texas. How wonderful to have a night to myself in a lovely hotel. I settle in, have a quiet dinner and review my questions for the next day. I feel like a budding journalist, and love this process of interviewing interesting people and then writing about them. I want to dig into their history, understand how they developed the dialogue, and hear more about Harville's relationship with Gene. I also want to explore ideas for my book and share the FSPD.

I sleep well, and next morning I make my way across the street. Riding up in the elevator to the penthouse floor, I feel a jittery and delicious nervousness, a feeling I am about to have a memorable experience. The door opens and a smiling young woman lets me in. Large windows reveal an impressive view of the city as I'm led into Harville's office. Warm rugs and lots of books fill the room with an inviting glow. It's clear that this space is a rich and vibrant one. We all settle in.

As the couple begin to share their story about the development of the imago dialogue, the felt sense of being with them forms inside me. The passion they have for each other and their work is contagious.

Their pleasure in being able to help is warm and enveloping. It reminds me of Rogers' (1951) concept of "unconditional positive regard". It becomes apparent to me how these two people have become so influential. I feel their capacity to create a sense of being held through skilful listening and curiosity.

Harville shares that the beginning of the dialogue process was in fact Helen's doing. They were in a heated argument and Helen said, "Stop, let's take turns listening to each other!" And so they did. Harville also shares how they unknowingly contributed to the patriarchy by not naming Helen as co-creator of the imago dialogue until recently.

"We realized much later that we were perpetuating the oppression of women. I hate the patriarchy!" Harville went on to say, "It makes me wonder what else I'm not aware of that I am doing." The capacity for both Harville and Helen to share their "shaky being" is part of what makes them such great teachers.

This leads us into a great discussion about the early days of feminism and Helen's deep commitment to the equality of women. She describes how the early work of feminist writers such as Jean Baker Miller impacted her thinking. Unlike the traditional Western male view of development that emphasizes the individuation of self as the end goal, Miller and others at The Stone Centre in Boston developed a relational paradigm. The self-in-relationship model sees the vehicle for growth and connection throughout life as a dyadic interaction. This relational paradigm is central to imago therapy and crosses beautifully with the interaction-first concept in focusing and the co-regulation concept in polyvagal theory.

Before I leave, Harville and Helen make sure to help me with my book. I share my model and the felt sense polyvagal dialogue (FSPD). They are curious and encouraging. Harville says I have to decide who I want my audience to be. Then I will be clear about the path forward. As I walk back to my hotel I begin to formulate my thoughts. Maybe I should write a book for therapists about what is close to my heart, de-pathologizing addiction. I feel a warm glow inside.

Some Imago Therapy Concepts and Points of Consilience

Let's briefly go through some imago therapy concepts. This will help give some context to the dialogue process. Then I will share the FSPD as it relates to addiction.

Helen and Harville sum up their message as follows: "We are born in relationship, we are wounded in relationship, and we heal in relationship"

(2007, p. 35). Imago theory suggests that the interaction between people, the *space between* them, is the source of life's energy. This interaction between people extends to all living creatures and plants within the universe. The space between also includes the space around us. Imago theory, like systems theory, stresses the importance of understanding that all living beings are connected to everything in the universe.

According to Hendrix and LaKelly Hunt, "What is happening in the universe is happening in us, and what is happening in us is happening in the universe" (2017, p. 5). When we shift into a bottom-up approach, we sense into the embodied connection with the world. Here we see a point of consilience between imago's relational paradigm and the concept of interaction first in focusing. Interpersonal neurobiology shares in this systems theory approach of interconnection within relationship and within the whole universe.

"When two people connect by being attuned, they experience a pulsating energy flowing back and forth, a "felt sense" that they are a point in an interconnecting universe. That awareness, stimulated by the quality of their interaction, triggers the neural sensation of Full Aliveness" (Hendrix & LaKelly Hunt, 2017, p. 6). This is similar to my concept of the relational felt sense (Winhall, 2014). This space holds the interaction of two beings. It is the space from which we co-regulate each other in polyvagal theory. Our nervous systems are finely attuned to the felt sense of each other. From the beginnings of life we are in an ongoing interactional process that is shaped by our lived experience.

The Primacy of Safety

Safety is a focal point of imago, focusing, interpersonal neurobiology, and polyvagal theory. "Safety is non-negotiable" state Hendrix and LaKelly Hunt (2017, p. 21). They have created a simplified version of the imago dialogue that can be used in any setting called *safe conversations*. It is a three-step process including mirroring, validating, and empathizing. Establishing a structured dialogue is an important step in establishing safety. The dialogue demands that we break old destructive patterns of communicating. By creating safe boundaries of containment, we are able to travel deeply into experiencing. This in turn creates the potential for empathy.

Imago: The Latin Word for Image

The concept of imago developed over time. As Hendrix discusses his early years of studying with Gendlin and other existential philosophers, we see his curiosity as he explores ways of understanding his clients:

> During this time in my clinical practice, I started listening to couples phenomenologically—that is, suspending my theoretical assumptions. I

had learned of the approach from Maurice Merleau-Ponty, a student of Husserl, to whom I had been introduced by Eugene Gendlin, a philosopher of phenomenology who had been a student of Carl Rogers ... While listening in a sort of reverie of suspended thinking, as couples described their frustrations with each other, I began to have images of them as children crying about unmet needs, complaining about their partners as they had complained about their parents. Even though I had attempted to suspend my assumptions, the transferential theory seemed validated by my observations. (2005, p. 19)

At first, he lets go of his theoretical assumptions. He listens in a kind of reverie of suspended thinking. And as he listens freshly, he notices the frequency with which couples transfer early attachment patterns from childhood onto their mates. The pattern resonates powerfully and frequently. He hears his client's early childhood pain and how it impacts their current relationships. He names this resonating pattern the imago.

Imago Felt Shift : Creating Moments of Couple Liberation

I relate to this process that Hendrix describes. For example, if we grow up with a parent who is explosive, we may find ourselves responding with excessive pleasing behaviour (fawning) and mating with a partner who lives in fight mode. The imago, or image, is stored in our felt-sense experience and resonates over and over again. In focusing language, we are in a *stopped process.* We cannot carry forward to heal in this state. This is where addiction often occurs to help us survive intolerable pain.

I am struck by how many people find a powerful felt sense that resonates back to childhood experiences with parents and powerful others. However, I do not impose this pattern on the client as an interpretation. Usually the client finds the imago pattern in their felt sense as we travel through the steps in the FSPD. If it doesn't come spontaneously, I might ask if this current experience with their partner is familiar. How far back does it go? Does it resonate with the memory part of the felt sense? Here I often see the client experience a powerful felt shift as I ask these questions. I watch their whole being shift into a ventral state as the body eases with this knowing. Often tears come, and a long pause. This is a significant moment in the healing process, a moment of liberation that is shared with the intimate partner. It begins the journey of decoding the trigger that sets off the conflict with the partner. The client begins to see the way in which the past is informing and often distorting the present.

Current attachment/trauma theory supports the concept of imago. While this is so, I can't stress the importance of this next point: If the imago doesn't fit for the client, I drop it. *I don't push experience into little boxes or units,* but rather, remain curious and open to the client's implicit intricacy. I recommend we welcome all that comes, freshly following our client's lead. It can take us to places where the concepts *don't* fit and bring the next creative steps in our thinking at the edge.

Focusing Practice: Finding Your Imago

Let's try the imago exercise.

Get yourself some paper and a pen and find a quiet space to take some time for yourself. Draw a large circle with a line across the middle. Allow yourself to drop down inside and find your child self. Welcome your felt sense of this place. Notice what comes when you invite your family into your memories. Let your body explore the space of your childhood home. On the top half of your circle, list all of the positive characteristics of your parents and any other people who influenced you. Don't worry about naming the people, just put them all together. Examples would be kind, generous, and supportive. On the bottom half, list all of the negative traits of influential people as they were in your childhood. Examples would be scary, selfish, or passive. *The list of positive and negative characteristics is your imago.*

Complete the sentences: "What I needed most as a child and didn't get was ..." And, "As a child I had these negative feelings over and over again ..." Take some time to let this into your body. Ideally find a person who can listen as you move through the practices in the book. Perhaps you can read together. You can also access a focusing partner or trainer on The International Focusing Institute website (www.focusing.org). Sharing your experience with a good listener will deepen it.

Next you can try the same exercise with your mate in mind. List their positive and negative characteristics and see how they relate to your imago. I suggest that you work through this in a felt sense way. Our heads often don't make these kinds of embodied connections. Many people find that there are a lot of similarities, or even one very strong characteristic that stands out in your parent and your partner. It only takes one strong characteristic to activate your imago.

First-Person Experiencing

I breathe down into the centre of my body. My hand goes to my heart. I'm engaging the aliveness of process with the containment of concepts. I feel into the deep knowing of my imago place. Something comes that feels new. Rather than a static concept I see imago as a process that carries forward with new knowing.

As I become more enlivened with thinking at the edge, I experience my own sense of imago differently. My awareness of the felt sense expands. I find myself bringing in a sense of curiosity about the carrying forward of imago. It is no longer limited by a moment in time. I see the image of a box inside my chest that morphs into a fuzzy floating imago that is alive and changing, guided by the wisdom of the body.

Hendrix and LaKelly Hunt explore the space of needing to define the concept and the importance of wonder, the implicit world of the felt sense:

Wonder moves us past the desire to understand what things and concepts are. When you define something, you limit it, in a way imprison it, by its definition. With definitions, you are limited by words, by a state of knowing, but Wonder goes beyond words to the state of not knowing. There is something so wondrous in not having the words to express what we are trying to say. (2017, p. 84)

As I go back down inside it feels good to get more clarity around defining and opening: top-down and bottom-up meet again in a delightful partnership. I take myself back to early days, tracing the changing patterns of my imago. In my first relationships I repeated an imago pattern from my father. I chose relationships that replayed deep wounds of abandonment, addiction and over-sexualizing. They also reflected great qualities in my dad like intelligence, curiosity, and playfulness. As I progressed in therapy I became aware of the need to not repeat patterns that had created such pain and chaos. These moments of liberation led me to choose different kinds of mates over time. My imago pattern began to take a new shape.

In my first marriage, my early imago began to heal around the edges as I consciously chose a partner who felt safe and dependable. I joke that I married my grandfather, the other father, the one who provided a safe nest for me. Unlike my dad, my grandfather and husband were accomplished and highly disciplined. In spite of my more conscious choice in partner, my relationship fell into a structured pattern. In Gendlin's process model (1997), this was a frozen cycle that blocked fresh experiencing and carrying forward. I played out more of the chaos flight/ fight state and my ex-husband played out immobility/fold. Sadly, what initially felt safe came to feel stuck. Over time my imago changed shape again as I moved through felt-sense experiences. I notice this fuzzy floating image of imago and pause here to explore more.

The Felt Sense Polyvagal Dialogue: The Model

Imago theory depicts the state of chaos and flight/fight as the hailstorm, and rigidity and fold as the turtle. In polyvagal language, we see how the sympathetic branch of the nervous system is like a hailstorm, and the dorsal branch is turtle-like in its shutdown response. (Figure 13.1)

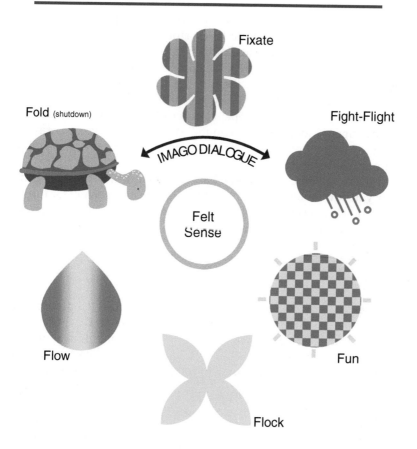

THE FELT SENSE POLYVAGAL DIALOGUE (FSPD)

Fixate

Fold (shutdown)

Fight-Flight

IMAGO DIALOGUE

Felt Sense

Flow

Fun

Flock

Adapted from:
Hendrix, H., LaKelly Hunt, H. (1990). *Getting the love you want: A guide for couples* (3rd ed.). St. Martin's Griffin.
Copyright © 2020 by Jan Winhall MSW, RSW, FOT. Focusing on Borden

Figure 13.1 FSPD (felt sense polyvagal dialogue).

The theory suggests that most people experience some degree of childhood wounding resulting from parents who were either too intrusive, or too neglectful. In response, we develop ways of defending ourselves that result in various degrees of emotional dysregulation. We either retreat, minimizing our reactions, or engage intensely, maximizing our reactions. Minimizers are called turtles and maximizers are hailstorms. The old adage that opposites attract applies here. Turtles are drawn to the vibrancy of hailstorms and hailstorms are drawn to the sense of containment of turtles. At first this can feel good, but then the very qualities that attracted us often become irritating, and a power struggle ensues.

The addicted partner will act out to shift the neurophysiological state from hailstorm to turtle, or turtle to hailstorm, in an attempt to soothe the underlying pain. Often when addiction is part of our early imago history we replay this in our relationships either by becoming the addicted person or the partner. In the traditional medical model this multi-generational addictive pattern is seen as evidence of genetic factors. But from an imago perspective, people re-enact old traumatic wounds that often accompany addictive behaviours. We then enlarge this way of thinking to include global and inter-generational traumas. We carry all of this in our relational felt sense.

I invite you to pause and explore hailstorm and turtle. Ask your body to show you how familiar each one is. Does hailstorm resonate? Or turtle? Or both? It helps to get to know your default mode, and your partners, in order to deeply appreciate how you interact with yourself and in your relationship.

The Addictive Imago, An Exit Extraordinaire

Imago therapists ask couples to make a commitment to the process for a 12-week period. Part of creating a safe container for doing the emotionally demanding work is to declare your commitment to the relationship. Engaging in the dialogue process requires an examination of what prevents you from being fully present to the relationship. Exits, as they are called in imago, are ways that people find to disengage, to avoid each other. Instead of expressing uncomfortable feelings, they are acted out. Some exits are not catastrophic. Examples include always inviting friends along to socialize, watching too much television, going to bed at different times, working too much, or spending too much time online. Catastrophic exits include suicide, divorce, murder, and insanity. In conversation with Harville we agreed that addiction would fit in the catastrophic category. Imago theory does not directly address it.

The Felt Sense Polyvagal Dialogue in Six Steps

1. *Asking for a Dialogue*

   Focuser: Ask your partner for an appointment to dialogue as soon as possible. You need one hour of uninterrupted time. Sit across from each other so you can connect in an open embodied way. You can give one sentence that describes the topic of the dialogue to help your partner begin the process.

2. *Clearing a Space: Finding A Welcoming Attitude*

   Listener: Pause and ask yourself the question: Is there anything coming between me and feeling really clear and available to listen? Then in your mind, take all the things that are preventing clarity and presence, and one by one, move them gently outside for the moment. You will get your turn to share, but for now, keep yourself out of it. Now you have a cleared space inside with which to welcome whatever comes. Good listening is an act of kindness. It includes a welcoming attitude of whatever comes into the room, whatever needs to be heard, as long as it is respectful.

3. *Mirroring: Resonating*

   Focuser: Begin by saying just enough to get the dialogue started. Often one or two sentences is all the listener can take in, especially at the beginning of learning how to listen deeply.
   Listener: Simply say back what you hear the focuser saying, feeling into it down in the centre of your body. Don't add any new information, but do ask for clarity. Say things like, "Let me see if I am hearing you ... Did I get you? Is there more about that?" Asking for more is an invitation for the focuser to take their time. Resonate back what you hear the focuser sharing; offer your digested version of what they are sharing with you.

4. *Asking into the Body*

   Listener: Invite the focuser to check to see how all of this feels in the body. Ask if there is a word or phrase or bodily movement that captures the quality of the felt sense. We call this word or phrase the *handle*. You receive it and hold it for them. You say it back to them, giving them a chance to shape it as they resonate back and forth between speaking and paying attention to the felt sense. As you create a safe space you will be amazed at how the speaker surrenders to their felt sense. You receive it and hold it for them. Remember to check to see if you got it right. In focusing we welcome being wrong because then we are prompted to inquire further, and to find what *is* right.
   The focuser holds the wisdom while you, as the listener, hold the space and silence. Welcome what comes, paying particular attention

to uncomfortable feelings and sensations. *Never push the focuser to ask into the body. This may frighten some people or it may not be where the focuser wants to go at the time.*

5. *Validating*

Listener: After accurately summarizing, the listener now validates the focuser's experience. The focuser always makes sense; you just have to see the sense it makes for them. Validation can be a difficult step as many people do not want to validate if they are not in agreement, but remember that validation is not about agreeing or disagreeing.

6. *Empathizing and Welcoming*

Listener: "So given all that, I can see why you are feeling ..." Just say back the feeling words and the handle only, without explanation. And then add, "Have I got your feelings and the felt sense of your experience?" Welcome whatever comes. The most uncomfortable places often give us the most information about our lives. Take time to be here and savour the moment of liberation that often occurs when your partner feels truly heard. These moments are the carrying forward of new growth within your relationship.

Behaviour Change Requests

Sometimes specific requests come from the focuser and they are worked through in the dialogue format.

As I introduce the imago dialogue, I explain how this process enables the couple to gain an intimate understanding of themselves and their partner. While they aren't each other's therapists, they do develop a keen awareness of their loved one's inner wounds, how these wounds impact their capacity for intimacy, and how they are the richest resource for each other's healing. These interactional insights form the basis of the imago healing journey. As this remarkable journey progresses, we witness couples moving through the *three D's*: They deepen their capacity for experiencing, develop, and depathologize their life stories, and do their daily practices through the FSPD.

When I am introducing the dialogue, I don't go into step four at the beginning unless the couple knows how to focus. Instead, I start by reading through the steps, first explaining them and teaching mirroring, validating and empathizing. Over time, as they gain the empathic listening skills, I introduce focusing. That way, they know that there is more to come, but we take our time. Asking into the body invites the relational felt sense into the process, deepening the couple's capacity for intimacy. As experiencing deepens, it accelerates the integration of the couple's healing journey.

Dialoguing with Triggers in Five Steps

I also offer a step-by-step process to use when one or both partners get triggered and need more containment in their dialogue. Try each step until you have enough containment.

1. Clear a space.
2. Name the issue that is triggering you and try to put it to the side for now.
3. Take turns mirroring short sentences so you don't have to wait too long.
4. Take a time out and come back in one hour.
5. If none of those things work, seek help from an experienced listener, or a psychotherapist.

This dialoguing for triggers is important in working with trauma and addiction since triggers occur frequently. People feel much safer knowing that this process is available any time that their nervous systems become dysregulated and hailstorms and turtles emerge. Taken together, working with the imago in conjunction with the felt sense model offers depth and safety to couples working to discover and heal addictive patterns. In the next chapter, we will meet Lily and Lucas as they travel through the FSPD.

References

Bierman, R. (1999). Focusing in changing abusive fighting to constructive conflict interactions. In *RWV therapy groups with domestically violent men. 11th international focusing conference*, Ontario, Canada.

Gendlin, E. T. (1962/1997). *Experiencing and the creation of meaning*. Evanston, IL: Northwestern University Press.

Gendlin, E. T. (1997). *A process model*. Evanston, IL: Northwestern University Press.

Hendrix, H. (2005). The evolution of imago relationship therapy. In *Imago relationship therapy perspectives on theory*. San Francisco, CA: Jossey-Boss.

Hendrix, H., & LaKelly Hunt, H. (2019). *Getting the love you want: A guide for couples* (3rd ed.). New York: St. Martin's Griffin.

Hendrix, H., & LaKelly Hunt, H. (2017). *The space between: The point of connection*. Franklin, TN: Clovercroft Publishing.

Rogers, C. (1951). *Client-centered therapy*. Boston: Houghton Mifflin.

Winhall, J. (2014). Understanding and treating addiction with the felt sense experience model. In *Emerging practice in focusing-oriented psychotherapy*. UK: Jessica Kingsley.

Winhall, J. (2018). Presentation at the fist felt sense conference, New York, May 18-20.

Winhall, J. & Falls, N. (2003). Focusing oriented psychotherapy and trauma. *Presentation at the 15th international focusing conference*, Pforzheim, Germany.

14 Lily and Lucas

The felt sense polyvagal dialogue (FSPD) comes to life when we see it in action. In this chapter, we will see how it facilitates the complex process between Lily and Lucas. We met Lily back in Chapter 10 when she was seeing me for alcohol addiction. During that time some issues had come up with her partner Lucas related to drinking. Lily was concerned that they were encouraging each other to drink too much so she wanted to address this with him in therapy. Lucas joined us for five sessions, and we developed a plan to reduce harm around their alcohol consumption. They both did very well and stopped therapy about one year ago.

The Call

Last week I got a call from Lily. Her voice was quivering as she told me that something terrible had happened and they needed to see me. They arrive this morning and we all sit down in our familiar places. Lucas and Lily are a very elegant-looking couple on the outside, but I am immediately alarmed. Lily's tall and graceful body is tight and her movement constricted. She is a dancer and her body usually flows beautifully even when she is struggling emotionally. Today she is lost.

Lucas met Lily at a ballroom dancing class. Young and handsome, he usually carries himself with ease. While his style is hip and lively, today his body shape is pulled in and down, protecting his centre. They both appear to be shut down in a dorsal state of shock and shame.

I make us some tea and then sit quietly while they find a way to begin. Lily has a real flair for adorning her body, wearing lots of interesting silver jewellery and gorgeous colourful scarves. Yet even though she is dressed in her usual vibrant style, her face has a deadened quality that is painful to see. I can't find a connection with her gaze. There is something so vulnerable about her slender being, but I hold myself back from reaching over to her. She is slowly making her way inside to find a way to speak. I sit still so as not to disturb her process.

"I found some stuff on Lucas' phone. I was suspicious because he spends more and more time on it, and he came home really late two nights last week. I thought he was having an affair." For the first time she looks at me. "I found stuff, sexual stuff, about hook-ups." We wait. I hold onto our space with a pause. Each word is so painful for her to speak out loud. "Meet-ups with men," she says. Ah, there it is. A huge source of painful betrayal for Lily.

"Oh boy," I say, "No wonder you are in shock!" At least now I understand this dorsal response. I've seen it many times in partners when they discover sexual betrayal. There is something so extraordinarily painful about this experience.

This is a very delicate moment where I need to connect with both of them. Lily needs to feel my acknowledgement of her deep pain, and Lucas needs to know that I can hear what is being revealed about him in a way that respects his dignity. He holds himself together, barely, as he looks over at me with a shameful expression. I look back respectfully. I've been here many times with clients. Good people in bad places.

As the session unfolds, Lily says that she and Lucas have begun to talk about what happened. He shared with her that he is struggling with his own sense of himself sexually and that he is deeply sorry for hurting her. Lily and Lucas have a caring relationship. They have many strengths in their shared life goals and their desire to heal from past traumas. They can also become quite disconnected and fall back into addictive patterns. Lily was beginning to feel more connected to him until a couple of months ago. She noticed that he began to spend more time on his phone and was often away at night.

It occurs to me that Lucas' sexual behaviour could be part of an addictive pattern. As he let go of the alcohol, he may have switched to or become more dependent upon sex. I don't mention this now though. Today, we focus on helping them find some resources to cope with the trauma.

Introducing FSPD

Over the next several weeks, I introduce the FSPD to Lily and Lucas as a way of helping them to work through their intense feelings towards each other. Lily is a skilled focuser but Lucas is not, so we begin by setting up the dialogue and practicing mirroring, validating, and empathizing. Through this process, Lucas shares that he knows he is addicted to pornography, specifically men with men. He has been using the sites and hooking up with guys for about ten years. This is completely new information for Lily, and she falls into a dorsal state of shock. I worry for both of them. It is such a painful journey. I suggest that they both need the support of a group and they agree. I refer Lily to a women's focusing-oriented therapy group, and Lucas to a male sex addiction focusing-oriented therapy group. These groups incorporate focusing practice in a group setting as a powerful way to activate the social engagement system and work on the three D's of healing: deepening the capacity to experience, developing and depathologizing the story, and doing daily practices.

The Three Circles

In group Lucas is supported to work through the three circles (Carnes, 2001) one of the components of the embodied assessment and treatment tool (EATT), as he develops his path of harm reduction. This work is shared with me through discussions with the group leader. We then bring it into the couples' session for Lucas to negotiate with Lily. Together we discuss Lucas' plan for keeping himself and Lily safe and committed to their relationship. Particularly with sex addiction, it is imperative for couples to commit to safe protocols. This discussion is extremely painful for both of them. Lily's intense feelings of panic and disgust are almost overwhelming for her, and she is struggling to stay in the relationship. They come to an agreement that they will commit to each other for a period of 12 weeks, and during that time they will not engage in any sexual behaviour, including using pornography, outside of their relationship.

As we bring the felt sense polyvagal model (FSPM) into our work, Lucas begins to recognize how his addictive behaviours help him to shift neurophysiological states. He knows that he is most comfortable in the turtle state of numbing. Lily recognizes that she normally flies into the hailstorm when she is stressed. However, since learning about Lucas sex addiction, she has been living in a turtle state, numb and in shock. Over the past couple of days she is aware that her body has begun to swing into hailstorm as the shock begins to wear off and she feels intense rage. Lucas' whole body shifts as he hears Lily describe her behaviour as a hailstorm.

Mirroring, Validating, Empathizing

"I've never heard you admit to yelling and attacking me before." As Lucas says this I suggest that they use the dialogue to continue.

Lily moves into step three and mirrors back, "You've never heard me admit that I yell and attack you sometimes."

"Yeah," says Lucas. I see a powerful moment emerging as they learn about their nervous systems. "It feels really good to hear you say that. When you yell, I die inside. It scares the shit out of me. In fact, right now my heart is racing!"

Lily pauses and takes this into her felt sense. "When I yell it scares the shit out of you, and now as you say that to me your heart is racing." I see how she is taking this all in. She is doing a great job in mirroring. I feel deep respect for her capacity to hear this from Lucas at a time when she is hurting so intensely. I am witnessing the power of the dialogue in providing the structure for such empathic moments to begin. Tears well up and spill down Lucas' cheeks as he searches Lily's face. Their eyes lock and then disconnect. Shy and shamed by his secret behaviours, he hangs his head.

Lucas' reference to his body suggests an opening to introduce step four, finding the felt sense. With my suggestion Lily asks Lucas to check down into the centre of his body and see what is happening now. "It feels shaky, like butterflies, like the fight/flight place on the model. It feels good though to talk openly with you, and for you to hear me."

Lily mirrors back and I see a moment of connection deepen between them for the first time since this all happened. Together, we help Lucas explore the world of the felt sense. As he connects with the butterflies in his stomach, he shares that it feels calmer in there now. I tell him that we call this the felt shift, when the body changes neurophysiological states. "Like going from flight to flock," he says.

"Yes!" I say, and we all laugh.

Lily moves to step 5 and validates: "I can understand that you would appreciate hearing me own up to yelling and attacking you at times. I know it's wrong and it hurts you. I also understand that you would shut down like a turtle hiding in your shell to protect yourself."

Step 6, empathizing and welcoming, emerges as this moment of empathy appears. It is enough for now. I see their faces soften together in the space between. I congratulate them on their progress in deepening their experiencing as a couple.

Developing Lily's Imago Story

Time passes and Lily goes in and out of being able to hear Lucas. Sometimes the pain and fear are overwhelming and we slow down, making space for it. She has agreed to commit to the relationship beyond the 12 weeks. This is a good sign. Lucas is learning to listen and validate her feelings. He is learning how to be with her pain without falling into despair. I can see how the support of the group is helping him to heal the shame. I suggest that they are ready to complete the imago exercise on their own and bring it with them to the next session.

It's Monday morning and I arrive to my office early. Coffee in hand, I let myself sit quietly, inviting a felt sense to form. Lily and Lucas are due in 20 minutes. I imagine them sitting across from me. Today, she is going to share her imago with Lucas. He will learn for the first time that his beloved Lily was sexually abused by her uncle and his male friend when she was eight years old. They were supposed to be taking care of her while her parents were visiting friends. Lily remembers them watching something sexual on television and touching each other's penises. They told her to sit still and watch. Another fragment appears of lying down on a couch and being touched in her "private place". Wispy images that vanish and reappear. This is going to be a tough session. My body feels the weight of it across my chest. If they get through this, they have a chance of healing together. I take a long, luxurious breath, and open the door to my beautiful, struggling couple.

Lily starts by asking for a dialogue with Lucas to share her imago. He feels into step 2 and clears a space as much as possible. He looks very anxious, and I remind him that the structure of the dialogue creates a safe container. If they get triggered we will pause. His shoulders relax slightly. Lily starts by sharing the positive and negative characteristics of her parents. Lucas mirrors back an imago picture that has some good memories for Lily: summer family camping trips, and her mom's yummy cakes. Her father's overbearing nature was always present in the house, and they were all afraid of him, including her mom. They were very busy working 12-hour days at the family hardware store and she longed for more attention from them.

Lucas is mirroring back and staying connected to her story. Then Lily stops abruptly and says, "There was someone else that I have to talk about." She begins to share the memory about her uncle and his friend. She tells him about her vague memory of them babysitting her and how terrified she was. Her body starts to tremble, and I watch to make sure that she stays present. She describes how they made her watch them touching each other's penises. She stops, and we all breathe. "I remember someone pulling down my underwear," she says. Her whole body seizes up, as Lucas looks to me for help. He is overwhelmed.

I say, "That's a lot to take in, and I am here with both of you." We pause and allow the new horrific information to seep into the room. I lead them both in a bit of grounding. I encourage them to take a breath, to feel their feet on the floor.

Lily's Imago Shift

The elephant in the room emerges with a fierce roar: the connection between Lucas' sexual behaviour and Lily's sexual abuse. Here is the imago moment where Lily's past and Lucas' present sexual experiences converge. I search Lucas' face to see if I can find any dawning awareness of how triggering his behaviour is for Lily. As we all shift in our seats, Lily flies into a rage. "Don't you see what you have done? You are just like them. Getting off on disgusting sex with guys you don't even know."

"Lily," I say, "You're triggered. Let's all slow down and breathe." A big pause is welcomed here. We pause again until I see our breathing slow down a bit. Adrenaline decreases as we all sit quietly. "You are confusing Lucas with the men in your life that hurt you when you were a little girl. Lucas isn't cold and threatening like your father. He didn't abuse any children like your uncle."

As I begin to help her decode the trigger, Lucas shifts in his seat, looking aghast. Within moments, and to my surprise, he says very clearly, "I did not abuse anybody. I never engaged in any sexual behavior with a minor, or without consent. I may be screwed up, but I know that I am not abusive."

Wow, I think to myself. Lucas is finding his voice. No turtles here. He is not hiding in response to Lily's hailstorm. I look over at Lily, and to my delight she is listening and appears a bit more settled. I imagine that she is feeling a sense of reassurance in Lucas' disclosure and his newfound voice. Partners often imagine the worst-case scenario when they first find out. She is beginning to shift her wounded imago. I don't kid myself though. I know we haven't seen the last of Lily's fight response. It's a powerful and undiscerning protector.

The beauty of this moment comes in realizing that Lucas' activation of her trigger enables Lily to feel the dissociated trauma experiences that she needs to access in order to heal. By finding these lost parts of herself through the imago triggers, Lucas inadvertently helps her to integrate her traumatic past. Because Lucas is also working on his own healing journey, attending group and containing addictive behaviours, the relationship provides a safe container for them both to access and reprocess their childhood wounds. In my experience, it can take several years and many rounds of being triggered and settling the nervous system before a couple with addiction/trauma histories can sustain an imago shift into a ventral state.

I suggest that they check inside and see how they are doing. We pause and drop down into the felt sense. "I think our nervous systems need a break, to settle and find some ventral energy," I say. They nod, and I tell them to take a ten-minute break and go for a walk in opposite directions. They laugh and off they go.

When they come back, we all check in to see if this is a good place to stop for today. They both say yes, they are exhausted. "Me too," I say. Lucas wants Lily to know that he is so sorry for her little girl, and he loves her. She hears him, and then looks away. Too painful a place to linger. I emphasize the importance of getting rest and being compassionate with themselves. As we trace this session's journey around the FSPM we arrive at the grounded place of flock. I commend them for the work they did today. Lily tamed her hailstorm, and Lucas spoke his truth. In doing so, they moved into a deeper place on the Experiencing Scale. They set the tone for more remarkable healing and integration of their traumatic pasts. While we will return to Lily's imago, next week we agree that Lucas will share. It's important to have both histories in the room so we can begin to understand the couple's dynamics.

Focusing Practice

I'm wondering how you are doing. Working with sex addiction is not for everyone. In my experience, it offers us powerful insights into human interaction. Our sexuality expresses some of the deepest aspects of who we are, sometimes in a disguised form. Often shrouded in shame, and perhaps therefore misunderstood by self and others, our sexuality longs to be free to breathe.

We therapists touch into such deeply painful places, and yet places that hold remarkably transformative experiences. By using the FSPD, what hurts us can eventually help us to heal. Please give yourself some time to pause and take in all that comes in your body.

Lucas' Imago Story

Monday morning comes again and Lily and Lucas arrive looking stressed. I ask how they are doing, and Lily says she feels like she is being tortured by images of Lucas acting out sexually. She says these images feel like they are "burned on her brain" and she can't escape them. I say that I hope Lucas' sharing will help diminish her trauma. I know that Lucas has been working hard in his group on the connection between his sexual struggles and his childhood wounding. Lily is about to learn that she isn't alone in her sexual wounding. Once Lucas shares his imago, we will be able to bring the child parts in each of them into the room. This will help us find their path of integration.

Lucas settles himself in his chair, takes a deep breath and asks Lily for a dialogue. This time Lily looks very anxious, as if some part of her knows what is coming. I work with her to clear as much space as she can, acknowledging that it is extremely hard to do. She says that she wants to listen. Good start.

Lucas describes a childhood that sounds quite nurturing and at the same time challenging. While his mom and dad loved him and his younger brother a lot, his dad's diagnosis of multiple sclerosis when Lucas was six threw the family into turmoil. Mom took on more work as an accountant, and dad left his full-time job as a music teacher and looked after things at home as best he could. There were increasing periods of time when Lucas took over for his dad. This was clearly too much for him, but he shouldered it without complaint. He learned early on to bury his overwhelming feelings. Lessons in assertiveness were nowhere to be found.

As Lily is nodding and mirroring back, I see her struggling to take in this revealing information about Lucas, the man that she loves, and at times hates. Lily's mind is wandering. She remembers safe Lucas who she wraps her naked body around to help her surrender into sleep. Safe Lucas who brings her espresso in the morning and kisses her lips ever so softly. And yucky Lucas who shares his naked body with strange men. The man that is her safe haven has become her source of deep betrayal. She wants so desperately to find her safe Lucas again, and she knows in her felt sense, as deeply as he does, that her man is a good and kind man. And she knows that life is messy and complicated and that she must listen to him now even though her limbs are burning up with the desire to fight and to flee.

I ask Lily gently if she is with us. She realizes that she had faded into herself and brings her attention back to the room. Lucas looks concerned and softly reaches over to say, "I have to tell you about other people too." He has rehearsed this sharing in group and is giving Lily a warning so her nervous system can prepare.

"Ever since this all came out I have been trying to figure out how it happened. Honestly, a lot of it I didn't remember until I started to talk about it in group. A lot of the guys shared things that happened when they were young and that got me thinking." Lily mirrors this back, looking concerned. "And then last week I started to have these weird feelings, and I remembered a time when the next door neighbour and I were masturbating together. I was about 7 or 8 and he was maybe 10." He takes a deep breath. "I wasn't really afraid of him, but I also couldn't say no, so I ended up doing things that I felt ashamed of. It went on for years. Sometimes his sister would come too. He would get her to masturbate us, and ..."

I look over at Lily as her body accelerates into flight/fight. I slow things down again. I ask her if she can stay with the dialogue and she says yes. I say that I will mirror Lucas' story and she looks enormously relieved. Some things are just too painful for partners to mirror back. "Would you like me to come closer?" They both nod and I move my chair up, just enough that we three are almost touching toes. A beautiful intimacy envelops the room. We are moving through new terrain and the window of tolerance is stretched to the limit. I keep the pace; the safety is in my hands now.

Lucas says he just wants to say one more thing today. There was another time with his gym teacher. He used to come into the boys' change room and one time he asked Lucas to come and see him after school. That became an abusive relationship that lasted for a few years until Lucas left high school. He doesn't know how he will be able to accept that this happened to him. "I'm afraid to go into those feelings, but I know that they have something to do with the sexual stuff with guys. I don't understand that kind of sex. I don't understand that part of me. I know how I feel about you. I love you and I love our sex. This stuff feels very different and it scares me." I mirror back his story and we all take a big, deep breath.

Lily starts to cry. "It scares me too."

I remind Lily that Lucas has committed to his three circles. "This commitment makes it safe for you to stay in the relationship and see how things go."

She nods her head. 'I'm so angry at that teacher!" she says.

This empathic response from Lily activates Lucas' imago pattern. "All my life I wanted someone to see my pain and to help me with it. I always felt so alone even though I know my parents loved me. It was so hard with my dad and we all just sucked it up."

I invite Lily to mirror this back and empathize with Lucas. She says, "I see how hard and confusing it must be for you with all that has happened to you. I see your pain. I wanted someone to see my pain too. It's still scary for me, what you did, but I am understanding more now." Lots of tears ensue.

A Couple Imago Felt Shift

"So we have little Lily and little Lucas, child parts that learned about sexuality in a scary way. A way that was confusing and robbed them both of the right to decide how and when to share that part of themselves." As I say this, we all start to cry. I try to honour my tears and at the same time, tuck them inside so I can be here for this wonderful moment of liberation for Lily and Lucas. As we unravel the triggered places, I invite us all to find the felt sense of this exquisite moment. "We will come back to this place as we continue the journey towards integrating these child parts. Now that they have found each other, we have to build a safe nest for each of them to grow and heal." And with that, we all stand and stretch and give each other a very well-deserved hug. I move back gently, letting this amazing couple linger in their moment of liberation.

Lily and Lucas continued working with me for two more years. During that time they journeyed in and out of triggered states, finding their way back to their safe nest. Lucas challenged the relationship in his need to explore his sexual orientation. Lily grew to accept that Lucas was attracted to many kinds of sexual expression, and she accepted this with respect, as long as he agreed to be committed to her and to keep her safe. They had a weekly practice of using the FSPD to explore ongoing boundaries. Lucas found that as he worked through the sexual trauma he felt no compulsion to act out sexually. He no longer identified as sexually addicted. He was grateful for Lily's capacity to welcome his sexuality in all its variations. He was now able to keep his little boy and her little girl safe.

Reference

Carnes, P. (2001). *Facing the shadow*. Carefree, AZ: Gentle Path Press.

Epilogue

I'm sitting at my writing table by the river, the same spot where I began this book one-and-a-half years ago. I hear the boats go by, the lap of the waves hitting the shore, my place in the sun. The wonderful group of women who gave me the inspiration to write this book are here with me. I don't want our journey to end. I pause, breathe, and turn my attention inward, into my felt sense.

As I drop down, I invite you to come with me. By now we are familiar with the place before words. Ah, the comfort that comes with silence. Notice what is around us, calling to us. I feel a stirring in my belly, a sweet, sulky sadness. The geese are calling, as they soar over the river. One by one they follow, travelling in packs, no one left behind. The comfort of each other, the comfort of knowing the path.

We humans need the comfort of each other. We have lost the path. Nowhere is that more evident than in the struggle with addiction. As I write these words, we are facing another wave of the Covid-19 pandemic. Addiction rates are soaring as we try to manage stressful times. The whole world must find a new path, a path of compassion, and connection with the felt sense, our embodied knowing.

Pausing to sense in. Sulky sadness comes back as I grasp for hope. Hope that we can find a way back to the body, not just for those suffering in addiction, but for the world. I want to end in hope, to carry forward the sweet sense of fresh energy.

The next generation of healers sometimes offer fresh eyes. When I am curious about challenging old patterns, I ask my children to enlighten me. My daughter Marika Heinrichs, a somatic practitioner, shares the following:

> I feel hopeful about movements. Movements for racial, economic, queer and trans, disability, and environmental justice are using and learning from somatics. There is a collective acknowledgement that our systems of domination and oppression are traumatizing. Within these systems, all trauma is political and cultural. A lot more people are waking up to that realization and doing something about it.

Many of us are imagining something quite different from the ways that mental health has traditionally been offered. That gives me tremendous hope.

Hope lies in social movements that deeply challenge top-down paradigms currently dominating our culture. People are creating spaces to treat trauma and addiction that challenge the current top-down medical model. The *felt sense polyvagal model* (FSPM) is my offering of a truly integrative approach that celebrates the body's natural response to trauma and addiction. It is my hope that the model will provide a framework for other de-pathologizing pathways of healing.

Maté, a leader in the harm reduction movement, continues to help healing communities to mobilize and find hope in the struggle. His insistence upon holding the medical world accountable is inspiring.

Poonwassie and Windego, indigenous focusing-oriented therapists, work with their people to find hope and help in connecting with the land, and with the ancestors. They see the addictive behaviours as helpers when there is no other way to survive. Poonwassie focuses on the complex trauma, paying little attention to the addictive behaviours. Windego takes groups of men out to the land to camp for weeks as they struggle to achieve sobriety. Through ceremonies and focusing practice, they find their way back to the body by connecting with the natural world. They invite their ancestors to help carry the weight of their intergenerational trauma. It is too much to bear alone.

Tatarsky (2002), grandfather of a harm reduction psychotherapy approach, draws hope from the community of healers that he has trained over the last decade at his Centre for Optimal Living in New York. The centre continues to flourish with the movement to de-pathologize addictions.

Haines has created a community that practices *generative somatics*. This approach integrates somatic healing and social justice. During these pandemic times, with the rise of the "Black lives matter" movement, this work is providing a powerful space to explore the healing journey. The community continues to thrive as it develops over time.

My Hopeful Space: Focusing on Borden

Focusing on Borden is the name of the focusing community that I started in 2012. Borden is the name of the street where we meet, except during Covid-19 times. We have a community of focusing trainers and focusing oriented therapists and many people who attend our groups throughout the year. We teach and practice focusing in partnerships and groups. We are moving away from having "addiction" groups. The FSPM teaches us to honour our ways of surviving, and many people who are struggling with addiction feel safe to share in the large group. This way no one is stigmatized.

The Borden Street clinic is also part of Focusing on Borden. In our clinic, we train graduate students, provide psychotherapy, and medication consultations. We do this in a democratic circle of care for our clients. What do I mean by that? In a de-pathologizing model, no single professional leads. Depending on the client issue, whoever is best qualified leads the process. In our small circle, we have managed to move beyond the narcissistic urge for power. Instead, we find nourishment in our common goal of caring for each other and the people who come to us for help. I believe this capacity to let go of the hierarchy comes from shifting into an embodied way of living. In deepening our experience, we embrace our vulnerability. Hope lies in our capacity to honour each other's shaky being.

In Conclusion: A Call to Action

We are currently living through dark times. Yet, there is a lightness that is awakening us to the realization that we are all part of each other. At a time like this, with a global pandemic upon us, we need to learn from those suffering from addiction. They tell us where we are failing as a culture. Understanding the struggle to regulate oneself demands a deeper and wider lens than we are currently using. The FSPM incorporates an understanding of the impact of power and privilege in our way of studying attachment, trauma, and addiction. By including the most marginalized communities, we create a more informed, inclusive, and humane way forward. This is the essence of healing.

Next Steps for Therapists

I sincerely hope you have enjoyed our journey of exploration into the embodied experience of trauma and addiction and have come away with a deep and compassionate understanding of both what drives addiction and how to treat the whole person. For those interested the most current details, models, and information on how to apply the FSPM, there is a resource page available at https://janwinhall.com/ and training information from the Polyvagal Institute at https://www.polyvagalinstitute.org/.

Reference

Tatarsky, A. (2002). *Harm reduction psychotherapy: A new treatment for drug and alcohol problems*. Lanham: Rowman & Littlefield Publishers.

Index

space 16; finding a handle 17–18;
getting felt sense of problem 16–18;
heart of 17; in partnerships 15–16;
practice 60, 64, 77, 83, 119, 121, 124,
126, 129, 136–137, 142; resonating
felt sense and handle 18;
session 19–20
The Focusing Dialogue 191
focusing-oriented therapists 174
focusing oriented therapy (FOT) 5–6,
11; psychotherapy 5, 14, 42, 82, 136
fostering 86
Frances, A. 28
free market capitalism 71
functional wholes 138

Galvanic skin response (GSR) 138–139
Gendlin, E. T. 14, 20, 22, 39, 45, 54–55,
75, 77, 130–134, 160; about
traditional scientific approaches,
137; body-environment unity
141–142; *Experiencing and the
Creation of Meaning* 18, 25, 136; felt
sense and felt shift, 139–141;
Focusing 14; focusing-oriented
psychotherapy 14, 136; functional
wholes 138; holistic approach 137;
holocaust story, 134–135;
importance of understanding
theories 137; *Let Your Body
Interpret Your Dreams* 133; manner
of experiencing 145; as a philosopher
135; *A Process Model* 24, 141;
process skipping 145; safe space 132;
view of neurobiology 138–139
Gendlin's process model 196
generative somatics 105–106
Ghomeshi, J. 103
global trauma 97, 99, 103, 113, 118
grounded aware presence (GAP) 177

habit-forming behaviours 2;
see also addiction(s)
Haines, S. 105
Hari, J. 60–62, 65
harm reduction model 86, 164
healing process 152
Hendricks, M. 24
Herman, J. 159
House Committee on
Appropriations 62

imago theory 192, 197–198

imago therapists 198
imago therapy process 191
immobilization with safety 11
implicit intricacy 21, 142–144
implicit memory 170
innate self-organizing capacity 81
insecure attachment 90, 96, 100
integration 3, 7, 76, 81–82
interoception 115, 120, 168
interpersonal integration 172
interpersonal neurobiology (IPNB)
2–3, 8, 75–78, 88
intertwining states 9–10, 90, 108
In the Realm of Hungry Ghosts (Maté)
58, 97, 103

journaling to track 55

kindness 103

language 11–12, 27, 37–38, 78, 80, 87,
98, 104, 111, 122, 125
left hemisphere of brain 25–26
Lewis, M. 50, 55; history of
neuroplasticity 46; *Memoirs of an
Addicted Brain* 43; views of
addiction 42–43
life-enhancing process 154
linkage 3, 82, 106
Lotte's holocaust story 132–134

maladaptive behaviour 12, 35
marginalization 59, 63, 71
marijuana 29, 31, 62
Maté, G. 103
Maternal Behavioral Q-Sort-mini
(MBQS-mini) 101
maternal sensitivity 101
McGilchrist, I. 25–26, 37
meditation 15, 36–37, 55, 88
Menakem, R. 64; about racism and
trauma 64; *My Grandmother's Hands,
Racialized Trauma and the Pathways
to Mending Our Hearts and Bodies* 64
mental models 170
Merrick, M. T. 69
Merzenich, M. M. 47, 53
metaphoric thinking 37
Mexican immigrants, drug abuse 62
micro aggression 58–59
midbrain 50–52
mind: definition 80; as relational
process 80